Dr. John C. L. Wong

G000294710

Methods for Cloning and Analysis of Eukaryotic Genes

Al Bothwell
Yale University School of Medicine
and the Howard Hughes Medical Institute

George D. Yancopoulos
Senior Scientist
Regeneron Pharmaceuticals, Inc.

Frederick W. Alt
Columbia University, College of Physicians
and Surgeons, and the Howard Hughes Medical Institute

JONES AND BARTLETT PUBLISHERS
Boston

Editorial, Sales, and Customer Service Offices

Jones and Bartlett Publishers
20 Park Plaza
Boston, MA 02116

Printed in the United States of America
10 9 8 7 6 5 4 3 2 1

Library of Congress Cataloging-in-Publication Data

Bothwell, Alfred.
  Methods for cloning and analysis of eukaryotic genes.

  Includes bibliographies and index.
    1. Molecular cloning—Laboratory manuals.
  2. Recombinant DNA—Analysis—Laboratory manuals.
  I. Yancopoulos, George. II. Alt, Frederick W.
  III. Title. IV. Title: Eukaryotic genes. (DNLM:
  1. Cloning, Molecular—methods. 2. DNA, Recombinant—
  laboratory manuals. 3. Genetic Engineering—laboratory
  manuals. QH 444.2 B749m)
  QH442.2.B67   1990   574.87'328   89-11058
  ISBN 0-86720-103-7

Cover illustration: Immunoflorescence micrograph of a rat kangaroo cell undergoing mitosis. Photo by Mark S. Ladinsky and Richard McIntosh, Department of Molecular, Cellular, and Developmental Biology, University of Colorado at Boulder.

Table of Contents

3   Genomic DNA Libraries   53

Al Bothwell
George D. Yancopoulos
Frederick W. Alt

4   cDNA Libraries   89

George D. Yancopoulos
Frederick W. Alt

5   Subtractive Hybridization Techniques   115

George D. Yancopoulos
Frederick W. Alt

6 Transfection Procedures   139
Al Bothwell

9   Nucleic Acid Probes   217

Al Bothwell

Preface

The aim of this laboratory manual is to provide a selected set of commonly used molecular cloning techniques. The protocols that are described in this cloning manual have been updated by many students and postdocs, and comments have been made by students in the Cold Spring Harbor Cloning Course over the last few years. Some of the methods have been developed or modified in the laboratories of the authors. The subtractive hybridization methods represent techniques they have developed over the past 15 years. As presented, they represent the current state of the art in that technology.

A number of recent technical developments are included here as well as current references (e.g., bacterial electroporation, lipofection, polymerase chain reaction, and pulsed-field gel electrophoresis). The developments are so rapid that newer ones appear quite commonly. The cloning of very large fragments of DNA in yeast vectors has been achieved but is still challenging to very experienced investigators. There are many basic procedures not included here, but it is assumed that individuals will consult several sources of information. We have attempted to include material that has been extensively used by the authors and present it in a very usable form.

It is increasingly possible to purchase a kit for an entire procedure or even several kits for several different steps of a procedure. In most cases these kits and their instructions are of high quality and save time. For this reason we felt that it was not necessary to cover certain topics here, such as dideoxy DNA sequencing or λgt11 screening procedures. The λgt11 system has been used to clone sequence-specific DNA binding proteins using DNA probes, but good references are available for those modifications.

There are also good kits for cDNA cloning. A detailed set of methods is presented in Sections 4 and 5 because there are no kits for the generation of subtracted cDNA probes. This is a topic not well covered elsewhere, and the application of these methods to a given problem often requires special considerations.

This manual has taken several years to develop and has had numerous contributions in addition to those specifically acknowledged. Invaluable contributions were made by members of Hans Lehrach's lab and by members presently or formerly in the authors' labs: Dean Ballard, Jeff Berman, Keith Blackwell, Peter Blier, Margot Bridgett, Robert Collum, Lori Covey, Ron DePinho, Elaine Dzierzak, Pierre Ferrier, Andrew Furley, Connie Gee, Khuda Dad Khan, Nancy Kohl, Ken LeClair, Sang Lee, Edith LeGouy, Elena Levine, Glen Lindwall, Stuart Lutzker, Steve Maher, Nancy Maizels, Barbara Malynn, Scott Mellis, Bill Philbrick, Roberta Pollock, Gary Rathbun, Michael Reth, Paul Rothman, Alfred

xi

Slanetz, Russell Smith, Bing Su, Mike Verneris, and Kathy Zimmerman. The section on retrovirus vectors was contributed by Paolo Dotto. The encouragement and advice from Joe Burns, executive editor at Jones and Bartlett, was crucial for the completion of the manuscript.

Al Bothwell
Section of Immunobiology
Yale Medical School

George D. Yancopoulos
Regeneron Pharmaceuticals, Inc.

Frederick W. Alt
College of Physicians and Surgeons
Columbia University

Preparation of DNA and RNA

PREPARATION OF CHROMOSOMAL DNA
FROM MAMMALIAN CELLS

General considerations

One needs to make DNA sufficiently clean to be suitable for restriction enzyme digestions and of high molecular weight to be representative with respect to large restriction fragments.

There are many methods; the one outlined below is very easy.

1. Treat with SDS and proteinase K to inactivate DNases and digest proteins associated with the DNA.

2. The proteins are then removed by extraction with organic solvents. The key is to be gentle in the extractions because high-molecular-weight DNA solutions will be viscous even at low concentrations and very subject to mechanical shear. Therefore one mixes the DNA solutions with organic solvents very gently (do not vortex or mix vigorously) and one transfers the DNA solution either with wide-bore pipettes (made by breaking off the narrow ends of glass pasteur pipettes after marking the glass with a diamond pen) or by gently pouring it off the top of the organic solvent (the viscous DNA solution can usually be poured off in its entirety with the inclusion of only small amounts of the organic solvent).

    First one performs extractions with phenol; then the DNA is extracted with chloroform. The use of the more hydrophobic chloroform for extraction complements the phenol extraction in its ability to remove proteins.

3. The DNA is precipitated by adding several volumes of isopropanol in 0.1 M NaCl. Isopropanol precipitation of DNA is used instead of EtOH precipitation because RNA remains soluble in the isopropanol solution. This achieves a very effective physical separation of RNA from the DNA and usually eliminates the need for treatment with RNase. DNA will clump out of the solution and can be removed using a hook formed by bending a pasteur pipette.

4. For storage, the DNA is dissolved in TE at pH 7.5. Neutral pH is used because at acidic pH DNA will depurinate and may then be degraded when the pH is raised to neutral or above (e.g., during restriction endonuclease digestion or other manipulations). The EDTA (1 mM) serves to inactivate DNase; the enzyme needs divalent cations for its activity.

    Store the DNA at 4°. Do not freeze because repeated freezing and thawing is disastrous for high molecular weight DNA.

3

5. One has to remember to continue to handle the DNA gently. For example, when doing restriction digests, treat with the restriction enzyme and then remix after the viscosity is reduced; there will be no problem with shearing after the size is reduced to below 10–20 kb.

6. DNA concentration: a DNA solution with an optical density at 260 nM of 1 has a DNA concentration of 50 μg/ml.

Isolation of DNA from cells in tissue culture

1. Start with approximately 5×10^6 to 10^7 cells and wash one time with PBS.

2. Resuspend cells in 3 ml of TNE solution (0.01 M Tris·HCl [pH 8], 0.1 M NaCl, 0.001 M EDTA). Use a pasteur pipette to force the cells into suspension. The cells can be frozen at -20° or -70° in TNE for processing at a later time or processed immediately.

3. Rapidly add an equal volume of TNE solution containing 1% SDS and freshly dissolved proteinase K at 400 μg/ml (referred to as *PK solution*); gently rock until a uniformly viscous solution forms. (When working with cells frozen in TNE solution, add the PK solution directly to the frozen cells, rock gently until thawed, and proceed as below; DNA can be made from a frozen cell pellet by thawing the pellet in a 1:1 mix of TNE and PK solutions).

4. Incubate at 37° for 1 to 4 hr or even overnight.

5. Extract once with an equal volume of Tris-saturated phenol. Rock gently for 15 to 20 min (rockers for this purpose can be purchased) and then separate the phases by centrifugation in a clinical centrifuge at room temperature. Remove the upper aqueous phase with a pasteur pipette whose narrow tip has been broken off, or simply decant (due to viscosity of the DNA solution it usually comes off as a unit).

6. Extract the aqueous phase with chloroform:isoamyl alcohol (24:1) twice as performed with phenol.

7. To the upper phase add 2 to 2 1/2 volumes of isopropanol at room temperature. Mix until a white cottony clump appears which is the DNA. The turbid solution contains mainly RNA. Do not let the white lump stay too long in the alcohol as it becomes dehydrated and more difficult to resuspend.

8. Remove the clump with a glass rod with a hook on the end (conveniently made by melting the tip of a glass pasteur pipette). Let it drain briefly on the side of the tube to remove alcohol and then plunge it into 1 ml of TE (0.01 M Tris·HCl [pH 8.0], 0.001 M EDTA). It may take several hours to resuspend completely even with rocking.

9. Store at 4° in the TE.

REFERENCE

Steffen, D., S. Bird, W. P. Rowe and R. A. Weinberg *Proc. Nat. Acad. Sci. USA* 76:4554 (1977).

Isolation of DNA from tissues

1. Mince tissue in a petri dish on ice (keep sample cold until step 7 below).

2. Transfer the minced tissue out of the petri dish into a cold 40-ml Dounce homogenizer with no more than 40 ml of cold RSB buffer (0.01 M Tris·HCl [pH 8.0], 0.01 M NaCl, 1.5 mM MgCl$_2$).

3. Dounce 10 times to break open the cells. The nuclei should remain intact throughout the procedure.

4. Transfer to a 50-ml tube. Pellet the nuclei at 3 krpm for 10 min at 4°.

5. Resuspend the nuclei in 30 to 40 ml of cold SDS buffer (0.1 M NaCl, 0.04 M Tris·HCl [pH 8], 0.02 M EDTA). If there is a white substance in the pellet or in the suspension remove it by spinning at 1 krpm for 1 min. If it still remains it will render the DNA resistant to further enzymatic treatments.

6. Centrifuge again at 3 krpm for 10 min at 4° to pellet the nuclei and remove the supernatant.

7. Resuspend the nuclei in 25 ml of SDS buffer (without SDS) at room temperature.

8. Quickly add an equal volume of SDS buffer containing 1% SDS and 400 μg/ml proteinase K. Gently vortex for 1 to 2 sec.

9. Incubate at 37° for 1 to 2 hr.

10. Phenol extract twice (gently, as in previous protocol).

11. Chloroform extract twice (gently, as in previous protocol).

12. Precipitate with 2 volumes of isopropanol and resuspend in TE (as described in previous protocol).

Isolation of DNA from small amounts of cells or tissue (example given for mouse tails)

1. Cut 1 to 2 cm of tail and place in a 1.5-ml microfuge tube. Mincing the tail is not necessary.

2. Add to the tube 0.7 ml of 0.05 M Tris·HCl [pH 8], 0.1 M EDTA, 0.5% SDS. Add 35 μl of a 10 mg/ml solution of proteinase K.

3. Incubate at 55° overnight on a rocking platform.

4. Remove tubes from 55° and add 0.7 ml of phenol. Gently mix for 3 min so that the phases mix completely.

5. Centrifuge in a microfuge for 3 min.

6. Transfer the aqueous phase to a fresh tube.

7. Add 0.7 ml of phenol:chloroform (1:1), mix for 2 min and centrifuge for 2 min.

8. Again remove the aqueous phase and transfer to a fresh tube.

9. Add 70 μl of 3 M sodium acetate (pH 6), and 0.7 ml of 100% ethanol at room temperature. Shake thoroughly to mix. The DNA should immediately form a stringy precipitate. A sodium acetate solution with a pH lower than 6 will cause the EDTA to precipitate.

10. Spin in the microfuge for 30 sec to precipitate the DNA. Remove and discard as much as possible of the ethanol supernatant.

11. Add 1 ml of 70% ethanol at room temperature to the tube, and vortex or shake vigorously to wash the DNA. This step is essential to remove traces of SDS and phenol.

12. Centrifuge in a microfuge for 1 min at room temperature. Remove as much ethanol supernatant as possible. Dry the DNA briefly *in vacuo*.

13. Add 0.1 ml of TE to the tube. Leave at room temperature overnight to dissolve. If necessary, the DNA can be dissolved more quickly by heating for 5 to 10 min at 65°. Use 10 to 20 μl of each DNA preparation for Southern blot analysis.

14. The DNA prepared in this manner will contain substantial amounts of RNA, but this does not interfere with restriction enzyme digestion or Southern blot analysis. When performing restriction enzyme digestion, add 5 μg of DNase-free RNase A to each sample along with the restriction enzyme. Digestion with certain enzymes may also be aided by adding 4 mM spermidine to the reaction.

RNA ISOLATION

General considerations

1. **RNA content** An average mammalian cell has approximately 10^{-5} μg of RNA. Therefore one can expect approximately 5–10 mg RNA/gram of cells (1 gram of cells consists of approximately 10^9 cells, which form a packed pellet of about 1 ml).

    a) rRNA (18S and 28S) comprises about 80% of the total cellular RNA and most of the remainder is other structural RNAs (4S RNA and 5S RNA). These are abundant and homogeneous in composition; therefore, they can be purified by size or density.

    b) mRNA is approximately 2% of the total and it is heterogeneous in size and composition. However, it can be isolated from the other RNAs because of its poly(A) tail (20–250 adenine residues at the 3′ end of the mRNA). These can be used for affinity purification on oligo(dT)-cellulose or poly(U)-sepharose columns.

    c) Cytoplasmic versus total RNA RNA prepared from whole cells (both cytoplasm and nucleus) contains the mature, processed forms of both structural RNAs and mRNAs, but in addition contains nuclear precursors of these RNAs (which for mRNA are also polyadenylated). RNA prepared from the cytoplasm contains only the fully processed forms of structural RNAs and mRNA.

2. **Important considerations** The key to RNA isolation is to minimize RNase activity:

    a) There is much RNase in tissues, some in reagents, glassware, hands, saliva, etc. Autoclaving is *not* particularly effective at destroying RNase activity.

    b) The basic idea is to inactivate RNase early and afterwards not to add it back (use "sterile" technique).

3. **Ribonuclease inhibitors**

    a) Strong detergents (SDS) are effective denaturants, but are by no means 100% effective. Guanidinium thiocyanate and urea are denaturants that, in conjunction with reducing agents (such as mercaptoethanol) that break the disulphide bonds of RNase, almost immediately destroy RNase activity. Remember, RNase can completely renature and regain function when the denaturing agent is removed.

b) Vanadyl ribonucleoside complexes or RNAsin (rat liver or placental protein inhibitors of RNase) are commercially available, are quite effective, and can be removed by phenol/chloroform extraction.

c) Diethylpyrocarbonate (DEPC) directly attacks amino groups at the active site of RNase, permanently inactivating the enzyme. DEPC treatment is frequently used to make solutions and glassware RNase free. However, DEPC also inactivates other proteins and acts on single-stranded nucleic acids and thus has to be removed following treatment (by autoclaving or by phenol extraction).

4. **Deproteinization (also removes RNase activity)**

a) Proteinase K (in SDS) at 37° followed by phenol/CHCl$_3$ extraction effectively deproteinizes.

b) *Direct phenol extraction:* Phenol is a very strong denaturant. However, in the cold mRNA partitions into the phenol rather than aqueous phases (due to the hydrophobic nature of poly[A] tails) unless the phenol is at an alkaline pH which tends to hydrolyze the RNA. At room temperature the mRNA partitions into the interface. With hot (60°) phenol, the mRNA partitions into the aqueous phase. The hot phenol extraction procedure is very useful for preparing RNA from small quantities of cells or tissue.

c) Extraction with a mixture of phenol:chloroform (1:1) partitions the RNA into the aqueous phase because the chloroform is more hydrophobic than phenol. This is a commonly used method when rapid deproteinization is needed.

Note: Phenol promotes RNA aggregation: Therefore, when the RNA is purified using phenol and is then to be used in other procedures (oligo[dT] selection, in vitro translation, cDNA synthesis, etc.) it should be disaggregated by heating to 68° for 3 min and then quick-chilling (in an EtOH/dry ice bath).

5. **Preparation of cytoplasmic RNA**   The procedure usually has to be optimized for a given tissue, because separation of nuclei from cytoplasm depends on cell type. The cells are lysed in a non ionic detergent which should keep the nuclei intact. The nuclei are removed by centrifugation and can be used for the isolation of nuclear RNA/DNA. RNA is then prepared from the cytoplasmic fraction. The most common method is to add one of the RNase inhibitors and deproteinize by proteinase K treatment or phenol/chloroform extraction.

6. **Preparation of total cellular RNA**   Total cellular RNA preparation is easy and does not usually have to be adapted for particular tissues or cell lines; RNA can be prepared from fresh cells and tissues or frozen samples (intact RNA has been prepared from samples that have been stored at -70° for over 10 years). The only problem with this type of purification is that one always isolates nuclear precursors along with the cytoplasmic mRNA. For many purposes this is not a problem, although it can pose problems in some cases (e.g., S1 nuclease analyses designed to map processed transcripts, and certain cloning situations).

    The most effective procedure, especially for large samples, involves homogenization of whole tissue or frozen cells in 4 M guanidinium thiocyanate also containing detergent and mercaptoethanol. This procedure rapidly disintegrates cellular structures, dissociates nucleoproteins, and leads to rapid denaturation. RNase activity is destroyed almost immediately.

    Once the tissue is dissolved one can isolate RNA by differential sedimentation of RNA through 5.7 M $CsCl_2$. Under appropriate conditions the RNA will pellet while the DNA and denatured protein will not.

    This procedure gives high yields of intact RNA from most tissue and cell lines (even tissues, such as pancreas, with high endogenous RNase levels).

    Other total cellular RNA isolation procedures are even more easily performed (i.e., hot phenol or lithium chloride/urea preparations) and are especially useful for isolating RNA from small amounts of cells or tissues. However, RNA isolated by these procedures may not be as intact as RNA isolated by the guanidinium thiocyanate procedure.

7. **RNA concentration**   After the purification steps involved in several of the RNA preparation protocols, RNA can be concentrated by conventional ethanol precipitation. Spectrophotometric analysis can determine quantity and purity of RNA samples. An RNA solution with an optical density(OD) at 260nm of 1 has an RNA concentration of 42 μg/ml. A solution with an OD of 20 has a concentration of approximately 1 μg/μl. The OD 260 to 280 ratio for pure RNA should be close to 2; less than that indicates high protein content.

8. **Isolation of poly(A) + RNA**   Total or cytoplasmic RNA can be passed over an oligo(dT)$_{12-18}$-cellulose column to separate RNA into fractions with or without poly(A)$^+$ tails; under high-salt binding conditions (400 to 500 mM NaCl, depending on the batch of oligo[dT]) only RNA with poly(A)$^+$ tails will bind to the column, which can then be eluted off using a low-salt buffer. One pass over a column yields a sample of about 50% purity (i.e., a 50/50 mixture of rRNA and mRNA); a second pass can be done if nearly absolute purity is required.

9. **Keeping purified RNA clean**   Once RNA is purified one must not add
    back RNase. Therefore, solutions and glassware (plasticware) must be
    "sterilized."

    a) Ribonuclease-free plasticware and (certain) chemicals can be pur-
    chased.

    b) Glassware can be sterilized by dry heat (250° for 4 hr or by DEPC
    treatment–rinsing the glassware in water containing 0.1% DEPC, fol-
    lowed by autoclaving to remove the DEPC) or by treatment with 0.1 N
    NaOH (which destroys RNase); remember to neutralize because base
    will hydrolyze RNA.

    c) Water and many solutions can be made RNase-free by treatment
    with 0.1% DEPC. DEPC will also react with amino groups on reagents
    such as Tris buffer and therefore cannot be used to "sterilize" all solu-
    tions. DEPC must be inactivated by subsequently autoclaving solutions
    (DEPC is a carcinogen; use in the hood). Autoclaving alone is not par-
    ticularly effective in removing RNase.

    d) Hands and mouth: wear surgical gloves; do not cough into tubes,
    and observe sterile precautions.

10. **Storage of purified RNA** The RNA is stable as an EtOH precipitate at
    -20° almost indefinitely. Purified RNA can be dissolved in water (which
    from most sources has a pH below neutral—RNA is less prone to hy-
    drolysis at neutral or slightly below neutral pH) or in 0.5 mM EDTA,
    pH 5.5 to 6.0 (EDTA binds divalent cations that lead to chemical break-
    down). The dissolved RNA should be stable at -70° for years. Note that
    although magnesium ions are often included during homogenization
    stages to protect nuclei and because they inhibit RNase, EDTA is in-
    cluded in purified RNA samples because RNase is no longer present
    and one is more worried about protection from chemical degradation.

RNA preparation using guanidinium thiocyanate

This procedure works well for even very large amounts of cells or tissue. See the end of this section for preparation of solutions used in this procedure.

1. Homogenize fresh tissue or cell pellet (cells do not have to be washed in any way) in 4 M guanidium thiocyanate (GnSCn) solution; use of a polytron homogenizer is convenient. Frozen tissues can be added directly to the 4 M GnSCn solution and homogenized immediately. Cells can be stored frozen at -70° as a cell pellet and GnSCn added directly to the frozen pellet. If no polytron is available fresh tissues have to be minced well, whereas frozen tissues or cells should be crushed almost to a powder (at -70° to prevent degradation), prior to vortexing in GnSCn. After dissolving the sample in the GnSCn solution, it is most important to destroy any remaining viscosity (due to DNA) by homogenizing or douncing; viscosity will hinder RNA from centrifuging through the GnSCn, decreasing yields substantially.

    One gm of tissue (or 10^9 cells) in 16 ml 4 M GnSCn yields 10 mg RNA.

2. Fill centrifuge tubes 1/4 with 5.7 M CsCl (2.7 ml for polyallomer SW41 tubes). Layer GnSCn homogenate on top (about 9 ml for SW41 tubes) and balance with added 4 M GnSCn.

3. Centrifuge in Beckman SW41 rotor for 12–20 hr at 32 krpm at 20°. (Procedure can be scaled up: 30 ml of homogenate can fit over 9 ml of 5.7 M CsCl solution in a single SW28 tube, which can be spun at 25 krpm for 20 hr.)

4. Dissolve RNA pellet.
    Important: At this point care must be taken to avoid RNase contamination, i.e., wear gloves, use RNase-free solutions, sterile tips, and sterile tubes.

    a) Remove all of GnScn layer and top of CsCl layer by vacuum aspiration (switch pasteur pipettes as soon as you enter CsCl layer to avoid contaminating CsCl layer with RNases—which can renature—trapped in GnScn layer). Quickly invert tubes to drain. Keep tubes inverted to prevent flow toward pellet.

    b) Cut off bottom of tube containing RNA pellet using a razor blade. Pellet resembles a contact lens.

    c) Rinse pellet 1x at room temperature with 95% ethanol (edges of pellet should turn white). From this point, keep RNA on ice.

d) Add RNase-free TE to dissolve pellet (300 μl first, then 100 μl rinse) and transfer to a microfuge tube. This takes a while: pipette up and down. Pellet looks like cellophane.

If there are problems dissolving the pellet (because pellet is very large) you can carefully push pellet into a 5–50-ml tube containing a larger amount of TE (1–5 ml); this tube can be vortexed to dissolve.

5.   Perform single extraction using an equal volume of phenol/chloroform.

6.   Ethanol-precipitate with 2 to 2.5 vol 100% EtOH and 1/10 vol 4 M NaCl at -70°; precipitates can be spun down in microfuges or at 3 krpm for 30 min for larger tubes.

7.   Redissolve pellet in RNase-free TE and reprecipitate with 1/10 vol NaCl and 2 vol EtOH. Redissolve and take an OD of an aliquot to determine yield. Store at -70°. Total RNA can be used to isolate poly(A)$^+$ RNA.

RNA preparation using guanidinium thiocyanate

Note: All solutions used after the initial GnSCn centrifugation step must be treated with diethylpyrocarbonate (DEPC) to get rid of RNase activity. This includes the following solutions: 4 M NaCl, ddH$_2$O, and TE as well as those described below in the poly(A)$^+$ RNA preparation procedure.

Add 20 μl DEPC per 100 ml of solution, let sit at least 1 hr at room temperature, then autoclave. Tris degrades DEPC so add Tris to solutions after DEPC treatment.

4 M guanidinium thiocyanate

50 g	Guanidinium thiocyanate (Fischer, #705)
0.5 g	Sodium lauroyl sarcosine (Sigma, No. L-5125)
2.5 ml	1 M sodium citrate pH 7
0.7 ml	β-mercaptoethanol
0.33 ml	30% Antifoam A (Sigma No. A-5758)

1.   First add GnSCn, sarcosine, and citrate. Bring to 100 ml with water, and stir till dissolved (can heat gently); verify that pH is about 7.0.

2.   Filter (Nalgene 0.45 micron filter).

3.   Finally adjust volume to 100 ml, add mercaptoethanol and antifoam.

4.   Store tightly sealed in amber bottle at room temperature, indefinitely.

5.7 M CsCl

CsCl (5.7 M)	95.8 g
NaCitrate (25 mM, pH 5.5)	<u>2.5 ml of 1 M NaCitrate, pH 5.5</u>
	Add ddH$_2$O to 100 ml

1. Pass through Nalgene filter.

2. DEPC treat.

3. Autoclave.

1 M sodium citrate (pH 5.5 or pH 7)

1. Start with 147 g sodium citrate.

2. Bring to 400 ml with ddH$_2$O.

3. Adjust the pH to 5.5 or 7 with HCl.

4. Bring to 500 ml with ddH$_2$O.

RNA preparation using LiCl-urea

Useful for small amounts of tissue or cells.

Adapted from Auffray, C., and O. Rougeon *Eur. J. Biochem.* 107:303 (1979).

1. Homogenize the frozen or fresh tissue (or harvested cultured cells) in 5–10 ml of 3 M LiCl/6 M urea per gram of tissue for 2 min at 0° using a polytron, ultra-turra dounce, Waring blender, or other device. We usually homogenize in 15-ml or 50-ml sterile Falcon tubes. If very small amounts of cells or tissues are used, homogenize in 0.5 ml (using microtip on polytron) and then transfer sample to microfuge tubes.

   A single mouse spleen, or less than 20 million cells, can be worked up in 1 ml.

   Expect about 10 μg total RNA for 10 million cells.

   3 M LiCl/6 M Urea: 126 g LiCl plus 360 g urea per liter of ddH$_2$O, then filter.

2. Keep homogenate greater than 4 hr at 0°-4°. (RNA will last indefinitely in the LiCl solution.)

3. For large preps in 50-ml tubes spin in a refrigerated benchtop centrifuge for 30 min at 3 krpm (2,000 x g). For microfuge tubes spin 30 min at 4°.

4. Pour off supernatant, add back 1/2 volume of cold 3 M LiCl/6 M urea, vortex or mix well and recentrifuge. Discard supernatant. If pellet is not tight after the first spin (i.e., it is viscous because all of the DNA is not sheared), shear the pellet by squirting through 21-gauge needle several times and then respin it.

5. Dissolve the pellet in 10 mM Tris·HCl (pH 7.6), 1 mM EDTA, 0.5% SDS (equivalent to elution buffer used in poly(A) + RNA prep) using 5 ml/ gram original tissue (i.e., about 1/2 vol of original homogenate).

6. Immediately add an equal volume of phenol:chloroform:isoamylalcohol (25:24:1) and extract 5–10 min with shaking. Often the RNA pellet is slow to dissolve so just add the phenol:CHCl$_3$ and vortex until it all dissolves; a white precipitate usually remains at interface. When you have many samples, keep them for 15–30 min at room temperature while vortexing each several times.

7. Centrifuge in microfuge or benchtop centrifuge and remove the top aqueous layer to a new tube; if there is a heavy interface re-extract the sample once more.

8. Add 1/10 vol 3 M sodium acetate (DEPC treated) and 2 vol EtOH. Store -20° or put on dry ice 10–15 min.

9. Harvest RNA by centrifuging, pour off supernatant, and wash with 70% EtOH.

10. Redissolve sample in DEPC treated ddH$_2$O. The RNA at this stage is fine for Northern analysis, oligo(dT) chromatography, or Sl or RNase protection analysis.

11. *Note*: If in the final EtOH precipitate it is apparent that some DNA has come through it can be removed by bringing the RNA in TE to 2 M LiCl and incubating overnight at 4°. Then pellet RNA by centrifugation, pour off supernatant, redissolve RNA in TE and EtOH-precipitate. This is rarely, if ever, necessary.

RNA preparation using rapid hot phenol method

Useful for small amounts of cells or tissues.

- Works for $5\text{--}40 \times 10^6$ cells. Yields $5\text{--}10$ μg RNA/10^6 cells.
- Take usual RNA precautions (gloves, etc.).
- Stock solutions:
  10% SDS made with DEPC-treated water
  3 M sodium acetate (pH 5.0), DEPC-treated
  DEPC-treated water.
  Phenol equilibrated with 50 mM sodium acetate (pH 5.0)
  100 and 70% ethanol made with DEPC-water

- Working solutions:
  Lysis buffer
  1% SDS/50 mM sodium acetate (pH 5.0)

Protocol:

1. Spin cells down and wash once in PBS. Resuspend in 1 ml PBS and transfer to a microfuge tube. Spin cells down in microfuge for 5 sec.

2. Remove supernatant and flick cell pellet loose (important).

3. Resuspend in 0.5 ml lysis buffer. Add 0.5 ml phenol.

4. Heat at 60° for 15 min while shaking vigorously.

5. Place on ice for 15 min. Spin 5 min at room temperature.

6. Transfer aqueous phase to a new microfuge tube; add 40 μl 3 M sodium acetate and 1 ml of 100% ethanol.

7. Place on dry ice for 15 min. Spin in cold room for 15 min. Wash the pellet with 70% ethanol.

8. Resuspend in 50 μl DEPC treated water. Use 2–5 μl in an appropriate dilution to determine the concentration by optical density.

Preparation of cytoplasmic RNA

This is a rapid procedure that allows for the isolation of high-quality cytoplasmic RNA from large numbers of cells; similar scaled-down protocols allow isolation from small numbers of cells. Samples must be kept ice-cold in early steps to prevent RNA degradation!

1.   Harvest cells. Wash 1x in cold PBS.

2.   Resuspend cells in *ice-cold* lysis buffer (10^8 cells per 3 ml lysis buffer).
     Leave cells on ice for 5 min—the suspension should clear somewhat, indicating lysis; lysis can also be verified under the microscope.

3.   Centrifuge at 1500–2000 rpm for 5 min at 4°.

4.   Transfer cloudy supernatant to new tube containing 20% SDS. *Mix fast* by vortexing (use 10 μl of 20% SDS per 1 ml of supernatant).
     Take care to leave all pelleted nuclei behind (pellet of nuclei can be used separately for preparation of DNA or RNA).

5.   Add 6 μl of 20 mg/ml proteinase K per ml of supernatant. Incubate 15–30 min at 37°.

6.   Vigorously extract twice with phenol:chloroform:isoamyl alcohol (25:24:1).
     Extract once with chloroform:isoamyl alcohol (24:1)
     Add 1/10 volume 3 M sodium acetate and 2.5 volumes of EtOH.
     Incubate at -20° for at least 2 hr.
     Recover RNA by centrifugation (3000 rpm for 30 min at 4°), wash with ethanol and resuspend in RNase-free water or TE and store at -70°.
     Determine A_{260} of a diluted aliquot and use to calculate RNA yield and concentration.

     Lysis Buffer:

     50 mM Tris·HCl (pH 8.0)
     100 mM NaCl
     5 mM $MgCl_2$
     0.5% Nonidet P-40
     _____

Add NP-40 while solution is at room temperature or warmer—dissolve by pipetting solution vigorously—then make solution ice-cold prior to use. RNase inhibitors (RNAsin, vanadyl ribonucleoside complexes) can be added to this solution if degradation appears to be a problem (not usually necessary).

Oligo(dT)-cellulose chromatography: isolation of poly(A)+ RNA

(See the end of this section for preparation of required solutions.)

Column preparation

1. Swell oligo(dT)-cellulose resin (type 3 from Collaborative Research, Inc., Cat. #20003) in binding buffer 5–10 min at 37°; pour off fines twice to improve speed of column. One gram of oligo(dT) expands to about 3–4 ml in binding buffer, and approximately 10 mg of total RNA can be loaded onto a 1-ml column.

2. Pour 1-inch column (into disposable plastic columns; a small amount of tubing can be attached to the bottom of the column to allow it to be regulated using a hemostat) using approximately 1 ml of resin. When pouring and washing columns the flow rate should be adjusted so that resin does not pack too tightly as this will slow the flow rate enormously.

3. Wash column with 10–20 volumes (10–20 ml) of 0.1 N NaOH + 1 mM EDTA (column will turn yellow in color as pH indicator); this will hydrolyze both RNase and any contaminating RNA.
    Then wash with 10–20 ml elution buffer.
    Then 10–20 ml binding buffer.
    For the first wash with a new buffer use 3 x 1 ml fractions first to equilibrate column and then add large volumes.

    The column is now ready for loading RNA in binding buffer.

Loading of RNA onto column

1. Take the OD of RNA and dissolve in elution buffer so that the OD is less than 10 or the RNA concentration is less than 0.4 mg/ml (can load maximum of 5–10 mg in 10 ml).

2. Heat to 68° for 3 min and quickly cool in EtOH/ice bath (important to cool completely); then add NaCl to 400 mM or 500 mM (depending on batch of oligo(dT); check specifications for each batch). RNA is now in binding buffer. If solution gets cloudy, warm to room temperature to get SDS back into solution and load onto column immediately.

3. Run RNA thru oligo(dT) column (previously equilibrated in binding buffer as described above) 3–4 times to ensure binding.

4.   Wash column with 30 ml binding buffer to get rid of non-poly(A)+ RNA. Wash first with 3x 1 ml fractions to get rid of bulk of non-binding RNA, and then wash with larger volumes.

5.   Elute poly(A)+ RNA with elution buffer: let column run until binding buffer is right at top of resin. Add 3 ml of elution buffer, 1 ml at a time: collect all 3 ml in 500 μl fractions. Most of sample comes off in 2nd and 3rd 500 μl fractions. You can check RNA concentration in fractions by OD as long as the blank contains an equal amount of elution buffer.

6.   Now the Poly(A)$^+$ RNA is in a maximum of 3 ml of elution buffer. To precipitate (any or all fractions) add 1/10 volume 4 M NaCl (DEPC treated) and 2 volumes EtOH and sequentially precipitate into 1 or 2 microfuge tubes (freeze samples in dry ice in between sequential precipitations). Alternatively, whole volume can be spun down in baked Corex tubes at 5–8 krpm for 30 min.

7.   Precipitated RNA can be redissolved and A_{260} (of a dilution) determined; for subsequent enzymology (e.g., reverse transcription) it often helps to do an additional precipitation to ensure removal of residual SDS.

To regenerate column

Columns can be reused for months if regenerated. Store columns in binding buffer at room temperature.

1.   Wash with 20 ml 0.1 N NaOH and 1 mM EDTA.

2.   Wash with 10–20 ml elution buffer.

3.   Wash with 10–20 ml binding buffer.
     Once again, when changing buffers, wash with 3x 1 ml fractions first to equilibrate the column and then wash with larger volumes.
     The column is ready for loading the next RNA or for storage.

Solutions for preparation of poly(A)$^+$ RNA

Solutions must be treated with DEPC as described in the previous section.

Elution Buffer	*for 500 ml*
0.5% SDS	25 ml 10%
10 mM Tris·HCl (pH 7.4)	2.5 ml 2 M
1 mM EDTA	1 ml 0.5 M

Binding Buffer   *for 500 ml*

0.5% SDS   25 ml 10%
10 mM Tris·HCl (pH 7.4)   2.5 ml 2 M
1 mM EDTA   1 ml 0.5 M
400 mM NaCl*   50 ml 4 M NaCl

Note: Check specifications of oligo(dT)-cellulose and use 400 or 500 mM NaCl as recommended by manufacturer. SDS can be removed from these solutions (although it helps prevent enzymatic degradation of the RNA), but then higher amounts of NaCl may be necessary for binding.

Analysis of DNA and RNA

POLYMERASE CHAIN REACTION

General considerations

The polymerase chain reaction (PCR) is a procedure used to amplify nucleic acid sequences using repetitive polymerization of DNA sequences. The polymerization is initiated by oligonucleotide primers usually 17–25 nucleotides in length. In the first polymerization cycle, a product should be made that extends beyond the location of the second primer for an unknown and probably variable distance. After the extension step, the entire sample is denatured by heating, reannealed and then extended again using the *Taq* DNA polymerase. This enzyme is resistant to the repetitive heat treatments and does not need to be added for each new extension reaction. During the second extension cycle the primers anneal to all possible templates, which include the original template plus all extension products of the first reaction.

The most common case is the amplification of a small region of DNA 100–400 bp by 10^5-fold or more. As diagrammed in fig 2.1A, primers (represented by arrows) at the termini of the region are usually made about 20 nucleotides in length corresponding to the termini of opposing DNA strands. During the first PCR cycle (1) the primers anneal to the homologous sequences. The polymerase generates a long extension product on both templates.

During the second PCR cycle half of the reaction products are equivalent to those produced in the first PCR cycle. However the other half are products initiated on the PCR products from the first cycle and terminate at the site of the first primers. During each subsequent cycle of denaturation, annealing, and extension there is an exponential accumulation of this type of product, which is the region between the two primers.

The reaction is also very capable of amplifying sequences present in mRNA after they have been converted into cDNA. Recently it has been used to isolate the 5' and 3' termini of cDNAs. In the case of the 5' terminal regions the DNA sequence for an oligo primer is unknown but can be replaced by homopolymer tailing procedures (see Loh et al. *Science* 243:217–222, 1989; Frohman et al. *PNAS* 85:8998–9002, 1988).

As diagrammed in figure 2.1B the first primer (labeled 1) is used to synthesize cDNA. Subsequently homopolymer tails of poly(dG) or poly(dA) are added using terminal deoxynucleotidyl transferase. A second strand primer containing poly(dC) or poly(T) is used to synthesize the second strand sequence. Extra nucleotides, indicated XYZ, are usually added to this primer to facilitate subsequent subcloning of the reaction products as well as increase the specificity of the second strand reaction. To begin the PCR amplification a second primer (labeled 2) can be used (in step 3) to increase the specificity of the PCR products. For sequences of relatively high abundance this second

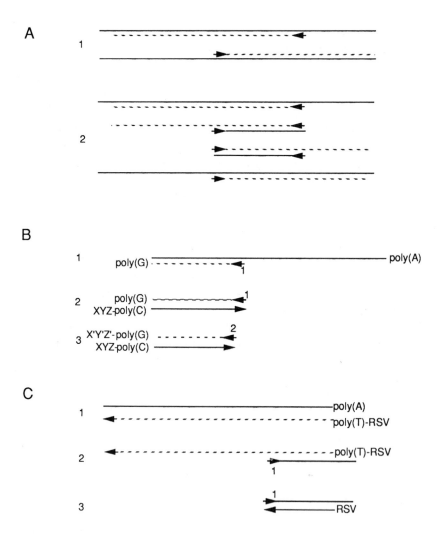

Figure 2.1. Amplification strategies for the polymerase chain reaction.

primer may not be necessary. The XYZ-poly(C) primer or an XYZ primer can be used to synthesize the second strand in the PCR amplification steps.

Amplification of the 3' ends of known sequences is more straightforward. A poly(T) primer containing DNA sequences RSV is used to synthesize cDNA. The PCR amplification can then be set up using the primer 1 and either poly(T)-RSV or RSV. In these reactions the primers XYZ, RSV, and ones located in known sequences should have restriction sites in them to facilitate molecular cloning of the PCR products.

This technique is incredibly versatile and has been used to detect point mutations in DNA, to analyze RNA splicing patterns, to determine DNA sequences without the need for prior molecular cloning, to analyze transfected cells for certain patterns of integration prior to cellular cloning, to isolate sequences from single cells, and for many other purposes. A recent review by C. Oste can be found in *BioTechniques* 6:162–167(1988). The PCR may be performed manually but it is certainly more easily done by a Thermal Cycler machine. This was first designed by Perkins-Elmer Cetus in Norwalk, Connecticut. Less expensive machines are available from Coy Laboratory Products, Inc. in Ann Arbor, Michigan and USA/Scientific Plastics, Ocala, Florida.

PCR conditions for DNA samples

Assemble the reaction for the *Taq* polymerase in this order:

61 µl	ddH$_2$O
10 µl	10x mix (100 mM Tris·HCl [pH 8.3], 500 mM KCl, 15 mM MgCl$_2$, 0.1% gelatin)
8 µl	2.5 mM dNTPs
5 µl	20 µM oligonucleotide primer 1 (about 130 µg/ml of a 20-mer)
5 µl	20 µM oligonucleotide primer 2
10 µl	DNA template (the amount can vary but 1 µg is fine)
1 µi	*Taq* polymerase (2.5 units)
100 µl	

PCR conditions for samples of total RNA

The conditions described here are appropriate to amplify DNA between two oligo primers of known sequence. If one wishes to use homopolymer tailing steps prior to the PCR additional steps must be inserted(see references listed above).

1. Assemble the reverse transcriptase reaction. These conditions are set up so the PCR is done directly on the total reaction products after the synthesis of the cDNA.

61 µl   5x buffer (250 mM Tris·HCl [pH 8.3], 375 mM KCl,
          50 mM DTT, 15 mM MgCl$_2$)
10 µl   2.5 mM dNTPs
2.5 µl   20 µM antisense oligonucleotide
2.5 µl   reverse transcriptase (500 units)
24 µl   ddH$_2$O
<u>1 µl</u>   total cellular RNA at 1 µg/ µl
50 µl

2. Incubate 60 min at 37° and then place on ice.

3. Add 50 µl of the following solution. If one has multiple samples one can
   scale up this solution appropriately.

10 µl   0.1% gelatin
2.5 µl   20 µM antisense oligonucleotide
5 µl   20 µM sense oligonucleotide
12.5 µl 0.1 M KCl
<u>20 µl   ddH$_2$O</u>
50 µl

4. Run the PCR reaction after adding 2.5 units of *Taq* polymerase to the
   reaction. Overlay the sample with mineral oil.

The following reaction conditions are suitable for products between 100–400
nucleotides in length.

1. Denaturation: 95° for 4 min.

2. Cycle (use between 20–90 cycles; 30 cycles would be a reasonable number to use initially).

   a) 72° to 95° over 1 min

   b) 95° to 55° over 1 min

   c) 55° to 72° over 30 sec

   d) 72° for 2 min

3. Final extension: 72° for 5 min. This step is designed to insure that all
   reaction products are full length.

4. Soak: 4°. This enables the user to run a PCR overnight and have the
   products waiting the next morning "on ice."

SOUTHERN BLOTS

Introduction

The analysis of DNA fragments in agarose gels is one of the most basic forms of analysis. The hybridization and analysis of DNAs in the conventional size range (0.5 to 20 kb) produced by many commonly used enzymes may be done using common procedures with a few variations. The variations in technique occur after the gel has been run. For DNAs in the conventional range the transfer is generally adequate. However there are two ways to nick the DNAs in the gel to facilitate the transfer. The DNA can be photo-nicked with UV light or depurinated.

Next there is a choice of membranes to use. Nitrocellulose has been more commonly used but the newer nylon membranes are more durable and can be reused more successfully. If one wishes to use nitrocellulose membranes to perform the hybridization one must first denature the DNA and then renature it. The transfer is generally in 10x SSC or 20x SSC. The higher salt may enhance the transfer of larger DNAs but requires more reagents. After the DNA is transferred the membrane is rinsed with 2x SSC, air dried, and baked at 80° to fix the DNA on the membrane. Batches of nitrocellulose can vary considerably in the degree to which they can be hydrated prior to setting up the transfer. One way to test a batch of nitrocellulose is to cut a narrow strip from a roll and set it on fire. If it burns very quickly it is good. If it does not burn quickly it may not wet well.

If one chooses to use nylon membranes one can perform the transfer directly in alkali (0.4 N). The DNA is directly coupled to the membrane and no baking is needed. After the DNA is on the membrane there are three different hybridization methods available. There are the standard aqueous conditions and formamide conditions both of which may also include the use of dextran sulfate to enhance the rate of hybridization. The conditions developed by Church and Gilbert employing BSA, SDS, and phosphate buffer are also very sensitive.

Many of these conditions work very well. Experience will result in the development of certain preferences. At present this author would recommend no form of nicking for conventional gels. Photo-nicking is preferable to depurination for large DNAs. The depurination is hard to perform reproducibly. It is easy to overnick the DNA and then it is difficult to detect with the probe. The alkali denaturation and transfer to nylon membranes is easier and probably results in a greater amount of the DNA being available for hybridization on the membrane. Finally, the use of hexamer primed probes using the Gilbert and Church conditions gives very good sensitivity. The choice of hybridization conditions may be less important. A new device called a Stratalinker produced by Stratagene may be very useful for many cross-linking purposes. It is able to monitor its output so that the appropriate amount of exposure is achieved.

Conventional Southern blots

1. Digest DNA with the appropriate restriction enzyme. Typically one uses a total of 10 μg of DNA per digest. If the volume of the digest is large, heat-kill enzyme and EtOH-precipitate. Resuspend the DNA in 1x sample buffer. Heat the samples 10–20 min at 65° to dissolve before loading.

2. Fractionate the DNA on a horizontal 1% agarose gel, using E buffer in the gel and in the running buffer (analytical gels using cloned DNA can be run in TBE). Recirculate the buffer. Continue electrophoresing until the bromophenol blue migrates about 14 cm, about 30–35 volts overnight.

3. Stain the gel for 10 min in ethidium bromide (about 0.5 μg/ml) dissolved in E buffer and photograph.

4. Expose the gel to UV to nick the DNA if desired. The UV box should be titered to achieve optimal nicking. Five min on a Fotodyne transilluminator works well.

    For a transfer to nitrocellulose continue to step 5. If you are going to use a nylon membrane go to 5A.

5. Denature the gel in 0.5 N NaOH, 0.6 M NaCl for 1 hr.

6. Neutralize in 1 M Tris·HCl (pH 7.4), 1.5 M NaCl for 1 hr.

7. Transfer DNA to nitrocellulose. Saturate 2 sponges in blot box with 10x SSC. Fit a piece of filter paper over and down the sponges and along bottom and up sides of box. Place gel over paper, smoothing out any air bubbles. Layer with a piece of nitrocellulose the size of the gel soaked in 2x SSC. Place a piece of wet filter paper over the nitrocellulose, smoothing out any air bubbles. Repeat with 2 more pieces of wet filter paper. Layer 7 more pieces of dry filter paper on top. Layer with 2–3 inches of dry paper toweling. Place a dry glass plate on top and weigh down. Let sit for at least 6 hr, generally overnight.

8. After the DNA is transferred, remove towels and filter paper. Wash nitrocellulose with 2x SSC to remove any pieces of gel. Dry, then bake in an 80° vacuum oven for 2 hr.

9. Process according to the conditions described for dextran sulfate/formamide or Church and Gilbert hybridization in section 9 on probes.

5A. Denature the gel in 0.4 N NaOH for 30 min at room temperature.

6A. Set up the transfer just as in step 7 but the transfer buffer is 0.4 N NaOH. Sponges may deteriorate over time and leach contaminants onto the filter. Paper wicks are a good alternative.

7A. After the transfer, rinse the membrane in 2x SSC if you are going to use SSC in the hybridization solution. Process according to the conditions described for dextran sulfate/formamide hybridization. If you are going to use the Church and Gilbert conditions you can rinse the membrane in 0.5 M phosphate buffer (pH 6.8) (see the Church and Gilbert hybridization conditions in the section 9 on probes). Check the pH of the solution after 2–3 rinses to make sure it is not alkaline.

Blotting minigels and cloned DNA

Use the same procedure for blotting minigels of cloned DNA except that denaturation/neutralization times are reduced to 30 min each and transfer is adequate after 2 hr.

Reduced stringency Southern blots

Three parameters can easily be varied to affect the stringency of hybridization: 1) temperature of hybridization, 2) percentage formamide in the hybridization mix, and 3) temperature and salt of the wash solutions. Generally, we have found it convenient to vary the percentage formamide and the temperature of the washes, keeping the temperature of hybridization constant at 42° and the salt in the wash solution constant at 2x SSC in 0.1% SDS. Reducing the stringency of hybridization is achieved by reducing the percent formamide or by decreasing the temperature of the wash solution. Of these two parameters the percent formamide is usually more important in determining stringency. Typical reduced stringency parameters are: formamide at 30–40% in the hybridization solution, washing at 56° (but these parameters usually have to be worked out empirically depending on the specific probe used). The effective hybridization temperature is reduced approximately 0.7° for each decrease of 1% in formamide concentration. Reduced stringency under aqueous conditions can be achieved by reducing the temperature of the hybridization or the wash (i.e., a 65° hybridization followed by a 56° wash or a 56° hybridization followed by a 56° wash). There are occasions where these aqueous conditions work very well and the other methods were completely unsuccessful.

Pulsed-field gel electrophoresis (PFGE)

Analysis of DNA fragments larger than 20 kb by Southern blotting procedures was not very adequate until the development of pulsed-field electrophoresis. This technique has now made possible the construction of restriction maps up to 13,000 kb (see Compton et al. 1988; Orbach et al. 1988). Recent modification of the electrophoresis conditions permits the resolution of individual fragments 12 mb in size.

DNA fragments larger than 50 kb electrophorese in a conventional unidirectional electric field in a size-independent manner are often modeled as a one-dimensional, wormlike migration termed *reptation*, and are consequently not resolved. Alternating the orientation of the electric field apparently forces the DNA molecules to reorient their path of migration, which is a size-dependent phenomenon and thus allows fractionation into the megabase range. Molecules whose reorientation time is approximated by the switching interval will be most affected by the alternating field. A window of resolution can therefore be made to encompass a particular molecular weight range by judicious selection of pulse times.

Orthogonal field alternating gel electrophoresis (OFAGE) employs two diode-isolated nonuniform fields, opposed at 90° or 120° (45° or 60° from the axis of DNA migration). As a result, the outer lanes display an increasing curvature, sometimes compromising the ability to make size comparisons.

Field inversion gel electrophoresis (FIGE) utilizes the periodic inversion of a single uniform field through a full 180° and so can make use of a conventional gel tank. With this technique, lanes track in straight lines, but display a mobility minimum in a molecular weight range characteristic of the switching interval used. This can be overcome by the use of pulse time ramps in which the length of the switching interval is increased over time so that molecules of increasing size can be brought into resolution range.

In *transverse alternating field electrophoresis* (TAFE), orthogonally opposed fields traverse the depth of a vertical gel at 45° from the gel axis. As a result DNA lanes run true and ramping is unnecessary. Buffer volumes, however, especially with larger gels, can be considerable.

Finally, electrophoresis via a contour *clamped homogeneous electric field* (CHEF) uses a series of equal resistors interposed between multiple electrodes, thus forming an enclosed perimeter. Because this is a modification of the orthogonal field method, reorientation angles are generally 90° or 120°. The uniform fields generated by this design allow for distortion-free, straight lanes with a good monotonic relationship between migration and molecular weight.

Parameters that have been implicated as critical to good resolution are: 1) *reorientation angle*–better resolution occurs at the greater angle; 2) *temperature*-buffer recirculation is required to maintain uniform temperature and to minimize differential heating effects (gels are generally run at 5° to 15°); 3) *voltage*–in general lower voltage potentials produce sharper bands, both by minimizing heating and by reducing the migration rate relative to the reorientation rate.

The following table may be used as a guideline for orthogonal-type and inversion gels, respectively.

Table 2.1. Separation of DNA on orthogonal type gels

Pulse time	Resolution range
1 sec	10–40 kb
5 sec	60–90 kb
25 sec	200–300 kb
45 sec	400–550 kb
100 sec	700–900 kb

Separation of DNA on field inversion gels

Forward: reverse ratio	Forward ramp	Resolution range
2:1	0.06–1.2 sec	10–50 kb
3:1	0.03–6 sec	100–300 kb
3:1	0.3–30 sec	500–800 kb
3:1	0.3–60 sec	700–1000 kb
3:1	3–75 sec	1000–2000 kb

The agarose gel concentration is typically 1% (0.8% to 1.5%) and the running/gel buffer is usually 0.5 x TBE (45 mM Tris base, 45 mM boric acid, 10 mM EDTA [pH 8.3]), although other buffers such as Tris-acetate may be used. The large tanks required for OFAGE necessitate a setting of 330 volts or more (100 to 120 mA in 0.5 x TBE) to achieve 10 V/cm across a 20-cm x 20-cm gel.

A similar FIGE gel can be set up to run at 140 V or 7 V/cm (50–60 mA in 0.5 x TBE).

Useful enzymes for PFGE are: *Apa* I, *Bcl* I, *Bss*H II, *Cla* I, *Eag* I, *Kpn* I, *Mlu* I, *Nae* I, *Nar* I, *Not* I, *Nru* I, *Pvu* I, *Sac* II, *Sal* I, *Sfi* I, *Sma* I, *Spe* I, and *Xho* I. The use of enzymes that recognize sequences containing one or more CG dinucleotides is a double-edged sword, however. The ability of the sites to be methylated has made them suitably rare in the genome, but partial methylation may then render some fraction of sites impossible to cleave. Size markers are best made by embedding yeast cells or whole λ phage in agarose at 5×10^8 to 5×10^9 cells/ml (load 0.5 to 5 μg) and 30 to 300 ng DNA/ μl (load 0.5 to 2 μg), respectively, and following the standard protocol. Note that the extent of λ multimerization is controlled by the concentration of DNA during the incubation step.

Preparation of high molecular weight DNA

Homogenize one fresh mouse spleen with a few strokes of a Dounce homogenizer in 1 x PBS at 4°. Spin for 5 min at 2 krpm in a clinical centrifuge. Resuspend in 10 to 25 ml of cold PBS, count, spin, and resuspend at 50 x 10^3 cells/ µl in PBS at 42° (an average spleen will contain 100 to 300 x 10^6 cells). Add an equal volume of 1% low melting temperature agarose (BRL LMP agarose or FMC Incert) in PBS at 42°. Dispense into commercial molds or 1/8-inch I.D. Tygon tubing and allow to set for 15–20 min at 4°.

Remove from the molds or tubing (the latter produces an agarose worm which must be cut into 1 cm plugs). These plugs or inserts are then lysed at 50°-56° for 48 hr in a solution of 0.5 M EDTA (pH 8.0), 1% sodium lauryl sarcosine and 2 mg/ml proteinase K (50 ml is sufficient for 1 spleen). If a rotating bath is not available, occasional inversion is adequate.

After the incubation is complete, wash the plugs with 50 ml of sterile TE(10 mM Tris·HCl [pH 8], 1 mM EDTA) buffer four times, 30 min each at 50°–56°. Then wash in 50 ml of TE with 40 µg/ml PMSF (from a 40 mg/ml stock made fresh in isopropanol) three times, 1 to 2 hr each at room temperature (or overnight at 4°). Store the plugs at 4° in TE or TE/PMSF.

Restriction digests

For restriction digestion, quarter a plug by cutting into 0.5 cm plugs and then slicing perpendicularly (each one quarter plug contains about 20 µl for a total of 500 x 10^3 cells or, at approximately 5 pg DNA/mouse cell, a total of 2.5 µg DNA). A typical digest takes place in 100 µl: 20 µl DNA, 10 µl 10x buffer, 1–10 units of enzyme/ µg DNA and H_2O. The final concentration of restriction buffer is 10 mM Tris·HCl (pH 7.5), 10 mM $MgCl_2$, 10 mM 2-mercaptoethanol, 100 µg/ml acetylated BSA (BRL) and 0, 50, 100, or 150 mM NaCl. Special buffers may be required for enzymes such as *BssH* II, *Not* I, *Nru* I and *Sfi* I. Triton X-100 at 0.01% (membrane quality, Boehringer-Mannheim) or spermidine at 5 mM may help some enzymes.

Digests are incubated for 30 min on ice to allow equilibration, then activated at the appropriate temperature for 6 to 8 hr or overnight. Following digestion, individual plugs are washed with 1 ml of TE and then held in TE with bromophenol blue on ice for at least 30 min.

Plugs are loaded into wells with their flat surface against the front of the well using forceps or a bent pasteur pipette and then sealed with low melting temperature agarose. The gel can then be immersed in the tank and electrophoresis begun.

Gel transfer and hybridization

Following the run, the gel is stained for photography with ethidium bromide at 0.5 µg/ml for 20 to 30 min, then destained for 10 to 15 min. The DNA is photo-nicked by exposure to the transilluminator UV source for 5 min.

If a nitrocellulose membrane is to be used, denature the gel for 60 min in 0.5 N NaOH, 1.5 M NaCl and then neutralize it for 60 min in 1 M Tris·HCl (pH 5), 3 M NaCl. After transfer with 20x SSC for 24 hr, the nitrocellulose filter is washed briefly in 2x SSC, blotted dry, and baked for 2 hr at 80°.

Prehybridize for 3 hr at 65° in 4x SSC, 5x Denhardt's, 0.1% SDS, 0.1% sodium pyrophosphate, 10% dextran sulfate and 200 µg/ml denatured salmon sperm DNA.

Hybridize at 65° for 24 hr with 1 x 10⁶ cpm/ml. Wash in 2x SSC, 0.1% SDS, 0.1% pyrophosphate at the same temperature.

If a nylon membrane is used (BioRad Zetaprobe), rinse briefly in 50 mM sodium phosphate buffer (pH 6.8 to 7.2) following transfer in 20x SSC, bake for 2 hr at 80°, then cross-link the DNA to the filter with shortwave UV for 2 min.

Alternatively, these membranes can tolerate direct alkaline transfer. Following photo-nicking, denature in 0.4 N NaOH and transfer in the same solution using Whatman 3MM paper wicks instead of sponges.

These blots are hybridized by a modification of the method of Church and Gilbert. Prehybridize for 1 hr at 65° in 0.5 M sodium phosphate buffer, 7% SDS, 1 mM EDTA, and 200 µg/ml denatured salmon sperm DNA. The probe is added to 3–5 x 10⁶ dpm/ml and the filter hybridized for 24 hr at 65°.

Washes are 40 mM sodium phosphate buffer containing 1% SDS, twice for 5 min at room temperature, then 1 to 2 hr at 65°. Stripwash filters for rehybridization with 0.1x SSC, 0.1% SDS at 95° for 4 times 15 min for each wash.

REFERENCES

OFAGE	Schwartz, D. C., and C. R Cantor *Cell* 37:67 (1984).
FIGE	Carle, G. F., and M. V. Olson *Nucl. Acids Res.* 12:5647 (1984).
TAFE	Gardines, K., et al. *Somatic Cell and Mol. Gen.* 12:185 (1986).
CHEF	Chu, G., et al. *Science* 234: 1583 (1986).
	Anand, R. *TIG*, Nov., 278 (1986).
Transfer	Reed, K. C., and D. A. Mann *Nucl. Acids Res.* 13:7207 (1985).
λ multimers	Waterbury, P. G., and M. J. Lane *Nucl. Acids Res.* 15:3930 (1987).
Yeast markers	Carle, G. F., and M. V. Olson *Proc. Nat. Acad. Sci. USA* 82:3756 (1985).
Hybridization	Church, G., and W. Gilbert *Proc. Nat. Acad. Sci. USA* 81:1991 (1984).
Higher resolution	Compton, D. A., M. M. Weil, C. Jones, V. M. Riccardi, L. C. Strong, and G.F. Saunders *Cell* 55:827–836 (1988).
	Orbach, M. J., D. Vollrath, R. W. Davis, and C. C. Yanofsky, C. C. *Molec. Cell. Biol.* 8:1469–1473 (1988).

YEAST CHROMOSOME MARKERS FOR PULSED-FIELD GELS

1. Grow 100 ml of the desired strain of yeast to saturation (200 OD) in YM media at 30°. Harvest the cells by centrifugation at 5 krpm for 5 min. Resuspend the cells in 15 ml of 50 mM EDTA (pH 7.5). Repeat the centrifugation step and again resuspend in 15 ml of 50 mM EDTA (pH 7.5). Repeat the centrifugation step and resuspend in 3 ml of 50 mM EDTA (pH 7.5).

2. Dissolve by heating a 1% low-melting-point agarose solution in 125 mM EDTA (pH 7.5). Cool to 38° and add 5 ml to the resuspended cells.

3. Add 100 μl of Zymolase 20T or 100T and mix (prepare and use within one week in 10 mM sodium phosphate (pH 7.2), 50% glycerol). The 20T or 100T refers to 20,000 or 100,000 units per g. Dissolve an appropriate amount so that you add 200 units of enzyme/100 μl.

4. Pipette onto parafilm or plastic wrap about eighty 100 μl aliquots of the solution as individual beads or plugs.

5. After about 10 min they will be cool. Add the plugs to 5 ml of 50 mM EDTA, 10 mM Tris·HCl (pH 7.5). Bring the β-mercaptoethanol to 5%. Incubate 2–8 hr or overnight at 37°.

6. Remove the solution by draining and replace it with about 6 ml of 10 mM Tris·HCl (pH 8.8), 50 mM EDTA, 1% N-Lauroyl sarcosine or SDS containing 1 mg/ml proteinase K. Incubate overnight at 50°.

7. Dialyze the plugs by soaking in 50 mM EDTA, 10 mM Tris·HCl (pH 7.5) at room temperature for 30 min. Store the beads in this solution at 4°. They should be good for several years.

   The beads can be melted at 67° and loaded into wells using a 100-μl capillary pipette which preserves the integrity of the DNA. Use about 20 μl per lane. Therefore 400 lanes worth of DNA are obtained from 100 ml of a yeast culture.

Zymolase (Code #320921) from ICN Immunobiologicals, P.O. Box 1200, Lisle, IL 60532

YM media

1/10 vol YNB
1/10 vol 20% glucose
Supplements if required by the yeast strain

YNB

1.7 g Difco yeast nitrogen base (w/o amino acid and $(NH_4)_2SO_4$
5 g $(NH_4)_2SO_4$
100 ml H_2O

REFERENCE

Mike Snyder, personal communication.

SLOT BLOTTING PROTOCOLS

Cytoplasmic RNA dot blots

1. Harvest 10^6 to 10^7 cells. (Numbers in parentheses indicate values for 10^8 cells.)

2. Pellet by centrifugation (1 krpm for 10 min).

3. Resuspend in 1 ml PBS.

4. Repellet in a sterile 1.5 ml tube (microfuge for 15 sec).

5. Resuspend in 45 μl of ice-cold TE (180 μl).

6. Lyse cells by addition of two 5 μl (20 μl) aliquots of 5% NP-40 with 5 min of mixing on ice in between.

7. Pellet nuclei in a microfuge for 2.5 min. A fuzzy pellet is formed.

8. Add 50 μl (200 μl) of the supernatant to 30 μl (120 μl) 20x SSC and 20 μl (80 μl) 37% formaldehyde in sterile 1.5 ml tube.

9. Incubate at 60° for 15 min.

10. Store at -70°.

11. For analysis, dilute 5–20 μl of each sample with 20x SSC and slot blot onto nitrocellulose. Bake, prehybridize, and hybridize as usual.

    Note: Cellular debris may make slot blotting difficult. For this purpose, it is sometimes better to spin the sample for 10 min at 4° in the microfuge and take off the supernatant (leaving debris in the pellet)—this should go through the slot blotter much more quickly.

REFERENCE

White, Bruce A., and F. Bancroft *J. Biol. Chem.* 257:8569 (1982).

RNA slot blots

1. Wet nitrocellulose in ddH$_2$O and then soak it in 20x SSC at 42° for at least 1 hr.

2. Rinse the slot blot apparatus with 0.1 N NaOH. Then rinse it with ddH$_2$O very well.

3. To assemble the apparatus: wet 2 sheets of blotting paper in 20x SSC. Place on the bottom of the apparatus. Smooth the nitrocellulose onto the underside of the top. Put the two parts together.

4. Rinse the wells twice with 10x SSC.

5. Denature the RNA in 50 µl:

	Final concentration
25 µl formamide	50% formamide
8 µl formaldehyde	6% formaldehyde
2 µl 20x SSC	1x SSC
15 µl RNA in ddH$_2$O	

Heat at 68° for 15 min. Cool on ice. Make appropriate dilution.

6. Add 200–400 µl of 20x SSC.

7. Load samples without suction. Apply vacuum. Rinse twice with 10x SSC. After the last rinse, leave the vacuum on for 5 min.

8. Rinse the filter with 10x SSC. Dry. Bake in a vacuum oven at 80° for 2 hr. Prehybridize and hybridize as usual.

9. Rinse the apparatus as described above (NaOH + H$_2$O) and let air-dry at room temperature.

DNA slot blots

1. Wet nitrocellulose and blotting paper in 2x SSC. Assemble the apparatus as described above.

2. DNA Sample Preparation:
Denature for 10 min using 0.2 N NaOH.
Chill on ice.
Dilute with 10x SSC.
Load onto slot blotter as above.
Rinse as above.

NORTHERN BLOTS

Northern blots reveal hybridization to RNA that has been separated in denaturing in agarose gels. The denaturation can be accomplished by glyoxal/DMSO or formaldehyde. After the electrophoresis the RNA is transferred to nitrocellulose. Glyoxal gels can also be transferred to nylon membranes which are more durable and easier to handle. The hybridization can be achieved by several different methods. The hybridization conditions developed by Church and Gilbert using BSA, SDS, and phosphate buffer work very well for this Northern procedure. These conditions are excellent for many purposes including pulsed field Southern blotting. The glyoxal Northern procedure is highly recommended. The use of RNA probes on Northern blots does not work well because of the interaction of probe with rRNAs. Washing conditions can be adjusted to reduce the background but the results are still not satisfactory for many purposes.

Northern blot (glyoxal denaturation)

Electrophoresis

1. Add 20 μl of 1.5x sample buffer to 10 μl of RNA in DEPC-treated ddH$_2$O (may contain up to 20 μg RNA) and denature by incubating at 50° for 1 hr.

2. Place on ice and add 2 μl of 50% sucrose containing 0.025% bromophenol blue dye.

3. Load onto a 1.5 to 2.0% agarose gel in 10 mM phosphate buffer. Electrophorese at 5 V/cm or less to avoid overheating. Buffer recirculation is required to prevent glyoxal dissociation from RNA due to pH changes.

4. Transfer overnight with 20x SSC following standard procedures (see Southern blot). The gel is kept 10 mM phosphate and is not preequilibrated in transfer buffer. Wet a nylon blotting membrane (Zetabind, AMF-Cuno) with H$_2$O and place on top of the gel. After the transfer the membrane is washed briefly with 2x SSC, blotted dry, and then air-dried for 30 min.

5. The RNA is then cross-linked to the filter by exposure to shortwave UV light (260 nm) for 3 min and can be visualized during this step.

6. Generally it is wise to photograph the gel at this stage using the standard UV light box. In this case the source of UV is the hand-held shortwave UV light source which is directed from the side towards the gels for 10 sec from each of three sides. During this time the shutter is held

open by placing it in the B position. On many cameras this can be held in place by a set screw. The f-stop is set at 8 and a yellow filter is placed over the lens.

7.   Hybridize according to the Church and Gilbert conditions as described in Section 9.

Materials

Deionized glyoxal

Use technical grade 40% glyoxal (Kodak or equivalent) and deionize over Biorad AG 501-X8(D) mixed bed resin. Repeat passes until pH approaches neutrality. Aliquot and freeze.

Running/Gel buffer stock

1 M Na_2HPO_4 (dibasic)
1 M NaH_2PO_4 (monobasic)

Add monobasic to dibasic solution until the pH is 6.8 to give a 1 M stock. It is optional to DEPC treat it but autoclave the final solution.

Sample buffer (1.5x)

	2 ml	Final concentration
1 M phosphate buffer stock	30 μl	10 mM
SpectroGrade DMSO (Fisher)	1.5 ml	50% (v/v)
Deionized glyoxal	435 μl	1 M
10% SDS	30 μl	0.1%
DEP-treated ddH$_2$O	5 μl	

Mix well, aliquot and freeze at -20°.

Northern blot (formaldehyde gels)

Electrophoresis

Load 5 μg of "denatured" total cellular RNA per lane.

Mix 1 vol RNA plus 2 vol 1.5 x sample buffer.
Denature by heating at 65° for 5 min then quick-chill.
Add 1/2 vol 5x loading buffer, then load gel.

Run at 25 volts (12 mA) overnight, recirculating the buffer. With such low ionic strength buffer, good recirculation is critical. Higher voltage is not appropriate.

1. Staining. One may visualize the rRNA in the sample by staining with 33 μg/ml acridine orange and viewing the gel under UV light. Ethidium bromide (used at 0.5 μg/ml) stains RNA, but poorly. If the gel has been stained, the stain must be removed prior to transfer. It is by far most convenient to load a side lane with a rRNA (or other marker) sample, and to cut this lane off and stain and visualize it alone while separately transferring the rest of the gel. Be sure to orient the marker lane with respect to the rest of the gel by keying the two with india ink.

2. Transfer. Take the unstained, untreated gel, flip it onto 3 or 4 sheets of 3 MM saturated with transfer solution, and transfer just as with a Southern, using 10x SPE or 10x SSC to transfer the RNA to nitrocellulose. The transfer should proceed for 12–18 hr. After transfer, *do not* rinse the nitrocellulose (this removes the RNA)—bake the filter directly, at 80° for one hour.

3. Hybridization and washes as with a Southern blot.

Materials

IMPORTANT: Formaldehyde vapors are toxic. Work in the hood when preparing solutions, and keep gel boxes covered whenever possible. Formaldehyde gels are slippery, and horizontal gel apparatuses are best suited to them.

Formaldehyde (HCHO, MW 30) comes as a 37% (i.e., 12.3 M) solution.

1 M Na_2PO_4 (pH 6):   97 gm NaH_2PO_4 (MW 138)
                          44 gm NaH_2PO_4 (MW 142)
                          per liter
    This solution is pH 6.0 at 1 M, and the pH rises to 6.7 at 10 mM. Sterilize solution by autoclaving before storing.

1% agarose, 1.1 M formaldehyde gel in 10 mM NaPO₄:

1 gm agarose
90 ml ddH$_2$O
1 ml 1 M NaPO$_4$ (pH 6.0)

Microwave to melt agarose.
Cool solution to 60° and then add 9 ml 37% formaldehyde.
Mix solution and pour gel.

Running buffer

0.5 M HCHO   40 ml HCHO
10 mM NaPO$_4$ (pH 6.7)   10 ml 1 M NaPO$_4$ (pH 6.0)
                   per liter

Sample buffer

                   for 3 ml 1.5 x s.b.

50% formamide   2.15 ml formamide
2.2 M HCHO   0.8 ml HCHO
10 mM NaPO$_4$ (pH 6.7)   45 µl 1 M NaPO$_4$ (pH 6.0)
0.5 mM EDTA   4.5 µl 0.5 M EDTA

Loading buffer

                   for 1 ml 5 x 1.b.

0.1% SDS   24 µl 20% SDS
5% glycerol   0.5 ml 50% glycerol
5 mM EDTA   50 µl 0.5 M EDTA
50 µg/ml BPB dye   50 µl 5 mg/ml BPB dye
                   0.38 ml ddH$_2$O

Notes: One need not sterilize buffers or take other antinuclease precautions during gel electrophoresis of RNA. These low ionic strength gels are designed for effective transfer of RNA to nitrocellulose. Rinse the gel apparatus and the pump with distilled water before using. Rinse afterward, too—this buffer is not reusable.

REFERENCE

Meinkoth and Wahl *Anal. Biochem.* 138, 267 (1984).

ANALYSIS OF RNA USING SP6 RNA PROBES

SP6 probes can be used like M13 probes in protection type experiments. Transcription is carried out as described in section 9. Probes synthesized according to this protocol are of very high specific activity and degrade rapidly; they should be used the same day they are synthesized. Probes of lower specific activity are more stable and seem to work well in these experiments (use 1 μl of ^{32}P-rCTP; add cold rCTP to final concentration of 15 mM).

The hybridization conditions (% formamide, temperature, salt) are the same as those for S1 mapping with M13 probes. Digestion of unprotected probe can be carried out with RNase A/RNase T1 or S1 nuclease. Samples digested with S1 nuclease have less background. Regardless of which method is used for digestion, the enzyme should be titered (digest an aliquot of the probe and carrier with increasing amounts of enzyme, and assay for TCA precipitable counts).

For RNase A/RNase T1

Add 350 μl 10 mM Tris·HCl (pH 7.5)/5 mM EDTA/300 mM NaCl containing 40 μg/ml RNase A and 2 μg/ml RNase T1.

Incubate for 30 min at 30°.

Add:

5 μg proteinase K
10 μl 20% SDS

Incubate at 37° for 15 min.
Samples are phenol-extracted, precipitated, and analyzed on a sequencing gel as described for M13 protection experiments.

IN SITU HYBRIDIZATION

This protocol describes the analytical methods used to detect the presence of RNA by hybridizing to cells that are maintained in culture and fixed on slides using a cytocentrifuge and tissue sections.

Cytocentrifuge preparations

1. The cells should be at least 80% viable. Wash them with sterile PBS containing 5 mM $MgCl_2$.

2. Resuspend the cells at 10^6 cells/ml in the PBS/5 mM $MgCl_2$/20% FCS. Different cell types will need to be titrated for the correct cell density to achieve an uncrowded monolayer of cells on the slide. We resuspend a fibroblast cell line, Meth A, at about 10^5 cells/ml.

3. Add 0.2 ml (2 x 10^5 cells) to the cytocentrifuge funnel applicator. Use microscope slides with etched surfaces from an unopened box. Centrifuge at 750 rpm in a cytocentrifuge for 5 min at room temperature. Allow the slides to air-dry for 1–5 min.

4. Fix the preparations in 4% paraformaldehyde prepared in sterile PBS at room temperature for 30 min. The 4% paraformaldehyde solution is prepared by dissolving paraformaldehyde with a pellet of NaOH while stirring, neutralizing the solution to pH 7.3 and filtering through a 0.45 μm filter. The solution should be prepared fresh every day.

5. Store the slides at 4° in 70% EtOH. The preparations are good for a month and may be used up to five months.

Prehybridization

Prehybridization and hybridizations are done in Wheaton staining dishes. All solutions should be prepared with DEP-treated H_2O. Do not let the slides become dry between solutions.

1. Rehydrate the cytocentrifuge preparations by incubating in 2x SSC at room temperature for 10 to 15 min.

2. Acetylate the samples by incubation in 0.1 M triethanolamine/HCl at room temperature. This solution is prepared by adding 6.6 ml of stock triethanolamine and 1 ml conc HCl to 500 ml H_2O. Immediately prior to immersing the slides in the staining dish containing the triethanolamine/HCl, add 1.25 ml acetic anhydride. Mix quickly and thoroughly

with a pipette, then immerse the slides. Acetic anhydride is extremely unstable in aqueous solution having a halflife of less than 1 min.

3. Rinse the slides twice briefly in 2x SSC.

4. Incubate in 0.1 M Tris (pH 7.2)/0.1 M glycine at room temperature for 30 min.

5. Rinse twice in 2x SSC.

6. Incubate in 50% formamide (EM Scientific, 4X0421–1)/2xSSC at 50° for 30–120 min.

7. Dehydrate through 30, 60, 75 and 95% EtOH for 2 min each.

8. Prewarm slides at 50° prior to adding the hybridization solution. Place the slides on end in a finger rack and put in an incubator. Prewarming is optional.

Paraformaldehyde fixed tissue sections

1. Remove tissue aseptically from the animal.

2. Place in a sectioning cassette and fix overnight in 4% paraformaldehyde/ PBS.

3. Rinse in PBS at 4° with several changes.

4. The following section on dehydration and embedding can at some locations be performed by pathology service facilities.

Dehydration and embedding

All operations are carried out at room temperature unless otherwise stated.

50% EtOH	10–30 min
70% EtOH	10–30 min
80% EtOH	10–30 min
95% EtOH	10–30 min
100% EtOH	3x, 10–30 min each
100% Xylene	2x, 10–30 min each
100% Xylene	30 min at 60°
Xylene:paraffin (1:1)	3 hr at 60°
Paraffin	3 hr at 60°

| Paraffin | overnight at 60° |
| Paraffin | cool to room temperature |

After cutting 5-μm sections float onto microscope slides at 40° using freshly boiled water. Air-dry. Bake overnight at 45°.

After sectioning the following pretreatment is performed at room temperature.

Xylene	2x, 10–15 min each
95% EtOH	2x, 10–15 min each
70% EtOH	2 min
60% EtOH	2 min
30% EtOH	2 min

Hybridize as for cytocentrifuge preparations.

Hybridization

1. Precipitate the ^{35}S-labeled RNA probe with sodium acetate and EtOH in the presence of 10 μg of carrier yeast tRNA. Wash with 70% EtOH and air-dry.

2.. Resuspend the pellet in hybridization buffer to give RNA at a concentration of 0.1 to 0.4 μg/μl. For instance, one might precipitate 50 x 10^6 cpm and resuspend the RNA in a volume of 25 μl.

   Hybridization buffer

   50% formamide
   2x SSC
   10 mM DTT
   1 mg/ml sheared salmon sperm DNA
   1 mg/ml yeast tRNA
   2 mg/ml BSA

3. Denature the probe by incubation for 10 min at 90° and place at 55° until ready to hybridize.

4. Place 5 μl of hybridization solution containing approximately 10^6 cpm/μl of denatured ^{35}S-labeled RNA probe at 55° onto the edge of an 18 x 18 mm methanol-rinsed air-dried coverslip and carefully lower onto the sample using forceps to hold the slide. First lower the edge of the slide with the probe on it, and gradually set down the rest of the slide. Exclude all air bubbles and seal the edges with rubber cement. A P-1000 pipetteman with the pipette tip trimmed works fine to dispense the

cement. Fresh rubber cement should not require prewarming. Over time, rubber cement will harden and prewarming may be needed to allow use of a P-1000 pipetteman to dispense the cement.

5. Hybridize in a humidified incubator at 50° for 8 to 12 hr. A plastic chamber (a large petri plate) soaked with paper towels is a suitable humidifier. Prewarm the chamber before adding the slides.

Washing

1. Peel off the rubber cement from the coverslips. The cement will have dried but should still form an intact seal around the slide.

2. Immerse the slide containing the sample in 2x SSC/0.1% 2-mercaptoethanol at 50°. Allow the coverslip to float off.

3. Wash in 50% formamide (EM Sciences)/2x SSC/0.1% 2-mercaptoethanol at 55° for 30 min.

4. Wash in 2x SSC/0.1% 2-mercaptoethanol twice at 55° for 30 min. To reduce background in tissue sections, incubate with 50% formamide/2x SSC/10 mM DTT/1 mM EDTA/20 mM Tris·HCl (pH 8.0) at 60°–70° for 10 min.

5. Rinse twice briefly in 2x SSC at room temperature (no 2-mercaptoethanol).

6. Incubate with DNase-free RNase at 50 μg/ml (Boehringer-Mannheim) and RNase T1 at 1 μg/ml (Boehringer-Mannheim) in 0.5 M NaCl/10 mM Tris·HCl(pH 8) at 37° for 30–60 min. This solution can be reused about 4 to 5 times, but increase the incubation times with age. Store at 4°.

7. Wash in 2x SSC/0.1% 2-mercaptoethanol at 55° for 30 min.

8. Wash three times in 0.1x SSC/0.1% 2-mercaptoethanol at 60° for 30 min.

9. Dehydrate samples through EtOH containing 300 mM ammonium acetate:

   30% EtOH for 4 min
   60% EtOH for 4 min
   75% EtOH for 4 min
   95% EtOH for 4 min

10. Air-dry and mount on a cardboard with transparent tape and expose overnight with XAR-5 film. The time needed for autoradiography can be estimated from the signal on this film.

Autoradiography

1. Melt Kodak nuclear track emulsion NTB-2 at 43° in a light-tight darkroom for approximately 15–20 min. Preassemble the water bath and wrap with foil to cover lights. Preset the water bath so that it maintains 43° with the top off (a setting of 50° on some baths). This emulsion is very light sensitive so any exposure to light should be avoided. Some darkroom safe lights are too intense. Use only a portable safe lamp pointed away from the work area.

2. Aliquot the NTB-2 in 10 ml aliquots. Store unused aliquots in a light-tight box at 4°.

3. Dilute the emulsion with an equal volume of 600 mM ammonium acetate prewarmed to 43° (10 ml emulsion/10 ml ammonium acetate).

4. Use a narrow container such as a plastic slide mailer to dip the slides. Mix the emulsion well with a blank slide. Do 2 blank test slides first to check for bubbles. Dip the slides for 8–10 sec and place horizontally on a metal plate cooled to 0° (on ice) for 5–10 min to harden the emulsion.

5. Place the slides in a rack (flat or upright) for at least 2 hr in the dark at room temperature to allow the emulsion to set or leave at room temperature in a closed drawer sealed with aluminum foil and masking tape.

6. While still working in a light-tight room transfer the slides to a light-tight slide box and carry out the autoradiography at 4°, usually for 3–10 days.

7. Develop the slides in Kodak D19 developer at 15° for 2 min. Get the solutions to 15° by putting staining dishes containing the solutions on a metal plate on ice for at least 30 min. Rinse in H_2O at 15° for 30 sec.

8. Fix in Kodak Rapid Fix at 15° for 4 min. Rinse in H_2O briefly and place in fresh H_2O at 15°. Allow slides to reach room temperature before removing them from the H_2O (1–2 hr). This is important because the emulsion is heat-sensitive and rapid temperature changes cause the emulsion to crack on the slide.

9. Stain the slides using routine stains for 2–5 min in 10% Giemsa stain (Fluka). Wash 30 sec under running tap water, air-dry and view under a microscope. There is also a "Diff-Quik Stain Set" (American Scientific Products). Using this kit, one dips the slides 5 times for 1 sec each in the red cyto stain, blots the bottoms of the slides on a towel, dips the slides again for 5 times for 1 sec each in a blue nuclear stain, blots, washes under tap water, and allows to air dry.

REFERENCE

Simon Carding, personal communication.

RNA PREPARATION USING GUANIDINE-HCL FROM SMALL NUMBERS OF CELLS FOR RNase PROTECTION ASSAYS

This procedure is very good for very small numbers of cells for this assay.

1. Wash cells in PBS containing 20 µg/ml cycloheximide. From a stock solution of 1 mg/ml, dilute 200 µl into 10 ml PBS.

2. Dissolve cells in 5 M guanidinium thiocyanate, 100 mM EDTA (pH 7.0) at a concentration of 10 x 10^6 cells/ml. The solution is made by dissolving 59 g guanidinium thiocyanate in 20 ml of 0.5 M EDTA.

3. Freeze aliquots of 10 µl at -20°.

4. Hybridize the 10 µl aliquots with 2.5 µl of an SP6 probe (about 5 x 10^5 cpm).

5. Incubate for 5 min at 60° and then for 18 hr at room temperature.

6. Add 300 µl of RNase solution and incubate for 50 min at room temperature. The RNase solution is 0.3 M NaCl, 0.001 M EDTA, 0.03 M Tris·HCl (pH 7.5), 50 µg/ml RNase A which can be made and stored for a month at 4°.

7. Treat the sample with 3 µl of 20 mg/ml proteinase K for 20 min at 37°.

8. Extract with an equal volume of phenol:chloroform (350 µl).

9. To the aqueous phase, add 10 µg of tRNA as a carrier, 35 µl of 3 M sodium acetate, and 700 µl EtOH. Let sit 30 min on ice and then centrifuge 30 min in a centrifuge.

10. Dry the pellet and resuspend in 5 µl of loading buffer. Heat at 90° for 2 min prior to loading on a urea/acrylamide sequencing gel.

REFERENCE

Firestein, G. S., S. M. Gardner, and W. D. Roeder *Analyt. Biochem.* 167:381 (1987).

PURIFICATION OF mRNA BY HYBRID SELECTION ON NITROCELLULOSE

1. Cut nitrocellulose into 1 cm square pieces.

2. Boil linearized plasmid (about 5 µg) for 1 min in H_2O, quick-cool and spot onto nitrocellulose.

3. Air-dry and bake for 2 hr in a vacuum oven at 80°.

4. Hybridize in a 100 µl volume containing: 2–10 µg poly(A)$^+$ RNA, 65% formamide, 0.01 M 1,4-piperazine diethanesulfonic acid (PIPES) at pH 6.4, and 0.4 M NaCl at 50° for 1–2 hr (5x = 2 M NaCl, 0.05 M PIPES).

5. Remove solution and wash with 1 ml of 0.15 M NaCl, 0.015 M sodium citrate, 0.5% SDS 10 times. All solutions should be at 60° throughout the wash procedure. Vortex tubes for several seconds after each addition of wash buffer.

6. Finally wash twice with 1 ml of 0.002 M EDTA at pH 7.9 for 5 min at 60°.

7. Elute the RNA by boiling for 60 sec in 300 µl of double-distilled H_2O and then quick-cool in an ethanol dry-ice bath.

8. Remove fluid and adjust to 0.2 M sodium acetate and add 5 µg of calf thymus tRNA. Precipitate RNA with 2.5 volumes of ethanol at -20°.

9. Centrifuge at 12 krpm for 10 min at 4° in a microfuge. Wash twice with 70% ethanol and dry under reduced pressure.

10. Resuspend in 50 µl H_2O and use 25% in an *in vitro* translation assay.

REFERENCE

Ricciardi, R. P., J. S. Miller, and B. E. Roberts *Proc. Nat. Acad. Sci. USA* 76:4927–4931 (1979).

Genomic DNA Libraries

CLONING OF CHROMOSOMAL DNA

The molecular cloning of eukaryotic chromosomal DNA is achieved by the use of bacteriophage or cosmid cloning vectors. In both circumstances the large chromosomal DNA is ligated into phage or cosmid vector DNA fragments. These molecules are packaged *in vitro* into infectious particles, which are then introduced into cells by infection. The bacteriophage vectors are lytic viruses and remain so after the insertion of the foreign DNA. Thus foreign DNA can be inserted into regions of the phage that are nonessential for lytic growth.

There is a size limitation on the amount of DNA that will still be packaged into an infectious phage particle. The actual size that is infectious is 78% to 105% of the size of λ DNA. This means that in some vectors up to 8 kb may be inserted and in others about 8–23 kb. Cosmid vectors containing larger DNA insertions are packaged into infectious particles using the same procedures as for phage DNAs. After entering bacterial cells they remain in the cell as a large circular plasmid because they lack the necessary regions of the phage DNA for lytic growth. Cosmid vectors typically possess only the terminal *cos* sites that are needed for packaging (200–500 bp from each end) and a gene for antibiotic resistance so the large plasmid DNA can be selected. Because cosmids lack the genes for lytic growth they can accomodate much larger insertions of foreign DNA (36–45 kb). The generation, screening, and maintenance of a phage library is much easier than for a cosmid library so most chromosomal DNA cloning is performed using phage vectors. In practice, most cosmid libraries are generated, screened immediately, and discarded, or sometimes aliquots of unplated cosmids are stored in liquid nitrogen.

CONSTRUCTION OF GENOMIC DNA LIBRARIES IN BACTERIOPHAGES

Phage libraries are used to generate virus stocks that contain a relatively random representation of chromosomal DNA segments, usually 15–20 kb in length. If one knows very little about the gene of interest then this is the most valuable form a library can have. Perhaps the most commonly used library of this type is a partial *Mbo* I digest in the EMBL3 vector. Recent derivatives, EMBL3*cos* and EMBL3*cos*-Not, are now preferable because the point of insertion of the chromosomal DNA is very near the *cos* site at one end of the phage. This greatly facilitates the restriction mapping of the recombinant phage by partial mapping (Whittaker et al. *Nucl. Acids Res.* 16:7625, 1988). The restriction enzyme *Mbo* I recognizes the sequence GATC and this should occur on average in a random sequence once every 256 bp. Thus, a partial *Mbo* I cleavage that produces DNA fragments 15–20 kb in size should be a good approximation to random cleavage of chromosomal DNA. For a mammalian genome, if all clones of this type were nonoverlapping, about

150,000 clones would contain the entire genome. One has a reasonable chance of obtaining the desired clone by screening about 500,000 or a 99% chance by screening about 700,000 clones.

The use of the EMBL3 vector is particularly attractive because the vector as well as the insert can be made without size selection of the DNA. Many times, however, one does perform size selection of the insert DNA. In addition, there is a biological selection (Spi phenotype) for recombinants vs. parental phage which is very efficient. The parental phages can not grow on P2 lysogens. One can measure the percentage recombinant phage by plating on the restrictive cells (NM539 or [P2] 392) and the nonrestrictive cells (NM538 or LE392) and generally less than 1% of a library is of the parental type. An additional restriction system called Mcr (modified cytosine restriction) reduces the survival of the recombinant phage. By removing this system genetically (strain NM646) there can be up to a 10 fold enhancement in the number of recombinant phages (see Whittaker et al. reference given above). The EMBL3 vector has a small polylinker at the two points of insertion in the vector having the sites for *Eco*R I-*Bam*H I-*Sal* I in which the *Bam*H I is the site for ligation of the *Mbo* I partial ends. The vector EMBL4 has the polylinker sequence in the opposite orientation relative to the cloning site. The EMBL3 vector-insert junction can be cleaved with *Sal* I which is an extremely convenient means of locating the terminus of the inserted DNA. One can also calculate that 1 out of 4 junctions theoretically should generate a *Bam*H I site at a given vector-insert junction.

If you already know some information about restriction enzyme sites around the gene it is sometimes advantageous to choose a particular vector with the appropriate restriction enzyme site for insertion. It may also be possible to enrich for the desired sequence by size-selecting the DNA before cloning by sedimentation on a sucrose or salt gradient or fractionation on an agarose gel. For instance, if one wished to clone a *Hin*d III fragment that was less than 8 kb one could use the Ch21A vector. If the fragment was between 8 and 22 kb one could use Ch35. Other examples of available sites in phage cloning vectors are indicated below. Derivatives of EMBL 3 and EMBL4 have been constructed that have several additional restriction sites that can be used for insertion (Chinali *Nucl. Acids Res.* 16:8734, 1988).

In principle, cloning into the bacteriophage λ vectors is very straightforward. There are two types of vectors: insertional vectors, in which the phage is able to propagate without any insert DNA at all, and replacement vectors, in which the phage requires some minimum size insert once the parental "stuffer" DNA is removed. This DNA is nonessential DNA for lytic growth of the phage. Selection of the appropriate vector is based on (1) the size of the insert DNA that is to be cloned, and (2) the restriction enzyme used. Each of the vectors has a specific range of insert sizes that it will accept; within this range, the recombinant molecule is able to be properly packaged and multiply in the appropriate bacterial host. Each vector also contains a limited number of restriction sites suitable for cloning.

Table 3.1 Properties of λ cloning vectors

Vector	Type	Enzyme(s)	Size Range (kb)
EMBL3 or 4 EMBL3*cos*	Replacement	*Bam*H I	8–23
Charon 4A	Replacement	*Eco*R I	8–22
Charon 30	Replacement	*Bam*H I	6–19
	"	*Eco*R I	4.5–17.5
Charon 35	Replacement	*Bam*H I	8–22
	"	*Eco*R I	"
	"	*Hin*d III	"
	"	*Sal* I	"
	"	*Xba* I	"
Charon 16A	Insertion	*Eco*R I	0–8
Charon 21A	Insertion	*Eco*R I	0–8
	"	*Hin*d III	"
	"	*Sal* I	"
	"	*Xho* I	"

The steps for cloning into phage vectors are outlined here and described in detail in later sections:

1. Vector preparation

For replacement vectors there are two different methods to prepare the vector depending on which vector is used. The simplest is the EMBL3 vector in which either a *Bam*H I or a *Bam*H I plus *Eco*R I double digest is adequate. The stuffer fragment doesn't need to be physically removed because there is a biological selection for recombinant viruses lacking the stuffer DNA. For other vectors such as Charon 35, Charon 30, or Charon 4A one must digest with the appropriate enzyme and remove the stuffer DNA usually on a sucrose gradient. For insertional vectors, the DNA is cleaved with the appropriate enzyme and the ends dephosphorylated by a CIP digestion. This prevents the arms from ligating to each other and regenerating the parental vector structure.

2. **Insert preparation**

After either a partial or a complete digestion with the restriction enzyme the DNA is cleaned up with phenol and ether extractions and then precipitated. A size-selection step on a sucrose gradient or out of a low-melt agarose gel can be used to enrich for inserts of a particular size range.

3. **Ligation**

Generally vector and insert DNAs are mixed and ligated overnight. Usually the vector alone and several ligations in which the amount of vector is held constant and the amount of insert is varied are performed.

4. **Packaging and titration of library**

The recombinant phage DNA molecules obtained from the ligation reaction are packaged *in vitro* (into infectious phage particles) using extracts from two strains of *E. coli* lysogenized by mutant λ phage genomes. These extracts contain the phage proteins required to package the recombinant molecules. The titer of the library is determined by plating out small aliquots of the packaging reactions. The purpose of the titration is to determine the best ratio of vector and insert to produce the largest number of recombinant phage.

5. **Library screening**

This step includes plating out usually on large petri plates, transferring the phage to nitrocellulose, and "probing" the library filters. Positive clones are purified by rescreening.

PREPARATION OF INSERT DNA

Preparation of size-selected insert DNA

1. To establish conditions for partial digestion of high-molecular-weight DNA for your particular DNA sample assemble a reaction consisting of 10 μg of DNA in a volume of 200 μl in an appropriate buffer for *Mbo* I. Remove 40 μl of the reaction of the undigested sample. Some samples of DNA are either partially degraded prior to the partial digestion or contain RNA that could be interpreted as DNA when analyzed in an agarose gel.

2. Preincubate the reaction mixture at 37° and then add *Mbo* I. The amount must be titered but as a suggestion one could add 1 unit to this reaction. At 10, 20, 30, and 60 min after the enzyme was added remove 40-μl aliquots, add EDTA to a final concentration of 10 mM, and heat-inactivate at 68° for 15 min. Analyze the products on a 0.5% agarose gel using a *Hin*d III digest of λ DNA as markers to determine the appropriate digestion conditions. Some fractions may be appropriate or some pooling of fractions can be done. Segments of chromosomal DNA (either rich or poor in *Mbo* I sites) might be underrepresented in a library, so pooling of digests might overcome that problem.

3. Once the appropriate conditions have been determined, a preparative digest using 20–40 μg may be performed using identical reaction conditions. After the preparative digest, phenol-extract the DNA and precipitate with EtOH. Use the restriction enzyme in exactly the same manner that was used to titer the digestion. Do not, for example, do analytical partial digestions using a diluted restriction enzyme and then do a preparative digest with undiluted enzyme.

4. Resuspend the DNA in 1x CIP buffer and add 3 units of CIP/10 μg of DNA for 30 min at 37°. Add EDTA to a final concentration of 10 mN, heat-inactivate the phosphatase by heating for 15 min at 68°, and EtOH-precipitate the DNA. If the DNA is to be size selected the following treatment with phosphatase is optional. The DNA may be size-fractionated on a gradient either before or after the phosphatase treatment.

5. Check the DNA on a gel prior to using it in ligation to determine both the size and approximate DNA concentration in the sample.

PREPARATION OF THE PHAGE CLONING VECTOR

For EMBL3, EMBL3cos or Charon 35 a *Bam*H I digest is sufficient for cloning *Mbo* I partials. For EMBL3 one can also perform an *Eco*R I digest to remove the *Bam*H I site from the ends of the stuffer fragment. The size fractionation for EMBL3 is optional but essential for Charon 35. After digesting about 10 μg of EMBL3 with *Bam*H I one can anneal the *cos* sites by adding MgSO₄ to 10 mM and incubate the DNA for 1 hr at 42° prior to running a gradient if desired. Some people prefer to actually ligate the *cos* sites prior to size fractionation of the vector on a gradient. In this case, the DNA should first be phosphorylated at the *cos* sites by polynucleotide kinase and rATP followed by annealing of the *cos* sites in 10 mM MgSO₄ for 1 hr at 42° and finally ligated for 1 hr at 37°. We consider the kinasing and ligation optional and never do it.

The possibilities for the preparation of the EMBL3 vector are numerous. We prefer to minimize the number of steps and the exposure of the vector to different enzymes and experimental manipulations. For DNA that has been at 4° for any significant length of time the *cos* sites should already be annealed. Because there is such a complete biological selection of the recombinant phages the extra cut with *Eco*R I and size fractionation are not essential. Therefore, we prefer to digest 10 μg of vector using a 3- to 5-fold excess of *Bam*H I to ensure complete digestion followed by phenol extraction, ether extraction, and EtOH precipitation. The vector DNA is resuspended in 100 μl of ddH₂O and is ready to use.

For Charon 35 the procedure must include a size fractionation of the stuffer DNA fragments away from the vector arms. Charon 35 is *gam*+ and therefore the Spi selection won't work with this vector. The left arm is 19.5 kb and the right arm is 10.7 kb. In the gradient, then, the annealed arms would be 30.2 kb and the stuffer fragments, which are easily separated, are 6.3 kb, 5.7 kb, and 3.6 kb in length. Thus for Charon 35 vector preparations we recommend at least annealing of the arms in MgSO₄ prior to gradient fractionation and the ligation of the *cos* sites is helpful. Even very good libraries made with vectors for which there is no biological selection for recombinants have a few percent parental phage.

Preparation of Ch35 arms for use with *Eco*R I, *Hin*d III, or *Xba* I

Preparing Ch35 arms for cloning with *Eco*R I, *Hin*d III, or *Xba* I is basically the same as preparing arms for an *Mbo* I partial library. The difference is that after ligating the *cos* sites (and cleaning the DNA with phenol, ether extractions, and precipitations) one digests with the appropriate cloning enzyme (*Eco*R I, *Hin*d III, or *Xba* I). Digesting the phage DNA with the cloning enzyme can be followed by a digestion with *Bam*H I. This generates arms with the appropriate ends and at the same time cuts the stuffer DNA into smaller fragments for easy separation on a sucrose gradient. The *Bam*H I sites remain on the stuffer fragment after cleavage with these three enzymes.

SIZE FRACTIONATION OF DNA ON SUCROSE GRADIENTS

1. Prepare stock solutions of 10% and 40% sucrose in 1 M NaCl, 20 mM
    Tris·HCl (pH 8.), 5 mM EDTA.

    It is convenient to prepare a 2x stock solution of 2 M NaCl, 40 mM
    Tris·HCl (pH 8.0), and 10 mM EDTA (gradient buffer).

    40% sucrose solution

    40 grams of sucrose
    50 ml of 2x gradient buffer
    Fill to 100 ml with ddH$_2$0.

    10% sucrose solution

    10 grams of sucrose
    50 ml of 2x gradient buffer
    Fill to 100 ml with ddH$_2$0.

2. Using a gradient maker, pour a 38 ml linear sucrose (10%–40% gradient
    in a Beckman SW28 ultracentrifuge tube (or equivalent). Clean the gra-
    dient maker with distilled water. Close both stopcocks. Add 19 ml of
    40% sucrose to the vessel closest to the outlet valve (stirred vessel).
    Open the stopcock between the two vessels to allow a small amount of
    liquid through so that no bubbles form and close again. Add 19 ml of
    10% sucrose to the other vessel. Make sure that the end of the outlet
    tube is secured against the inside of the centrifuge tube near the top and
    that the 40% sucrose solution is stirring. Open both stopcocks simulta-
    neously. Liquid should begin to flow into the centrifuge tube. The level
    of the sucrose solution in each vessel should decrease simultaneously.

    Alternatively, some find it more convenient to pour gradient from
    the bottom up. In this case, the 10% sucrose should be in the/vessel
    containing the outlet valve. The Tygon outlet of the gradient maker
    should be extended with a 100-µl capillary pipette which is placed in the
    bottom of the tube (against the side). After gradient is poured, be sure
    to take the capillary out gently.

3. Load the DNA onto the gradient (no more than 70 µg of phage or 200
    µg of cellular DNA per SW28 tube in a volume of 500 µl or less). Centri-
    fuge the sample at 24 krpm for 24 hr at 20° in a Beckman SW28 rotor (or
    its equivalent).

4. Put the centrifuge tube into a 50-ml syringe. Insert a 21-gauge needle
    attached to a length of Tygon tubing through the bottom of the centri-
    fuge tube, being careful to keep the tip of the needle as close to the
    bottom of the tube as possible. Collect 0.5 ml fractions.

Alternatively, fractions can be collected using a peristaltic pump. Carefully insert a 100-μl capillary tube attached to a length of narrow-bore tygon tubing and pump the fractions out. (A ringstand and clamp can be used to brace the capillary tube).

5. Remove a 50-μl aliquot from every third fraction and dilute with an equal volume of water. Add EtOH and precipitate. Resuspend in TE. Analyze by electrophoresis through a 0.5% agarose gel. Determine which fractions contain the relevant DNA fragments (DNA fragments in the 15–22 kb size range when making insert DNA for an *Mbo* I partial library or phage arms when making a substitutional vector).

6. Pool fractions containing the desired DNA fragments (i.e., omit those contaminated with stuffer fragments when making phage arms). Dilute with an equal volume of ddH$_2$O and precipitate with 1.5 volumes of isopropanol. Freeze in dry ice, thaw, and spin in SW41 tube at 35 krpm for 45 min at 4°. Precipitate again (may be done in a microfuge tube). Resuspend, and dissolve at approximately 1 μg/μl in TE. Determine the concentration by analyzing it on a gel and comparing the intensity with known amounts of DNA. It is ready to be used to make a library.

Set up ligations as described in the next section on genomic libraries without size selection.

SIZE FRACTIONATION OF DNA ON SALT GRADIENTS

Solutions

1 M and 4.5 M NaCl in 0.1 M Tris·HCl (pH 8), 0.01 M EDTA. Autoclave solutions.

1. Pour 1 to 4.5 M NaCl gradients in SW41 tubes. On the 11-ml gradient the capacity is 50–75 μg of DNA.

2. Centrifuge for 40 krpm for 4 1/2 hr at 15°. This puts the phage arms about 60% down the tube and is also suitable for preparing inserts.

For phage arms

1. Collect into a 96-well microtiter dish about 0.2-ml size fractions.

2. Run 10 μl of every other fraction on a gel with marker DNAs. Restriction-cut phage DNA is the best marker. Pool fractions with arms and no internal fragments and EtOH-precipitate. One must add an equal volume of water prior to adding EtOH or a large salt pellet form. For the best yield of phage arms, be sure the sticky ends are annealed prior to the gradient. Most stocks of λ DNA stored at 4° for some time will be annealed, but if the DNA preparation is new one can incubate 1 hr at 42° in 10 mM MgSO$_4$ before loading the gradient.

For genomic DNA

Collect 0.24 ml fractions into microfuge tubes, add 0.25 ml ddH$_2$O, 1 ml EtOH, and precipitate. Resuspend the pellet in 20–40 μl of 0.1x TE, run 5%–10% of every second or third fraction on a gel.

Comment: salt pellets—if it looks like one, it is. Reprecipitate with 0.2 ml 0.4 M sodium acetate and 0.5 ml EtOH.

PREPARATION OF DNA FOR INSERTIONAL VECTORS (Ch16A or Ch21A) AND COMPLETE GENOMIC DNA DIGESTS

The preparation of DNA for this type of cloning is very simple. One digests about 10 μg of chromosomal DNA to completion with the chosen enzyme, phenol-extracts the DNA, ether-extracts the DNA and EtOH-precipitates prior to setting up the ligations. Because the manipulations are minimal to the insert DNA it is a good idea here to include the ether extraction to remove the phenol as completely as possible.

For the preparation of the vector again a digest is performed on 10 μg for 60 min followed directly by the addition of 3 units of CIP for an additional 30 min at 37°. Add EDTA to a final concentration of 10 mM, heat inactivate the CIP by heating for 15 min at 68°, phenol-extract, ether-extract and EtOH-precipitate.

Set up ligations as described in the next section on genomic libraries without size selection.

GENOMIC PHAGE LIBRARY WITHOUT SIZE FRACTIONATION OF INSERTS

This procedure is a quick and easy one for generating a partial *Mbo* I library from chromosomal DNA. The recombinant vs. parental phages can be selected biologically using the EMBL3 vector and the chromosomal DNA can be prepared and used without size fractionation.

Preparation of vector

Cleave 10 μ of EMBL3 DNA with *Bam*H I in a 200-μl reaction. Use digestion conditions that would be 3–5 times the estimated titer of the enzyme to ensure complete cleavage but not overdigest the DNA. The volume should minimize any viscosity problems and be appropriate for easy phenol extraction. After phenol extraction add 1/10 volume of NaCl and EtOH-precipitate using a 30 min centrifugation in a centrifuge at 4°. Rinse with 70% EtOH and resuspend in 100 ml of ddH$_2$O. Examine the products on a gel along with the inserts for cleavage.

Preparation of the insert

Digest approximately 15 μg of DNA again in 200 μl with *Mbo* I at 37° such that the partially digested fragments contain a significant proportion of DNA in the 15–22 kb size range. Titration of the appropriate amount of enzyme is important and can vary from one sample to another. It is essential to titer the digestion of the DNA using exact conditions that will be used preparatively. In this analytical digest first preincubate the DNA at 37° for at least 10 min. Remove 30 μl to run on the gel as a control. Some of the RNA in the sample may contribute to the EtBr staining material in digested samples. Add *Mbo* I to the DNA and incubate for various lengths of time. Empirically we have found that approximately 3 units of enzyme is a good amount. At 5, 10, 20, 30, and 60 min remove 30-μl aliquots and add to separate tubes containing sample buffer and immediately incubate at 65° to inactivate the *Mbo* I. Each tube should contain approximately 2.5 μg of DNA which is enough to visualize as a smear in the appropriate region of the gel.

Analyze all of these samples on an 0.7% agarose gel using markers that allow one to determine the size of DNA in the range of 5–30 kb in size. The λ *Hin*d III digest is OK for this purpose. The goal is to determine the amount of enzyme and time of digestion that produces DNA in the correct size range. We have found that for many DNA samples, digestion for 5 min as described above generates appropriately sized DNA fragments. In some situations where the amount of DNA was extremely limited the 5 min digestion was performed without prior titration and was used to generate a good library. Once the appropriate digestion conditions have been determined, digest 15 μg of DNA and phenol-extract after the appropriate time and EtOH-precipitate the DNA.

In this method of constructing a library the *Mbo* I digestion produces many digestion products. The goal is to clone only a single intact fragment produced by *Mbo* I digestion and avoid cloning any religation products that might not be contiguous in the chromosomal DNA. To prevent this the partially digested DNA must be dephosphorylated using calf intestine phosphatase (CIP). Resuspend the DNA in the CIP buffer and digest for 30 min with CIP. Terminate the reaction by adding EDTA to a final concentration of 10 mM, phenol-extract, and ether-extract. Ethanol-precipitate the DNA and rinse the pelleted DNA with 70% EtOH. In several cases where it was examined the CIP treatment actually stimulated the number of recombinant phages. Presumably the ligation of DNA fragments that would generate DNAs too large to package is prevented by the CIP treatment. It is a good idea to check for the completeness of the dephosphorylation of the inserts by attempting to ligate them. Analyze the inserts in an agarose gel in adjacent lanes. Compare both ligated and unligated inserts and as a positive control ligate some of the insert DNA that you saved prior to the dephosphorylation step. The positive control should be very large DNA and the inserts should look as they did on the earlier analytical gel.

Setting up the ligations

In a 10-μl reaction set up analytical ligations first using 0.2 μg of vector plus 0.2 μg of partially digested DNA. In three similar ligations keep everything the same but decrease the amount of insert to 0.06 μg, 0.02 μg, and 0.0 μg. These are somewhat arbitrary and could be chosen differently. In many cases approximately equal amounts of vector and inserts have proven optimal. The amount of insert DNA is taken from the input DNA assuming 100% recovery. In some samples small amounts of insert DNA have been very efficient in generating recombinant phage. Set up standard ligation reactions and incubate at 17° for at least 12 hr.

Analysis of recombinant phage

Perform *in vitro* packaging on all or a portion of these analytical ligation reactions. Typically these amounts of DNA will produce 10^5 to 10^6 recombinant phage. If it is less, one can just scale up the reaction. If one analyzes 0.01% of each reaction there are appropriate numbers of phage to quantitate. Typically one would dilute the packaged phage into 1 ml of NZY broth, dilute that by 10^{-2} (10 μl into 1 ml NZY) and infect 0.3 ml of cells using 10 μl of the final diluted phage. The recombinant EMBL3 phage can be distinguished from parental phage by their Spi phenotype. The recombinant phage will grow on the P2 lysogen of LE392 cells called P2(392) whereas the parental phages will not. One can measure the parents plus recombinant phage by plating the phage on LE392 cells. Typically only a small percentage are recombinant phage if plated on LE392 but growth on P2(392) produces a library that is essentially all recombinant phages. The efficiency of the packaging extract will determine how much DNA will be needed to produce enough phage to generate a complete library. Typically 10^5 to 10^6 recombinant phage per μg of *Mbo* I digested DNA can be achieved.

REFERENCE

Frischauf, A.M., H. Lehrach, A. Poustka, and N. Murray *J. Mol. Biol.* 170:827–842 (1983).

SCREENING A PHAGE LIBRARY WITH A RADIOLABELED PROBE

Preparation of large plates for phage library screening

The use of large plates (24 cm x 24 cm from Nunc distributed by Vangard Scientific) to screen libraries reduces the number of filters that must be prepared. The plastic plates are reusable and can be adequately cleaned by rinsing with 70% EtOH and treating with UV in a sterile hood. Pour liquid NZY bottom agar (about 330 ml) into each plate. It is useful to place the bottom agar in a 67° bath after autoclaving. Pouring at this temperature seems to reduce the condensation on the plates after they have solidified. Use a flame or a sterile pasteur pipette to remove air bubbles. Let dry in an uncovered Laminar Flow hood under a UV light and air blower. Plates prepared in this way are ready for immediate use after about 2 hr. Do not overdry the plates. If a hood is not available the plates can be dried on the benchtop but be sure to adequately dry the plates in an incubator prior to use. Before plating phage it is a good idea to equilibrate the plates at 37° or at least at room temperature.

Plating phage

Equilibrate the top agarose at about 55°. It is convenient to aliquot 45 ml into a sterile 50 ml screw cap tube just after heating and then allow it to cool to 55°. In a separate tube an infection is performed using 3 ml of a saturated culture of the appropriate *E. coli* strain for the particular phage and the desired amount of phage. A fresh saturated culture works well but one can also use what are called Mg-cells. These Mg-cells are made by growing bacterial cells to saturation, harvesting the cells by centrifugation, and resuspending the cells in 0.5 volumes of sterile 10 mM $MgSO_4$. These cells are good for 2–5 weeks if stored at 4°. For this size plate up to 10^5 phage can readily be screened. This is the usual amount per plate for screening a mammalian genomic library. Usually one titers the library to determine the appropriate volume of the phage library to use for the large plate. After the infection has incubated 15 min at 37° or 25 min at room temperature it is added to the tube containing top agarose. The tube is mixed well by inverting 3 to 4 times. Tapping the tube on a benchtop a couple of times removes some bubbles that may have been generated. The mixture is poured onto the surface of the large library plate starting at one corner. The plate is then tilted to spread the top agarose uniformly across the surface. All of this must be performed within a few seconds before the agarose solidifies.

Filter replicas and hybridization

1. Cool the plates for a couple of hours at 4° after the overnight incubation to harden the top agarose surface.

2. Place a dry nitrocellulose sheet on the lawn of cells such that no air bubbles form between the agar and the filter. Let the phage adsorb for at least 3 min. Longer times up to 10 min are all right. If a second or third lift is made, adsorb the filters for 4 min for the second and then 5 min for the third lift. The nitrocellulose Benton-Davis lifts can be performed using square pieces of nitrocellulose that are 20–22 cm on each side. We commonly use precut filters that are 21 cm x 22 cm which fit into the Seal-a-Meal roll bags. During the adsorption use a syringe containing india ink to make holes through the filter and into the agar. This permits alignment of the autoradiogram of the filter with the library plate. For a plate of this size holes forming approximately a 5 cm x 5 cm grid are adequate for later alignment.

3. Carefully remove the filter from the plate. Peel back with forceps, taking care not to remove the top agarose.

4. Submerge the filter in a container with 0.1 N NaOH, 1.5 M NaCl for 1 min. Longer times are all right. With rubber gloves on, gently rub the surface that was in contact with the bacterial cells to dislodge any particles of agarose or cell debris. This is optional but does appear to reduce background signals.

5. Remove the filter and submerge in another container with 0.2 M Tris·HCl (pH 7.5), 2x SSCPE for 1 min. After several filters have been processed the solutions should be replaced.

6. Blot dry and let air-dry completely. At 37° or under a stream of air this occurs quickly.

7. Bake in a vacuum oven for at least 1 hr at 80° but not more than 2 hr. Longer times cause the filters to become very brittle.

8. Prehybridize and hybridize as for a Southern blot. For high-density screening it is a good idea to prehybridize the filter for several hours.

9. After the development of the autoradiogram, align the film with the filter in saran wrap and mark on the film the location of the holes marked with india ink.

10. Align the original library plate with the marked X-ray film for identification of the hybridizing plaques.

Plaque purification

1. After a region of the plate has been identified using the autoradiogram, pick a plug of agar from the plate using the large end of a pasteur pipette. Blow on the other end of the pasteur pipette to transfer the agar plug into a sterile tube containing 1 ml of TM media or NZY broth. Allow the phage to soak out into the media for an hour at room temperature or at least 10 min at 37°. Longer times are fine. The titer of phage in this solution will vary depending on the density of phage in the original lawn and the dryness of the bacterial plate and the phage vector being used. If a plate had approximately 10^5 phage then the ml of phage will usually contain 10^6 to 10^7 phage.

2. It is desirable to have a few hundred (300–600) phage on a 10 cm plate for rescreening the phage (for plating technique see section on preparation of phage stocks). This is called the secondary screen. For example, if one had a titer of 3×10^6 phage per ml and one replated using 10 μl of phage then there would be 3×10^4 phage on the 10-cm plate. This is too many phage to rescreen effectively. A 10-cm plate reaches confluent lysis at about 10^4 phage per plate. We usually make 100-fold dilutions so that calculation of the titer is simplified. If 10 μl of the original stock was added to 1 ml of NZY broth that produces a solution having a titer of 3×10^4 phage/ml. Now plating of 10 μl of the dilution should result in 300 phage on a 10-cm plate. The actual number of phage obtained will vary and your own series of dilutions will need to be determined empirically.

3. A nitrocellulose filter lift is made using 88-mm circular discs and processed using the same solutions as for the primary lifts. The secondary screen allows one to determine if the signal on the primary screen was real and should achieve a significant purification, perhaps 100-fold.

4. Once a positive signal has been identified on the secondary screen an agar plug can again be picked and phage-eluted from the plug. As the plaque becomes purer it is desirable to pick smaller plugs of agarose now with the narrow end of the pasteur pipette. To pick a pure plaque, one generally has to pick from a plate with no more than 150–200 plaques. It is easier from plates with less than 100 per plate. Once a pure plaque has been identified it can be amplified and large amounts of DNA made (see sections on preparation of phage stocks and phage DNA).

Preparation of an amplified library stock

1. Flood the large plate with 50 ml of NZY broth or λdil and place at 4° for several hr.

2. Pour the fluid into a 50-ml sterile tube and add a few drops of $CHCl_3$ to the tube and mix.

3. Store the stock at 4°. Never store the phage below 0° because they are completely killed by freezing. The titer at the beginning will be about 10^{10} pfu/ml (pfu is plaque-forming units).

CONSTRUCTION OF A COSMID LIBRARY

There are several very useful cosmid vectors. Some are designed with very specific goals in mind. This description of making a cosmid library will employ the use of the cosmid vector p*cos*-2EMBL. This vector has a gene for kanamycin resistance and 2 *cos* sites with a *Pvu* II site between them and a *BamH* I site for cloning *Mbo* I partials located in the tetracycline gene derived from pBR322. The vector is produced by cleaving the cosmid vector with *Pvu* II and dephosphorylating those sites. This inhibits the formation of polyplasmid cosmids and the separation of vector arms is unnecessary. After subsequent cleavage with *BamH* I the vector is ready for use. The *Mbo* I digested DNA can be produced in the same manner as was described in the previous section on constructing a library without size-fractionation of inserts, or size-fractionated inserts could be used.

Preparation of vector

1. Digest 10 μg of p*cos*-2EMBL DNA with *Pvu* II for 60 min at 37°. Then add 2 units of CIP directly to the reaction for an additional 30 min at 37°.

2. Add EDTA to a final concentration of 10 mM, heat for 15 min at 68°, phenol-extract, ether-extract and EtOH-precipitate the DNA.
    At this point one can check for the completeness of the dephosphorylation reaction by attempting to religate a portion of the linear vector to a circular form. Perform a ligation reaction under standard conditions and compare its mobility on an agarose gel with both linear and uncut p*cos*-2EMBL vector.

3. Resuspend the cleaved vector DNA in buffer appropriate for *BamH* I and cleave it with *BamH* I for 60 min at 37°.

4. Phenol-extract, ether-extract and EtOH-precipitate the vector DNA. Resuspend it in TE at a concentration of 0.25 μg/μl. The completeness of the *BamH* I digestion can also be monitored on an agarose gel. The vector is ready for use in ligations.

Preparation of *Mbo* I partials

The source of insert DNA can be prepared in the same manner as described for the phage libraries except the partials should be larger in size. The size can be judged on a 0.35% agarose gel using uncut λ DNA and a *Hind* III digest of λ DNA as markers. Resuspend the inserts at a concentration of 0.25 μg/μl.

Ligations

Standard ligation reactions should be assembled in a 10-μl volume. For an analytical ligation one could try different ratios of vector to insert as for phage cloning but one should initially try 0.5 μg of insert plus 0.25 μg of insert. Ligate overnight at 15°.

Testing the library

1. Package 1 μl of the ligation reaction and assay a portion of the sample. This can be accomplished by adding λdil to 100 μl total volume and using 5 μl to infect 100 μl of DH1 Mg-cells. This 5 μl would be 1/200 of the cosmid ligation reaction.

2. Adsorb the packaged cosmids to DH1 cells for 15 min at 37°. Add 1 ml of L broth and shake for 1 hr at 37°.

3. Concentrate the cells by centrifugation, resuspend in 150 μl and spread onto a plate containing kanamycin. Fifty colonies would correspond to an efficiency of $10^4/\mu g$.

4. Based on the analysis of the packaging results set up a preparative ligation. One might use 20 μg of *Mbo* I partials plus 10 μg of cosmid vector in an 80-μl reaction. After the ligation one should perform an analytical packaging reaction just to check the ligation.

5. Perform a preparative packaging reaction which is just a scaled up version of the analytical reactions.

Purification of cosmids

1. The cosmids should be purified over a CsCl step gradient prior to plating. Construct a step gradient using 0.5 ml of 54%, 42%, and 31% CsCl in λdil (54% would have 5.4 g CsCl plus 4.6 ml of λdil). Place the cosmid library on top of the CsCl solution and then fill the remaining volume in the tube with λdil.

2. Centrifuge for 3 hr at 18°. The cosmid should be underneath a white layer in the CsCl solution. Remove 1-ml fractions from the top using a pasteur pipette. When you are in the region of the cosmids take approximately 0.2-ml fractions.

3. Test for the cosmids by diluting 1 μl of the CsCl solutions into 50 μl of λdil and using 10 μl to infect DH1 cells.

4. Pool the fractions containing cosmids and dialyze against λdil. First place the dialysis bag in a small volume without stirring and later dialyze against large volumes of λdil. Change the buffer twice.

5. To plate the cosmids, add 2 ml of DH1 Mg-cells and incubate at 37° for 15 min. Add 10 ml of L broth and shake at 37° for 60 min. Collect the cells by centrifugation. Resuspend the cells in 1.5 ml L broth and spread on a large plate containing kanamycin. To make an amplified stock you can plate directly on an agar plate. For immediate screening see the section below.

6. Harvest the amplified cosmid library by scraping the cells off the plate into 20 ml/plate of L broth. Add 1/10 volume of 10x HMFH and freeze in aliquots in liquid nitrogen.

10x HMFH
6.3 g K_2HPO_4
0.45 g Na citrate
0.09 g $MgSO_4 \cdot 7H_2O$
0.9 g $(NH_4)_2SO_4$
1.8 g KH_2PO_4
44 g glycerol
ddH_2O to 100 ml

Screening the cosmid library

The cosmid libraries should be plated directly onto nitrocellulose filters placed on kanamycin-containing plates. They can be plated at a density of up to 10^5 per large library plate (22 cm x 22 cm sheets of nitrocellulose). Making replica filters is best done by transferring from one nitrocellulose surface to another nitrocellulose surface.

Assemble a few layers of 3MM paper on a flat surface and put the plated cosmids colony side up on the 3MM paper. Prewet a sheet of nitrocellulose by placing it on a fresh agar plate. Remove it and place it directly on top of the original plating of the cosmids on nitrocellulose. Place a few sheets of 3MM on top of that. Using a glass plate press the nitrocellulose sheets together as firmly as possible. Punch a few holes through the nitrocellulose filters for later alignment of the sheets after the probing has been performed. More than one copy of a plate may be made. Take the second sheet of transferred colonies and incubate it overnight at 37°. Place the original plate of cosmids at room temperature overnight and then at 4° for temporary storage. The second sheet will be used for probing but first the cosmid sequences can be amplified by placing the nitrocellulose sheet on a kan plate containing 50 μg/ml chloramphenicol for 4–10 hr at 37°.

This filter should be processed just as described for the bacterial colony hybridization procedure. Once positive colonies have been identified they must be purified. After localizing the region of hybridization on the plate of cosmids cut out about a 5-mm circle containing that region and place in 1 ml of L broth containing kanamycin. Plate out the cells at a density of about 100 cells per plate and repeat the screening procedure until a pure colony has been isolated.

REFERENCE

Poustka, A., H. Rackwitz, A. Frischauf, B. Hohn, and H. Lehrach *Proc. Nat. Acad. Sci. USA* 81:4129-4133 (1984).

PREPARATION OF PACKAGING EXTRACTS

Freeze-thaw lysate

1. Grow BHB2688 cells in L broth at 30° to 3 x 10^8 cells /ml. Use about a 1/20 dilution of 30° overnight culture.

2. Induce culture by vigorous shaking in a water bath at 43° for 15 min and then shake vigorously at 38° for 3 hr.

3. Chill the flask in ice water and centrifuge the cells at 8 krpm for 10 min.

4. Resuspend the cells from 1.5 L culture in 4 ml of cold 10% sucrose, 0.05 M Tris-HCl (pH 7.4).

5. Aliquot 2 ml each to 2 screw-cap Oak Ridge or Nalge centrifuge tubes. Add 0.1 ml of 2 mg/ml freshly dissolved lysozyme in 0.25 M Tris·HCl (pH 7).

6. Mix rapidly and freeze immediately by immersing in crushed dry ice or liquid nitrogen.

7. Thaw slowly and when viscous add 0.3 ml of M1* buffer. Mix gently and centrifuge at 35 krpm for 25 min at 2° in a precooled rotor.

8. Aliquot into 25–100 µl volume in microfuge tubes and freeze immediately by placing the tubes on crushed dry ice. Store at -70°.

M1* Solution

ddH$_2$O	0.110 ml
2-mercaptoethanol	0.001 ml
2 M Tris·HCl (pH 7.4)	0.0015 ml
0.05 M spermidine + 0.1M	0.300 ml
putrescine (adjusted	
to pH 7 with Tris	
1 M MgCl$_2$	0.009 ml
0.1 M ATP	0.075 ml
	0.500 ml

Add solutions in the order listed.

Comments

1. It is a good idea to test the temperature sensitivity of your strains.

2. One can increase the amount of M1* added by 2- to 5-fold and sometimes achieve greater packaging efficiencies.

Sonic extract

1. Grow BHB2690 cells in L broth at 30° and induce as before. Shake for 2 hr at 38° after induction.

2. Resuspend the cells from 1.5 L in about 8 ml of buffer A (0.02 M Tris·HC1 (pH 8), 0.03 M MgC1$_2$, 0.05% 2-mercaptoethanol, 0.001 M EDTA) and transfer to a clear plastic tube.

3. Sonicate, avoiding foaming.

4. Centrifuge the extract in a 15-ml Corex tube at 6 krpm for 10 min. The pellet should be very small. Remove the supernatant and 0.2 ml of M1* buffer per ml of resuspended cells.

5. Aliquot into 20 μl to 100 μl volumes in microfuge tubes and freeze on crushed dry ice. Store at -70°.

IN VITRO PACKAGING PROCEDURE

These extracts and procedures give high-efficiency packaging but there is some variability. One strategy is to use extracts prepared in one's own laboratory to titer the reactions used to achieve optimal ligation of recombinant molecules and then use the very high efficiency commercially available extracts for the final preparation of the library.

Mix only 90 extract, 88 extract and ligated DNA and incubate at room temperature for 1 hr. Dilute and plate phage. Dilute at least 250 μl with 0.01 M Tris·HC1 (pH 7.4), 0.1 M MgC1$_2$, 0.2% gelatin. TM or NZY broth also works fine. Typically one might mix 5 μl of each extract with 1–4 μl of ligated DNA. The volumes of each extract may be titered to give optimal yields. One can use 1 μl of each extract and 1 μl of DNA and package optimally. The volume of the DNA should not exceed the combined volume of the extracts and probably should not exceed half that volume. Smaller volumes of the ligated DNAs are better. Efficiences of 1–2 x 10^9 pfu/mg of DNA are achieved with these extracts. If one is careful to minimize the amount of time the extracts are thawed it is possible to freeze and thaw the extracts many times without significant loss of activity.

PREPARATION OF PHAGE STOCKS

1. Pick a pure (single) plaque as an agar plug from a plate and transfer it to 1 ml of λdil buffer (0.01 M Tris·HCl [pH 7.4], 0.01 M MgCl$_2$, 0.10 M NaCl, 0.01% gelatin). The NZY medium also works well. All phage should be stored at 4° when not in use. The phage from a single plaque will vary in amount from 10^4 to 10^6 (frequently about 10^5). To make a higher titer stock of the pure phage another infection is performed.

2. Mix 0.1–0.2 ml of the first phage stock with 0.3 ml of stationary-phase bacteria. If a phage stock has been stored over chloroform, no more than about 0.05 ml of the stock can be added to 0.3 ml of cells. Larger volumes of chloroform-containing phage stock are inhibitory. Chloroform may be cleared from a saturated solution by brief incubation at 37° in a loosely capped tube so vapors escape. The mixture is incubated for 10 minutes at 37°. Three ml of top agar (0.8% agar in medium) at about 55° is added to the mixture and quickly vortexed to achieve uniform distribution of infective centers. The solution is added to an agar plate and swirled to create an even layer of top agar. The top agar begins to solidify immediately and in a few minutes the plates can be placed at 37°. Ideally, complete or almost complete lysis of the bacterial lawn will occur. This is achieved if about 10^4 or more phage were used to initiate the infection.

3. A high-titer lysate is prepared by adding 5 ml of λdil buffer or NZY medium to the plate and putting it at 4° for about 2 hours. The phage will diffuse into the medium which can be removed by pouring it directly in a tube or removing the fluid with a pasteur pipette. Usually about 3 ml are recovered from a single 10 cm plate. The titer is usually 1–2 x 10^{10} pfu/ml. To this lysate 0.05 ml of chloroform is added and the solution is clarified by a low-speed centrifugation. For long-term storage of phage stocks, one can add MgCl$_2$ to 0.01 M and gelatin to 0.05%. If the lysis of the bacterial lawn was poor, continue to generate a higher titer phage stock using the second lysate.

PREPARATION OF PHAGE DNA

A reliable procedure for growing large amounts of phage, from which DNA is subsequently isolated on CsCl density gradients, is the following:

1. Bacteria (1.5 L of LE392 or an appropriate host for the phage in a 4-L Erlenmeyer flask) are grown in NZY medium to mid-log phase at 37°, OD_{590} = 0.5. With experience this is determined visually. To expedite this part of the procedure, one can add up to 40 ml of a saturated culture of LE392 to 1.5 L of medium. After about 1.5–2 hours the culture will be at the correct density.

2. Infect the bacteria at a MOI (multiplicity of infection) of 0.1. This means 1 pfu per 10 cells. This can be achieved be adding 3 ml of the high titer phage stock to the 1.5 L culture. Thus, approximately $5-10^{11}$ cells are infected by $5-10^{10}$ pfu. After addition of the phage lysate to the culture, the entire culture should be shaken for perhaps 20 sec to completely mix the two solutions.

3. The infected culture should be left stationary for about 10 min at 37° to permit effective adsorption of phage to the bacteria.

4. Continue vigorous shaking of the culture until lysis is obvious. There should be a rather synchronous lysis beginning about 4–5 hours postinfection. Complete or maximal lysis should then take 45–60 minutes when harvesting should begin. If the culture is not processed within the next 2 hours, significant readsorption of phage to cells and cell debris will occur. This can drastically reduce the yield of phage from a culture.

5. Add solid NaCl to a final concentration of 1 M NaCl (90 g per 1.5 L culture) and dissolve by shaking.

6. Centrifuge at 8 krpm for 20 min at 4° in JA-10 or JA-14 rotor to pellet any intact cells and cell debris. During this spin one can rinse the culture flask with distilled water which can then be used in the next step.

7. Gently pour the supernatants back into the rinsed culture flask.

8. The phage can be concentrated and precipitated from this large volume by the use of polyethylene glycol (Sigma PEG 6000). Solid PEG (105 g) is added to the supernatant while stirring at 4°. Usually about half the PEG can be added and stirred for 15–20 minutes and then the remaining portion added. The PEG should be completely dissolved, which usually takes at least 1 hr. At this point one could let the solution stir overnight at 4° if convenient.

9. Centrifuge again at 8 krpm for 20 min at 4°. One can conveniently use the same centrifuge tubes used to pellet the cell debris if they have been rinsed with distilled water.

10. Pour off the supernatant and let the inverted tube drain briefly onto a paper towel.

11. Resuspend the precipitated phage in TNM (0.01 M Tris·HCl [pH 7.4], 0.1 M NaCl, 0.01 M MgCl$_2$). From a 1.5 L culture, 40 ml is a good volume to use for resuspension. This works well for the next step gradient fractionation.

12. A partial purification of phage is accomplished by the use of a CsCl step gradient by adding 9 ml of 3 M CsCl in TNM to the bottom of an SW28 Ultra Clear centrifuge tube. Using 10 ml of 5 M CsCl in TNM in a 10-ml pipette, add 9 ml to the bottom of the tube containing the 3 M CsCl in TNM. Gently place the tip of the full pipette at the bottom of the tube and gradually release the 5 M solution which will remain below the 3 M solution. This might take a minute to do. The pipette can be removed from the gradient with less disturbance if 1 ml is left in the pipette. The 3 M CsCl solution contains 50.2 g solid CsCl per total volume of 100 ml TNM; 5 M contains 84 g CsCl per 100 ml. The resuspended phage solution in TNM is gently layered on top of the step gradient. About 20 ml is layered on top of each of two gradients.

13. The tubes are centrifuged in the SW28 rotor for 90 min at 24 krpm at 15°.

14. Place the tube in a clamp on a ring stand. At the interface between the 3 M and 5 M solutions, a white, opalescent band of phage should appear. Most of the cell debris will be near the TNM solution-3 M CsCl interface.

15. Remove the phage by inserting an 18-gauge needle in the side of the tube. The band can be visualized more clearly by holding some dark material behind the tube. Usually the band can be completely removed in 5 ml.

16. A further equilibrium density gradient purifies and concentrates the phage. About 10 ml of the step-gradient purified phage is placed in a SW41 Ultra Clear tube and centrifuged for at least 16 hr at 36 krpm at 15°. If necessary one can top up the tube with some 4 M CsCl in TNM.

17. The band of phage is again removed from the tube with a needle and then dialyzed against TNM buffer. Usually 1 hour is adequate.

18. An optional step, but worth doing, is to treat the dialyzed phage solution per ml with 40 µl of 0.5 M EDTA, 50 µl of 20% (w/v) SDS, and 10 µl of 5 mg/ml proteinase K in TE. Incubate 60 min at 65°.

19. The phage solution is then extracted with organic solvents until the interphase is clean. First, an equal volume of phenol (equilibiated with 0.2 M Tris·HCl [pH 8]) is added and mixed·on a rollodrum for 15–20 minutes at room temperature. The phases are separated by a brief spin in the table top clinical or TR-J centrifuge. The aqueous phase is reextracted with phenol. After 2 phenol extractions, the aqueous phase is extracted with chloroform repeatedly until the interphase is clear. Usually this takes at least 4 extractions, but frequently 6 or 7.

20. The aqueous phase containing purified phage DNA is then dialyzed vs. TE buffer (0.01 M Tris·HC1 [pH 8.0], 0.001 M EDTA). This dialysis should be done for 1–2 days at 4° with 3 changes of buffer.

21. Usually the DNA concentration is such that OD_{260} can be read using a 1/100 dilution. One OD_{260} unit is about 50 µg/ml.

Note: It is possible to obtain adequate amounts of DNA for many purposes from a 250-ml culture. In this case use 15 g NaCl, 17.5 g PEG, and resuspend the phage pellet in a total of 6 ml of TNM. This can be layered in an SW41 tube containing 3 ml each of the CsCl solutions and centrifuged 60 min at 36 krpm. The phage band can be rebanded to equilibrium in a total of 5 ml in an SW55 rotor for 16 hr at 45 krpm. If the phage band in the step gradient is relatively pure a quicker second step gradient can be run. To 1.5 ml of phage removed from the first gradient add 1.5 ml of TNM saturated with CsCl. Layer 1 ml of 5 M CsCl in TNM followed by 1 ml of 3 M CsCl in TNM. After a 60 min centrifugation at 45 krpm the phage band will have floated to the 3 M/5 M interface. Pull the phage band and extract the DNA as described above.

PHAGE DNA MINIPREP

The procedure described here and indicated as 2A, etc., is for very small analytical amounts of phage. It can easily be scaled up to prepare DNA fragments in sufficient quantity for gel purification and radiolabeling. The scaled up version is noted as 2B, etc.

1. Prepare a phage stock from a confluent plate as described for the bulk phage preparation. Add a few drops of chloroform and shake at 37° for 15 min (a rotating wheel in a warm room works well).

2A. Centrifuge about 1 ml of the supernatant in a microfuge tube. This serves to clear the solution of particulate matter.

2B. Spin down 5–25 ml of the phage stock either in a tabletop centrifuge or Sorvall for 5 min at 3 krpm.

3A. Transfer 0.7 ml of the supernatant to a new microfuge tube.

3B. Transfer up to 25 ml to a new 50-ml tube.

4A. Add 1 μl 5 mg/ml RNase A and 1 μl 5 mg/ml DNase I. Incubate at 37° for 5 min.

4B. Add RNase A and DNase I to a final concentration of 1 μg/ml and incubate for 5 min at 37°.

5A. Add 0.7 ml 20% PEG 8000/12% NaCl and vortex well. Incubate for at least 1 hr on ice. Spin in a microfuge for 15 min. Remove all of the supernatant with pipetteman or by aspiration.

5B. Add an equal volume of PEG/NaCl and centrifuge at 3 krpm for 30 min.

6A. Resuspend pellet in 50 μl 50 mM Tris·HCl (pH 8)/10 mM $MgCl_2$. Vortex until dissolved.

6B. Resuspend in 500 μl and spin in a microfuge for 15 min to remove debris.

7A. Add 2 μl 0.25 M EDTA (pH 8.0), 2 μl 2% SDS, 2 μl 5 mg/ml Proteinase K (in ddH_2O). Incubate at 65° for 30 min.

7B. Scale everything up 10-fold and incubate at 65° for 30 min.

8A. Add 150 μl ddH_2O.

8B. Don't add water.

9. Extract once with SEVAG (24:1 CHCl$_3$:Isoamyl alcohol) to get rid of the PEG.

10. Extract once with phenol/SEVAG (1:1).

11. Extract once with SEVAG.

12. Extract once with ether.

13. Bring to 0.3 M sodium acetate. Precipitate with 2 vol EtOH at room temperature for 10 min. Spin in the microfuge for 10 min at room temperature.

14. If desired, resuspend pellet in 200 μl 0.3 M sodium acetate and reprecipitate with EtOH at room temperature. Wash pellet with EtOH.

15. Dessicate pellet.

16. Take up pellet in 50 μl TE and 1 μl 10 mg/ml RNase A.

Notes

1. If the plate is not confluently lysed, DNA yields are very low.

2. Enough DNA is present in 20 μl to run one lane of an agarose gel. The scaled-up version can commonly result in yields of 10–20 μg of phage DNA.

3. This DNA should be cleaved by a slight excess of most restriction enzymes.

4. The DNA from this prep can be used for ligation. See later protocol.

SUBCLONING FROM PHAGE DNA

1. Ligation from phage DNA minipreps:

    Digest 30 μl: Bring up to 100 μl:
    2x phenol
    2x ether
    EtOH-precipitate and rinse with 100% EtOH.
    Bring up in 3 μl ddH$_2$0: ligate 2 μl of this and
    3 μl of a 1/10 dilution.

2. Ligation from a large scale phage DNA prep:

    Ligate vector with 50 ng and 250 ng of phage DNA that has been di-
    gested, extracted with phenol 2x and ether 2x, then EtOH-precipitated.

    Ligation

RNase	1μl of 5 μg/μl
Digested phage DNA	2 μl
Digested and CIP'd vector DNA (100 ng)	1 μl
4x Ligation buffer	1.5 μl
Ligase	0.5 μl
(control: no phage DNA)	

RNase is not necessary for ligation of DNA purified in a bulk phage prep.
Ligate overnight at 15° in a small microfuge tube or capillary. After incubation, add 50 μl TE. Transform with 35 μl.
   Colonies can be screened via Grunstein/Hogness method with the same
probe that was used to screen library.

PHAGE RESTRICTION MAPPING USING PARTIAL DIGESTS

Using this method of restriction mapping partial digests are fractionated on agarose gels and the products are visualized by ^{32}P-labeled 12-mer oligonucleotides which are hybridized to either of the two termini of the λ DNA. This procedure was developed by Lehrach and colleagues. Partial digests are prepared and the restriction enzyme reaction terminated with high EDTA concentrations. Labeled 12-mers are annealed to the partial digest and the products are fractionated on a 0.7% agarose gel. The gel is dried down and the products visualized by autoradiography. The sizes of products can be determined from known standards.

Partial digests

1. The extent of the partial digestion depends upon the purity of the DNA, the specific activity of the particular restriction enzyme, and the incubation time and temperature. For these reasons it may take a few trials to determine the optimal conditions. The following conditions have been chosen to give reproducible patterns:

   2 μl phage DNA (0.1–0.2 μg)
   8 μl enzyme mix

   The enzyme mix typically contains 6 μl of ddH$_2$O, 1 μl of a 10x restriction enzyme buffer mix appropriate for the particular enzyme, and 1 μl of a diluted restriction enzyme added in the order listed. The commercially available enzymes generally need to be diluted immediately prior to use in a 1x buffer appropriate for the enzyme. For example, we use a final dilution of particular enzyme lots of 4 units of *Eco*R I, 1 unit of *Bam*H I, 20 units of *Hin*d III, 10 units of *Eco*R V or 5 units of *Sac* I per μl. The enzyme mix is assembled and incubated at room temperature for about 15 min. The enzyme digest is initiated by the addition of 2 μl of phage DNA.

2. The enzyme reaction is generally incubated for 5 min at room temperature after which 5 μl of the digest is transferred to another microfuge tube. The reaction is terminated in the second tube by the addition of 1 μl of 0.2 M EDTA. The first tube is incubated an additional 5 min and then terminated by the same procedure. Then the contents of both tubes are combined. The time of digestion at room temperature varies with the enzyme used. For many enzymes 5 min works fine. Some enzymes produce better partials if longer times are used. For instance we have done *Hin*d III using 10 min plus 10 min and *Sac* I for 20 min plus 20 min. The partial digestions may be stored for long periods of time at -20° before the gel analysis is performed.

Hybridization of 12-mer oligonucleotides

The two dodecamers ON-L(5'-dAGGTCGCCGCCC-3') and ON-R(5'-dGGGCGGCGACCT-3') are complementary to the left and right termini of λ DNA, respectively. These are labeled at their 5' termini using T4 polynucleotide kinase and γ-^{32}P ATP. The kinased oligos are separated from the unincorporated label using the spin columns. Typically 50–100 ng of oligonucleotide is used to prepare the labeled oligo. Only very small amounts of what is labeled are used per digest.

3.   Add 1 μl of 1 M NaCl and 5 μl (about 5000 cpm) of the kinased oligonucleotide and incubate at 75° for 2 min. Transfer immediately to 42° for 30 min. The samples may also be stored at -20° after this step.

Agarose gel analysis

4.   Add 5 μl of loading buffer (36 mM Tris·HCl [pH 7.8], 30 mM NaH$_2$PO$_4$, 60 mM EDTA, 0.25% bromophenol blue, 0.25% xylene cyanol and 50% glycerol) to each tube.

5.   Layer onto a 0.5% agarose gel and run at 40–68 volts for 10–16 hr (about 2 V/cm). The electrophoresis is done using 1x E buffer with recirculation and the buffer is changed once about halfway through the run.

 The agarose gel must be dried down before autoradiography. After an agarose gel is frozen once it loses its form and turns to slush. The drying can be accomplished by placing it in a gel dryer or by using the following procedure. We prefer to avoid the gel dryer because of the possibility of ^{32}P contamination of equipment that is generally used more for experiments with other isotopes.

6.   Place the gel in methanol to dehydrate it for at least 30 min.

7.   Dry the gel by placing a sheet of 3 MM paper on top of a glass plate. Put the gel on top of the 3 MM paper. Put a single layer of gauze on top of the gel followed by 2 sheets of 3 MM paper. Place some paper towels on top of that and a light weight. After about an hr the gel attached to the bottom sheet of 3 MM paper can be removed, wrapped in saran wrap, and autoradiographed with an enhancing screen. An overnight exposure is usually sufficient.

Analysis of the products

Useful markers to include in the gel are the parent vector for the recombinant phages being mapped. For EMBL3, a *Sal* I or *Bam*H I partial digest allows one to determine where the vector/insert junction is located in the gel. The restriction map of several standard vectors has already been determined (see the reference cited below). Because very large molecules are being fractionated it is advisable to position all the digests of a given phage in adjacent wells. It is not possible to compare the relative mobility from the lane on one side of the gel to a lane on the other side to assign an absolute length. This is extremely useful in mapping the relative order of restriction sites in a phage much like one reads a sequencing gel. By combining this information with the sizes of fragments from a complete digest a very good map can be determined very easily.

REFERENCE

Rackwitz, H., G. Zehetner, A. Frischauf, and H. Lehrach *Gene* 30:195–200 (1984).

cDNA Libraries

GENERAL INFORMATION

Introduction

This chapter is designed to provide the reader with a detailed understanding of cDNA cloning procedures and is not intended to be a list of steps to be blindly followed. Sufficient detail is included to allow for analysis and troubleshooting of the procedure at each step. The reader should go through this entire chapter and feel comfortable with it before attempting cDNA cloning. The accompanying flowchart (figure 4.1) outlines the procedures to be used in cDNA cloning. A list of necessary reagents, their sources, and their preparation is provided at the end of this introductory section.

The two methods that are most commonly used to make cDNA libraries basically differ in the way that the cDNA is converted into a double-stranded form. Currently, the most popular method uses the "nick-translation" procedure developed by Gubler and Hoffman (*Gene* 25, 263–269[1983]); this method utilizes the mRNA that served as a template for the first strand of cDNA as a primer for synthesis of the second strand. Prior to the development of this procedure most libraries were made by the "hairpin-extension" method in which a hairpin structure at the 5′ end of the first strand of cDNA is used as a primer for synthesis of the second strand of cDNA; the hairpin structure is removed by cleavage with S1 nuclease. The double-stranded cDNA produced by either the nick-translation or hairpin-extension method is then inserted into a phage or plasmid cloning vector using linkers. There are times when it is useful to use existing cDNA clones to obtain longer

cDNA Library Flow-Chart

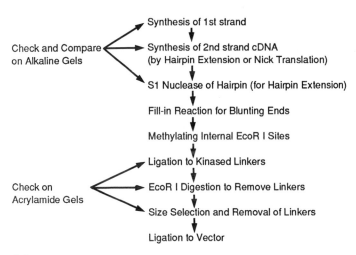

Figure 4.1

91

cDNAs containing more 5' sequences. This could be because the mRNA is very large in size or because the mRNA has secondary structure which impedes reverse transcription. A useful procedure for using primers from existing clones to extend cDNAs is presented at the end of this section.

Several procedures have not been included in this section. A method that selects for full-length cDNA clones which are inserted directly into an expression vector was developed by Okayama and Berg (*Mol. Cell Biol.* 3:280, 1983). Another procedure that uses vector primers was developed by Noma et al. (*Nature* 319:640, 1986). These methods may be necessary for particular cloning experiments. A variation on the S1-hairpin method not described here is the use of different linkers to orient the cDNA inserts into a plasmid (5' to 3') to facilitate the expression of the protein product (Helfman et al. *PNAS* 80:31, 1983).

The process of cDNA cloning requires the adept use of several general techniques:

1. *Gel exclusion columns (regular or spin columns)* are used to quickly change salt/buffer conditions or to remove free nucleotides from incorporated nucleotides.

2. *Ammonium acetate precipitation* is used to specifically precipitate DNA without also precipitating free nucleotides or free linkers.

3. *Trichloroacetic acid (TCA) precipitation* can also be used to specifically precipitate DNA but not free nucleotides. This precipitation is used as the basis of a quick assay to determine the amount of radiolabel in DNA versus free nucleotides.

4. *S1 nuclease and RNase H assays* are used to determine if radiolabeled cDNA is in single-stranded, double-stranded, or hybrid (DNA:RNA) form.

5. *Alkaline gels* are used to determine the size of denatured, single-stranded DNA.

    Gel exclusion columns, ammonium acetate precipitations, and alkaline gels are described later in this section; S1/RNase H assays and TCA precipitations are described within the cDNA cloning procedures, and further details are given in section 5 on subtractive hybridization.

Reverse transcriptase

Reverse transcriptase (RT), a retroviral enzyme that uses RNA as a template to make DNA, has made cDNA cloning possible. Multiple vendors provide RT derived from either the avian leukemia virus (ALV) or the Moloney murine leukemia virus (Mo-MLV). The quality of the various RT preparations varies considerably. For example, Life Sciences makes an "XL" quality ALV RT which yields significantly longer cDNA than their regular ALV RT. Thus it is useful to optimize conditions for a particular batch of RT. The effectiveness of the RT reaction is judged by quantitating the net synthesis and monitoring the size of the cDNA product. In assaying a batch of RT, both parameters are considered, but for most cloning purposes size is usually picked as the index of optimal activity. For titering purposes, small (10-µl) reactions can be done to save reagents. Some of the variables worth testing are the following:

1. *Quantity of RT per reaction.* Until recently, RNase contamination in the RT preparations was a frequent problem, and titering the amount of RT used per reaction was routine. We now use the maximal amount of RT that can be added to a 30-µl reaction (about 20 units/µg RNA), because commercial preparations have improved. However, one should remember the potential problem of nuclease activity.

2. *Temperature and pH.* ALV RT reactions seem to work best at 42°–48°, at a pH (at that temperature) of 8.3; conditions may differ for Mo-MLV RT, especially those encoded by fusion proteins. Heating RNA (100°, 30 sec) and quick cooling prior to cDNA synthesis eliminates aggregation and can result in higher net synthesis or in higher relative synthesis of full-length cDNA.

3. *dNTP concentration.* Reverse transcriptase reactions are not processive; the enzyme will fall off the template if substrate levels are low. Thus the reactions are performed using high concentrations of dNTP as well as an excess RT. When making cDNA for cloning purposes, we use each unlabeleled nucleotide at a concentration of 500 µM. When cDNA is made for probing purposes, we use fewer unlabeled nucleotides to increase the incorporation of radiolabeled nucleotides at the expense of cDNA length and net synthesis—for details see the subtractive hybridization section on making cDNA probes.

4. *KCl and DTT.* The RT reactions seem to work best in the presence of at least 5 mM KCl and 10 mM DTT.

5. *Sodium pyrophosphate (NaPPi).* NaPPi can be added to the reaction to inhibit RNase activity in the reverse transcriptase. Placental or pancreatic RNAse inhibitors can also be added, especially if methyl mercuric hydroxide is being used (see below).

6. *Methyl mercuric hydroxide (MeHgOH).* MeHgOH denatures mRNA by reacting with the amino groups of uridine and guanosine, resulting, under some conditions, in longer cDNA products following reverse

transcription. In particular, this treatment was very effective in cloning RNA sequences prone to certain types of secondary structure or aggregation. MeHgOH must be inactivated by addition of thiol (in the form of DTT or 2-ME) before the RT reaction. MeHgOH must *never* be used if NaPPi is to be used in the reaction, because an insoluble precipitate will form. We currently prefer the use of NaPPi in the reactions and do not routinely use MeHgOH.

7. *Actinomycin D (Act. D).* Reverse transcriptase can use the 3'-OH end of the cDNA it is synthesizing (- strand) to prime synthesis of a second strand (+ strand) complementary to the first strand, thus yielding short "snap-back" cDNA in which the first and second strands are covalently linked. Actinomycin D binds to double-stranded DNA as it transiently forms, preventing reverse transcriptase from extending these hairpin structures into snap-back DNA.

   Practically, only the effect of different RTs, of heating the RNA prior to synthesis, or of using MeHgOH is routinely tested. Individual mRNA species may be affected differently than the cDNA population as a whole. Optimizing various treatments with respect to a specific mRNA can be tested rather easily. Simply make unlabeled first-strand cDNA under the various conditions, run the reactions on an alkaline gel and blot the alkaline gel directly onto a nylon membrane. The nylon membrane can then be hybridized with a probe specific for the mRNA of interest, and cDNA products from this mRNA can be examined for relative length and amount under the different conditions.

General techniques used in cDNA cloning

1. *Ammonium acetate (NH₄Ac) precipitation to remove free nucleotides and linkers.* Use a half-volume of a 6 M NH₄Ac stock (filter-sterilized, not autoclaved) to the aqueous volume (for a final concentration of 2 M NH₄Ac), and then add a two-fold excess of EtOH. The sample is placed in dry ice for 15 min, thawed to room temperature (which redissolves nucleotides and linkers but not longer nucleic acids) and then spun in the microfuge at 4°. This first supernatant contains >90% of the free nucleotides or linkers and is carefully removed with a pipette; a 100% EtOH wash is performed and the sample is then ready to be either redissolved for a sequential precipitation, or dried and dissolved for a subsequent reaction.

2. *Columns.* Reaction products will often have to be purified through G-50 (or G-100) columns. A variety of such columns is commercially available. If you are making your own columns, use disposable material (e.g., columns or syringes) to avoid cloning contaminating molecules.

Fractionation uses either 5-ml disposable pipettes or standard 3-cc spin columns containing Sephadex G-50. The G-50 is prepared by autoclaving Sephadex in ddH$_2$O (10 g makes ~160 ml). The swollen resin is washed with ddH$_2$O 5–10 times to remove soluble dextrans that are EtOH-precipitable and will inhibit your cDNA reactions. The Sephadex is finally equilibrated in TE.

a) A column can be poured using a 5-ml disposable pipette plugged at the bottom with siliconized glass wool. The column is partially filled with water and the Sephadex is then added; about 10 ml dH$_2$O (or TE) should be run over the column to ensure removal of dextrans. Adding bromophenol blue to the sample prior to loading will mark where unincorporated nucleotides/linkers travel in the column.

b) An alternative method is to use a spin column (see discussion on radiolabeled probes in section 9) preequilibrated with TE and yeast tRNA. A spin column is faster and more convenient because the excluded peak is usually eluted in less than 400 µl (appropriate for precipitation in 1 microfuge tube).

Note: Ether extractions do not need to be done following phenol extractions if reaction product is to be loaded on column. Phenol does not come out in excluded peak. Spin columns can be pre-wet prior to loading sample to reduce nonspecific sticking to a dry column.

3. *Alkaline Gels.* The length of labeled, single-stranded(ss) DNA molecules can be monitored via alkaline minigels:

a) Alkaline electrophoresis buffer: 30 mM NaOH/1 mM EDTA
For 2 Liters: 4.8 ml 12.5 N NaOH + 4 ml 0.5 EDTA

b) Make a 1.2% agarose gel in 1 mM EDTA, boil, cool to 60°, and add NaOH to 30 mM.

c) Run ~5000 counts per lane for quick exposures.

d) Run end-labeled marker DNA (such as *Hin*f I cut pBR322).

e) Run gels lengthwise for better separation. Be sure to recirculate the buffer!!

f) Run at 30–45 volts in a horizontal gel apparatus. (Gels can also be run quickly at 100–120 V in which case you must watch them carefully and leave the lid off the gel apparatus to prevent overheating).

g) To visualize DNA, dry down gel and obtain autoradiographic exposure.

Note: The average size of the 1st-strand cDNA should be approximately 1000 nucleotides with some material extending beyond 2–3 kb. The second-strand cDNA should be about twice the size of 1st-strand cDNA if the second strand is made by the S1-hairpin method. After S1 treatment cDNA should ideally be the same size as first-strand cDNA.

2x Alkaline Gel Loading Buffer
(Make up fresh because dye degrades in base.)

100 mM NaOH	80 μl 12.5 N NaOH
2 mM EDTA	40 μl 0.5 M EDTA
20% glycerol	2 ml 100% glycerol
Dyes	400 μl saturated bromophenol
	80 μl saturated xylene cyanol
	To 10 ml with ddH$_2$O

4. *Other Hints*

   a) cDNA samples should be saved at every step of the way for size comparison (only small amounts necessary) as well as for repeating procedures in case of problems. For example, it is a good idea to save at least 1/2 of initial first-strand cDNA.

   b) Carrier tRNA or carrier glycogen should be added after double-stranded (ds) cDNA is made to help precipitation.
   Remember to treat samples with RNase A before ligations since RNA added as carrier can significantly inhibit ligations.

   c) All buffer stocks, etc. should be stored at -70°. Aliquots can be kept at -20° for short periods.

cDNA reagents and their sources

5 mM dNTP:
   Purchase dNTPs in solution from Pharmacia; these are about the same price and purportedly more stable than the dry form (the dry form tends to disproportionation reactions); dATP:#27–2050–01; dCTP:#27–2060–01; dGTP:#27–2070–01; dTTP: #27–2080–01. These come from Pharmacia in convenient and pH-adjusted 100 mM solutions. Make a mix containing 5 mM of each dNTP (total dNTP concentration is 20 mM).

Oligo(dT)$_{12-18}$: Stock 1 mg/ml in H$_2$O (20 u = 1 mg: 5 u in 250 μl = 1 mg/ml); Cat # 12136, Collaborative Research (store at -20° or -70°).

Reverse transcriptase (Life Sciences, 2100 U/60–150 μl
-titered roughly, see protocol)

α-^{32}P dNTPs: We use NEN/Amersham 50 μCi/5 μl.

Klenow: DNA polymerase I large fragment
-New England Biolabs #210, about 5 units/μl

Sl Nuclease: Boehringer-Mannheim, Cat# 818–330 (1 x 10^{4}u)
-This is titered as described in protocol.

*Eco*R I methylase: New England Biolabs #211

S-adenosyl-L-methionine: iodide salt grade I from Sigma #A-4377: Make up as 20 mM stock in 5 mM H_2SO_4 with 10% EtOH. It is stable as such for extended periods and through several thawings when kept at -20°. Immediately before use make 2 mM stock in H_2O for use in methylation reaction.

*Eco*R I linkers: (CGGAATTCCG) 1 OD unit = 50 μg: for a tube containing 1 u, take up in 100 μl H_2O (500 μg/ml).

T4 polynucleotide kinase: BRL, New England Biolabs, or Collaborative Research

γ-^{32}P-ATP: ICN, high specific activity (>95% ~150 μCi/μl)

10 mM rATP: purchased as 100 mM, pH 7.0 solution from Pharmacia (#27-2056-01)

HEPES: free acid, crystalline form from Sigma # H:3375

RNase H (*E. coli*): BRL #8021SB

DNA polymerase I (*E. coli*): Many vendors

Actinomycin D: Sigma #A4262. *Note:* Highly toxic and light-sensitive; therefore do not weigh out or spread powder around; just add 50% EtOH in water directly to bottle at ratio of 5 mg to 2.5 ml (final conc. 2 mg/ml). Store covered with foil at -20°.

RNase A: 10 mg/ml in 10 mM Tris·HCl (pH 7.5), 15 mM NaCl. Boil for 15 min to eliminate DNase activity. Allow to cool slowly to room temperature (so the RNase can renature).

Yeast tRNA: #XR-9001 from Sigma; Aliquots are 500 u (19.2 u/mg) which equals 26 mg, so you can dissolve it in 2.6 ml sterile water to achieve final concentration of 10 mg/ml. For cDNA manipulations you want clean tRNA that has been phenol/CHCl$_3$ extracted, precipitated, and redissolved in sterile water (check final OD to see correct concentration—a 1:200 dilution should have an OD_{260} of 1.25).

MAKING A cDNA LIBRARY

The integrity of the poly(A)$^+$ RNA to be used in making the library should be verified on a gel prior to proceeding with cDNA library construction. This RNA can then be used for first-strand cDNA synthesis.

First-strand cDNA synthesis

10x RT buffer	*For 10 mls*
0.5 M Tris·HCl (pH 8.3)	5.0 ml 1M Tris·HCl (pH 8.3)
1 M KCl	3.3 ml 3 M KCl
0.1 M MgCl$_2$	1.0 ml 1 M MgCl$_2$
4 mM DTT	200 μl 200 mM DTT

To 10 ml with ddH$_2$O, filter, *then* add DTT.

Reaction: Two representative reactions (HI,LO) are shown; see below.

HI CPM		LO CPM	
7 μl		12 μl	ddH$_2$O + 5–10 μg poly(A)$^+$ RNA (or MeMgOH-treated RNA)
3 μl	=	3 μl	10x RT buffer
3 μl	=	3 μl	oligo(dT)$_{12-18}$ of 1 mg/ml stock
0.6μl		4 μl	5 mM dNTPs(5 mM each for final 100 or 666 μM each)
3 μl	=	3 μl	0.04 M NaPPi (if not using MeMgOH)
1.5μl	=	1.5 μl	actinomycin D(2.0 mg/ml for final 100 μg/ml)
3 μl		0 μl	α-^{32}P-dATP
3 μl		0.5 μl	α-^{32}P-dCTP
3 μl		0.5 μl	α-^{32}P-dGTP
2–3 μl	=	2–3 μl	reverse transcriptase (titered before use)

Incubate 1–2 hr at 42°.

Note: If you are making second strand directly using the nick-translation method, at this point heat sample 10 min at 68° to stop the reaction and then proceed directly to nick-translation protocol.

Note: If you are continuing by hairpin-extension method, then stop the reaction: heat-kill 10 min at 68°, then add 170 μl ddH$_2$O and see below.

The HI/LO CPM reactions can be run and then combined to have a relatively cold, maximally long cDNA sample that includes a smaller amount of HOT (although shorter) cDNA which is used as tracer in the following reactions. The tracer cDNA is useful in assaying most of the reactions and in performing size-selection manipulations. This is most useful when you are making a subtracted cDNA library, in which case the separately synthesized first strands can be pooled after they are isolated and analyzed separately. The HI CPM reaction yields about 20 million counts whereas the LO CPM reaction yields several hundred thousand (Cherenkov) counts.

At this point you should save an aliquot of the first strand reaction mixture to be used in calculating the amount of cDNA you have synthesized. You can either do this easily and roughly (but adequately for most purposes) by just counting an aliquot (e.g., 2 out of 200 μl) of the original reaction mixture (used to determine "counts in"), which can be compared to the total number of counts incorporated in the cDNA after isolation on a column ("counts out"). The counts incorporated into cDNA can be measured after first-strand synthesis, or if you go directly to second-strand synthesis (with nick-translation protocol), after second-strand synthesis. Alternatively, you can do TCA precipitation with a 1–5 μl aliquot of the first-strand reaction mixture (only incorporated "counts out" are precipitated by TCA—see below) and compare it to an equal amount of unprecipitated reaction mix. Details of calculations will be described below.

To isolate counts incorporated into first-strand cDNA:
Run on G-50 spin column to remove unincorporated triphosphates.
Collect excluded peak, count:

Add 5 μg tRNA/tube.
EtOH-precipitate with 1/10 vol 4 M NaCl/2 vol EtOH.
Place on dry ice until solidified.
Spin 10 min at 4°.
100% EtOH-wash.
Dry 1 min in Speed-Vac (overdrying can cause cDNA to stick to tube).

(Through all of these and similar manipulations follow your radioactive counts with a monitor to avoid unexpected losses at any stage.)

Redissolve as described below for hairpin extension or other purposes.

Monitoring incorporation by TCA precipitation

Put 2 μl from 200 μl inactivated RT reaction plus 50 μg of carrier DNA (see subtractive hybridization section) into 1 ml of cold 5% TCA/0.5% NaPPi solution (stock = 50% TCA/5% NaPPi).

Incubate on ice for 10 min (precipitate forms).

Vacuum load onto filter (1.2-μm pore, 25 mm diam. American Scientific Product # F2895–11) using special vacuum manifold, and rinse several times with the 5%TCA/0.5%NaPPi solution. Reaction products greater than approximately 10 base pairs in length will be retained on the filter, whereas unincorporated nucleotides pass through the filter circle.

Place filter in counting vial, add 2–5 ml Aquasol (NEN# NEN-952) or equivalent scintillation fluid.

In another vial of Aquasol, add 2 µl aliquot from the original reaction mixture that was not TCA-precipitated.

Count both vials.

The TCA-precipitated sample represents incorporated counts (counts out) whereas the unprecipitated sample represents total number of counts used in the reaction mixture—this can be used to calculate the amount of cDNA made.

Calculating conversion into cDNA

If 4 µl of a 5 mM solution of the dNTP's were used,
this means 4 µl of 20 mM/L *Total* dNTP

$$= 20 \text{ µM/ml} = 20 \text{ nM/ul} \times 4\text{µl}$$
$$= 80 \text{ nanomoles of total dNTP} \times 330 \text{ ng/nmol}$$
$$= 26 \text{ µg cold triphosphates used per reaction}$$

Therefore (counts out/counts in) x 26 µg = µg of triphosphates converted to first strand.

To calculate % conversion, divide this number by the µg of poly(A)$^+$ RNA that you started with.

Note: At this point it would be a good idea to test the first strand synthesized for hairpin formation (snap-backs). This can be done by boiling the first strand and chilling it quickly on ice immediately before testing for relative amounts of single- and double-strandedness by assaying S1-sensitivity (see section on subtractive hybridization for details on S1 assays). Good first strand should be mostly (>90%) S1-sensitive (single-stranded). If it is not, you can try making new Act. D or using Act. D at a higher concentration (it should prevent hairpinning).

Thus, you should know at least two things about your first-strand cDNA at this point—the amount that you have and how S1-resistant it is. You might also want to determine its size on an alkaline gel.

Second-strand cDNA synthesis by hairpin extension

1. Redissolve precipitate from (2) into 0.5 mM EDTA at 10–20 µl/500ng. Make sure it dissolves (you can save some of this as first-strand cDNA).

2. Boil 2 min and quickly cool in EtOH-ice (then thaw).

    This is done to denature DNA/RNA hybrids.
    High EDTA protects DNA from nicking at 100°.

    Klenow is used to extend the hairpin at the end of the first strand. Use Klenow at 1 u/10 ng cDNA and dilute the enzyme at least 1:20.

For example:

20 μl	1st-strand cDNA (up to 1 μg)
40 μl	dNTP 5 mM
200 μl	2x Salts
120 μl	ddH$_2$O
<u>20 μl</u>	5 u/μl Klenow (100 u total) (add last)
400 μl	

Incubate at 15° overnight.

2x Salts	*For 10 ml of 2x salts*
0.14 M KCl	1.4 ml 1 M KCl
0.01 MMgCl$_2$	0.5 ml 0.2 M MgCl$_2$
0.02 M DTT	1 ml 0.2 M DTT
0.2 M HEPES	<u>4 ml 0.5 M HEPES (pH 6.9)</u>
	To 10 ml

Add 1/5 volume 5x STOP (2.0% SDS, 50 mM EDTA)
1x Phenol/CHCl$_3$

Run over spin column or add 5x dyes and run over G-50 column and collect excluded peak.

S1 Nuclease Treatment to Remove Hairpin

1. Adjust excluded peak with 10x S1 salts to 1x.
   Bring up to 0.5 mls with 1x S1 salts.

10x S1 Salts	*For 100 ml*
3 M NaCl	17.5 g NaCl
0.3 M sodium acetate (pH 4.5)	2.46 g sodium acetate
0.03 M ZnCl$_2$	<u>0.41 g ZnCl$_2$</u>
	pH to 4.6 with glacial acetic acid

S1 is used to cleave the single-stranded hairpin loop in the double-stranded cDNA made above. However, this has to be carefully titered because you do not want to overdigest and thus lose cDNA.

2. *To Titrate S1:*

Use about 0.03 u/ng cDNA (remember, you have doubled amount of cDNA by second-strand synthesis) according to unit definition of 1 unit enzyme releasing 1 μg acid-soluble dNMP from denatured herring sperm DNA in 1 min at 37°.

S1 should be titered and checked on alkaline gel. The size of second-strand cDNA should ideally be twice the size of the first strand and size after S1 treatment should ideally be back to the size of the first strand.

S1 concentrations that are usually appropriate:

0.03 u/ng 1 hr 37°
1/5 of this amount S1, 1 hr at 37°
0.03 u/ng S1 at room temperature, for 1 hr

You have to play around a little until you get the hang of it (play around with aliquots—in small volumes so ratio of S1 to cDNA remains constant; do not lose your whole sample).

To isolate the double-stranded cDNA after the hairpin is removed:

Add 10 μg tRNA/400 μl.
1x phenol/CHCl$_3$-extract.
2x ether-extract.
Precipitate with 1/10 volume 3M sodium acetate and EtOH.
Dry.

Fill-in reaction to form blunt ends and methylation of internal *EcoR* I sites

1.   Methylation

Resuspend the cDNA in:

5 μl 10x RI methylase buffer
2 μl 2 mM S-adenosylmethionine
2 μl *EcoR* I methylase (40 u/μl)

Bring to 50 μl with ddH$_2$O.

Incubate 1 hr at 37° followed by 10 min at 68°. Then cool on ice.

10x EcoR I methylase buffer

1.0 M Tris·HCl (pH 8.0)
1.0 M NaCl
10 mM EDTA

2. Blunting of ends

Add:

5.0 μl	0.1 M $MgCl_2$
5.0 μl	5 mM dNTP
<u>2 μl</u>	5 units/μl Klenow
62.0 μl total	

Incubate at room temperature for 10 min.

Add ddH_2O to 100 μl.
Phenol/$CHCl_3$ extract.
Ether-extract twice.
Precipitate with l/10 volume 3 M sodium acetate and EtOH.
70% EtOH-wash, 100% EtOH-wash.
Dry. Now cDNA is ready to be ligated to linkers (see below).

Second-strand cDNA synthesis by nick translation

If you are making second strand from purified first strand (or from RNA:DNA hybrid created by subtraction techniques) you must precipitate your cDNA with at least one (preferably 2) NH$_4$ acetate precipitations, then wash with both 70% and 100% ETOH, and redissolve in 130 μl H$_2$O and proceed as below.

If you are directly making second strand from first strand, you can just dilute your heat-killed first-strand reaction mixture up to 130 μl with H$_2$O and precede as below. In this case you will never be able to assay your first strand directly (i.e., for amount, S1 resistance, snap-backs, etc.) although these properties should also be reflected in the second-strand analysis described below. If you are concerned about performing these analyses you can take an aliquot of the first-strand reaction mixture and purify it over a column, analyze it, and use the rest of the reaction mixture directly in the second-strand reaction.

Finally, there are at least two ways to determine if the second strand worked. If you start with low-specific activity (or cold) first strand, you can make *hot* second strand and determine the amount of second strand made in the same way as with first strand (i.e., determine "counts in" and "counts out" roughly or via TCA precipitations). Comparing the amount of second strand made to the amount of first strand used as substrate will give you a rough idea of how much of the cDNA is now double-stranded. Alternatively, if you: (1) Don't want to make *hot* second strand, (2) Are going straight from first strand to this second-strand reaction and have not had a chance to determine the amount of first strand you made, (3) Want to know *exactly* how much of your cDNA is double-stranded, (4) You are making a subtracted library and thus your subtracted first-strand tracer has a high-specific activity which would obscure uptake by the second strand—in each of these cases you can directly assay the S1 resistance of your new double-stranded cDNA as described below.

(If you are testing your reagents for the first time, you might first try a small analytical reaction using an aliquot of your cDNA.)

Second-strand reaction

1st-strand cDNA:RNA hybrid	130 μl
1 M Tris·HCl (pH 7.5)	4 μl
0.2 M MgCl$_2$	5 μl
0.1 M (NH4)$_2$SO$_4$	20 μl
1 M KCl	20 μl
10 mg/ml BSA	1 μl
5 mM dNTP	5 μl

Second-strand reaction (*cont.*)

(Optional if you	[α³²P]dCTP	2 μl
want HOT 2nd strand)	[α³²P]dGTP	2 μl
RNase H (3 u/μl)		1 μl
E. coli DNA polymerase (5 u/μl)		10 μl

200 μl

Incubate at 12° for 60 min.
Incubate at 22° for 60 min.
Then heat-kill for 10 min at 68°.

1. *Blunting of ends*

    You are now ready to directly make this ds cDNA blunt-ended so it will be suitable for ligation to linkers; we often use both Klenow and T4 DNA polymerase (or either one) because they have slightly different activities at either filling-in 5' overhangs or removing 3' overhangs.

    Add 6 μl 5 mM dNTPs (final conc 200 μM).
    Add 2 μl of 1 u/μl T4 DNA polymerase.
    Incubate 15 min at 37°.
    Heat-kill 10 min at 68°.
    Add 2 μl of 5 u/μl Klenow.
    Incubate 15 min at room temperature.
    Heat-kill for 10 min at 68°.

    Phenol/SEVAG extract

    Isolate ds cDNA from free nucleotides on (spin) column. You may want to first count/save defined aliquot of reaction mix for assays to be described just below.
    Precipitate ds cDNA isolated on column with 1/2 volume NH acetate and 2 aqueous volumes of ethanol.
    70% EtOH-wash/100% EtOH-wash.
    Dry.

2. *Measuring second-strand efficiency*

    There are several ways that the efficiency of second strand can be measured:

    a) If you know how much first strand you had and you are making hotter second strand, doing TCA precipitations on an aliquot before and after the second-strand reaction (or roughly counting aliquots of the reaction mix as "counts in" and the column-purified as "counts out") will allow you to roughly determine how many μgs of second strand have been synthesized relative to the amount of first strand used. Don't forget to subtract from the second-strand sample the counts that the first strand contributes. If you went directly from first strand to second strand, this method could be used to determine how much total cDNA you have made (and % conversion) as described in the first-strand section, although you will still have to go to part *b* below to see how well the second strand worked.

b) After the second-strand cDNA is purified on a column, comparing S1 sensitivity of the second strand to the S1-sensitivity of second strand following RNase H treatment (which will degrade DNA:RNA hybrids) will not only tell you how much ds cDNA you have, but how much of it is DNA:DNA (which is what you want) and not leftover RNA:DNA from first strand. You can also assay the S1-sensitivity of a boiled/quick-chilled sample of your second-strand, allowing you to rule out "snap-back" ds cDNA (which you don't want). The combination of "S1" "boiling + S1", and "RNase H +/- S1" analysis on the second strand should allow you to evaluate not only your second strand, but also how the first strand must have worked if you went directly to second-strand synthesis and never assayed your first-strand. If you have saved an aliquot of the first strand it can be compared via the same assays, and thus will serve as a positive control for the RNase H step.

3. *RNase H assay*
    Cleaves only RNA:DNA hybrids, so first-strand should be sensitive (unless it has a lot of snap-backs), but second-strand should be resistant.

10 µg	ds salmon sperm DNA (this carrier required to prevent ss cDNA from sticking to tube at 37°)
2 µl	10x medium salt restriction buffer
0.5 µl	RNase H (3 u/µl)

1–5 k cpm cDNA to 20 µl with H_2O.

Incubate at 37° for 30 min.
Split in half to assay total cpm and S1-resistant cpm.

Methylation of internal *EcoR* I sites

Use of kinased *EcoR* I linkers (which are more efficient than nonkinased linkers that do not multimerize and thus do not require subsequent digestion with *EcoR* I) requires subsequent digestion with *EcoR* I which will also cleave *EcoR* I sites within the cDNA if these sites are not methylated.

Resuspend in:

40 µl ddH$_2$O
5 µl 10x *Eco*R I methylase buffer (see previous section)
2 µl 2 mM S-adenosyl methionine
2 µl *Eco*R I methylase

Incubate for 1 hr at 37°.
Heat-kill enzyme at 68° for 10 min.
Increase the volume to 200 µl with TE
Phenol/CHCl$_3$ extract twice.
Ether-extract twice.
Precipitate using 100 µl 6M NH$_4$-acetate, 600 µl EtOH.
70% EtOH-wash/ 100% EtOH-wash.
Dry (but do not overdry).
Resuspend in 8 µl TE for the ligation step.

Kinase of linkers

10x kinase/ligation buffer

For 400 µl

0.1 M Tris·HCl (7.5)	20 µl 2 M Tris·HCl (7.5)
0.1 M MgCl$_2$	40 µl 1 M MgCl$_2$
0.1 M DTT	200 µl 200 mM DTT
	140 µl H$_2$O

Kinase of 4 µg of linkers

8 µl	*Eco*R I Linkers (500 ng/µl in ddH$_2$O)
2 µl	γ-^{32}P-ATP
2 µl	10x kinase/ligation buffer
2 µl	T4 polynucleotide kinase
6 µl	ddH$_2$O
20 µl	

Incubate for 15 min at 37°.
Add:

2 µl	10x K/L buffer
2 µl	10 mM rATP
1 µl	T4 polynucleotide kinase
15µl	ddH$_2$O
20 µl	

Incubate for 45 min at 37°.
Incubate for 10 min at 68°.

Add 60 µl 1x K/L buffer: this is used directly below.
Store at -20° (4 µg linkers/100 µl).

Ligation of linkers to cDNA

Redissolve the double-stranded cDNA pellet prepared by the hairpin extension or nick-translation method in the following:

13 µl H$_2$O
20 µl kinased linkers
 2 µl 10 mM rATP
 2 µl 10x K/L Buffer
 1 µl RNase A (5 mg/ml)
_____
38 µl

Incubate 10 min at 37°.

Add:

1 µl T4 DNA ligase
1 µl T4 RNA ligase (optional)

Incubate at 15° overnight.
Stop at 68° for 10 min.
(Save aliquot to compare to product after digestion below.)

Note: Before using newly kinased linkers for ligating onto cDNA, you should do a test ligation to make sure that the linkers themselves have been labeled properly, and that they ligate under these conditions.

EcoR I digest to remove linkers

After heat-killing ligase, add to the above:

8 µl	0.2 M Tris·HCl (pH 7.1)
2.4 µl	100 mM MgSO$_4$
1.0 µl	5 M NaCl
1 µl	EcoR 1 (~100 u/µl)

Incubate at 37° 2 hr, then add 250 µl 1x EcoR I buffer + 2 µl high concentration EcoR I and let digest an additional hr.
Then incubate for 10 min at 68° to heat-kill the EcoR I.
Store at -20°.
While in second digest step, you should evaluate the ligation/digestion by

checking equivalent aliquots of the cDNA before and after *EcoR* I digestion by running on an 8% acrylamide gel (dry the gel and get an autoradiographic exposure). It is also instructive to load free γ-ATP and unligated linkers onto the gel for comparison. You should note that *cut* linkers migrate differently than the virgin, unligated linkers, providing further verification that ligation and cutting went well.

It is *very* important that all the linkers be removed from the cDNA sample before ligating the cDNA into a phage vector. This can be done in several different ways. In any case it is probably worthwhile to do two NH_4Ac precipitations (see [b] below) to get rid of most single linkers (which can smear backwards) before using purification methods in (a) below. You should also treat your sample with RNase A just before loading in (a) below because carrier tRNA that has been added can affect mobility/smearing of small cDNA fragments.

a) Isolate the cDNA from ultrapure agarose by electroelution (see section 9 on fragment isolation). Basically, the steps are as follows:

Fractionate the DNA on a 0.8%-1.5% agarose gel in TBE buffer (% gel depends on the size you want to resolve—1.2% is usual).

Visualize the gel with a longwave UV lamp. It should be possible to expose *only* the size markers with the UV, thus not exposing your cDNA to damaging UV light.

Cut out agarose containing cDNA; try to minimize the volume of agarose that the cDNA is in.

The cDNA can be purified by electroelution.

b) By differential precipitation using sequential NH_4Ac precipitations: add 20 μg tRNA, bring up to 2 M NH_4Ac and add 2 volumes EtOH. Freeze in dry ice, then thaw to room temperature (this helps increase ratio of linkers in supernatant to pellet) and spin in microfuge at 4°; unincorporated labeled dNTPs in the supernatant can be carefully removed with a pipette. This can be repeated (at least 5x) one last time after no more counts come off in supernatant. The counts left should be comparable to the counts of cDNA you initially put into your linker-ligation reaction.

REFERENCE

Gubler, U., and B. J. Hoffman *Gene* 25, 263–269 (1983).

Litigation to phage vector

After any of these methods, the purified, double-stranded cDNA with *Eco*R I linkers attached should be phenol/SEVAG extracted twice, ether extracted twice, and NH$_4$Ac-precipitated again. It can then be taken up in an appropriate volume and used to set up ligations to phage vector. Once it is diluted, we add 1 μl RNase A and let it digest 15 min at 37° before using cDNA in ligations. We have found that the tRNA carrier necessary to precipitate the cDNA inhibits the library ligation >2-fold, but not after RNase A treatment.

We find that saving 1/2 the cDNA at this stage, and using the remainder and a 1:4 dilution of it in two ligation points, each with 1μg phage vector DNA, usually works sufficiently to yield a library of >1 x 10^6 independent clones starting with 5 μg of RNA.

In contrast to genomic libraries, cDNA libraries are often of small size, especially if size selection, subtractive hybridization, or other techniques are used which will decrease your final yield of cDNA. Thus it often becomes important to be able to distinguish recombinant and nonrecombinant phage, or even to exclude nonrecombinants in some fashion. For this purpose we use three *Eco*R I cloning vectors, Ch16A, λ-ZAP (from Stratagene) and λgt10. The Ch16A and λ-ZAP have color-coding tests that distinguish recombinant phage (which disrupt the lac gene) as white against a blue background of wild-type phage (see below), although the λ-ZAP color assay does not work as well. (Note that the color test works much better in the recently improved λ-ZAPZ vector.) Recombinant λgt10 have disrupted the phage repressor gene cI, which results in clear plaques in a bacteria strain (C600) in which the wild-type forms turbid plaques. The turbid plaques result from high numbers of unlysed bacteria bearing a lysogenized wild-type phage which only rarely undergoes a lytic cycle due to the presence of an undisrupted cI gene. Furthermore, plating λgt10 on a bacterial strain with the "high frequency lysogeny" mutation (C600Hfl) efficiently prevents plaque formation by non-recombinants altogether, allowing you to not only distinguish recombinant phage, but also to screen plates bearing only recombinants. *Note:* All three of these phage vectors are limited to inserts less than about 9 kb in size, and phage with only linkers for inserts still register as "recombinants" by these assays.

Using λgt10

1. λgt10 seems to grow better on plates than in liquid culture. To grow it up we use large circular plates (150 mm) with NZY bottom *agarose* (use of bottom *agar* will yield phage DNA that will not cut well due to inhibitors in the agar), plating out λgt10 at about 5 x 10^4 per plate in 0.6 ml C600 (grown overnight in NZY + 0.2% maltose) plus 7 ml top agarose, let grow about 10 hours, and then overlay with 15 ml TM (Tris-Mg used in diluting phage). We generally grow up 30–50 such plates, pool

the overlays, and from this step proceed as in regular phage prep; EcoR I cutting and phosphatasing are done as for other vectors. It is also a good idea to check your λgt10 stock for relative level of background clear plaques in the C600 strain (should be <1:1000).

2. Library titerings are done in C600—this allows you to see the ratio of recombinants to wild-type; this ratio is fixed for a given batch of λgt10 and thus eliminates the need for packaging controls. Thus, the first time you use a new batch of λgt10 arms you should determine about how many wild-type plaques you get per μg of unligated arms, and the ratio of clear to turbid plaques. Subsequent ligations can be judged on these two facts: (1) if the library ligations work then the ratio of clears to turbids goes up manyfold (i.e., 10 to 1000-fold); (2) if the packaging doesn't work the ratio is still up many fold but the total number of plaques is not increased proportionately. The library plates for screening are plated on C600Hfl to eliminate the need to screen nonrecombinants.

3. Phage DNA from λgt10 recombinants can conveniently be assayed using miniprep procedures (see phage section 3); this provides enough DNA to see small inserts and to isolate fragments for nick translation. Because inserts are often small (hundreds of bp in length) it is often useful to screen phage not for EcoR I inserts but for changes in size of a 1.2 kb Hind III/Bgl II fragment that spans the EcoR I insertion site in λgt10 (this fragment can also be isolated for use as a probe on genomic DNA and RNA).

Ch16A Color Test

To use 16A color coding test on libraries one must plate them (or at least plate titering plates) on JM103. Just add 40 μl of 2% Xgal in the mix of phage/bacteria/top agarose used in the plating procedure—recombinants will appear white, and wild-type will be light blue. If IPTG (40 μl of 100 mM) is also added, the wild-type will yield uniformly royal blue plaques with blue halos whereas recombinants will yield light blue plaques with white centers and no halos. We have not strictly examined consequences of 16A growth in JM103, but the plaque size and plating efficiency is identical to LE392. Clearly, this assay can also be used to evaluate genomic libraries and eliminate the need for a packaging control as described above for the λgt10.

λ-Zap

Directions for use are provided by Stratagene. A subsection in section 5 notes how probes can quickly be made from this vector.

PRIMER EXTENSION cDNA LIBRARY

This protocol describes the synthesis of primer-extended cDNA and ways to optimize its synthesis. After the cDNA has been extended a cDNA library can be constructed as described in previous sections.

1. Preparation of primer

The primer is a terminally labeled, single-stranded fragment of DNA. Protocols are given elsewhere for phosphatasing, kinasing, and strand separation gels that can be used to obtain end-labeled fragments; synthesized oligo-nucleotides are often used as primers.

2. Synthesis of first-strand cDNA

Synthesis of first strand consists of annealing the primer to the RNA and reverse transcription. It is beneficial to optimize the annealing and reverse transcription conditions using small amounts of primer and template (RNA) before doing a large scale reaction. Variables to test include addition of MeHgOH (removes secondary structure from RNA), actinomycin (prevents self-priming of primer in reverse transcription reaction), yeast tRNA (nonspecific template to control for specificity of primer extension), no RNA (negative control), and high and low salt 10x R.T. buffer. A typical analytical annealing reaction is the following:

deionized formamide	16 μl
10x hybridization buffer	2 μl
primer (10–50,000 cpm)	1 μl
RNA (~2 μg of cytoplasmic RNA)	1 μl
	20 μl

To determine the effect of MeHgOH:

a) To RNA add 1 μl 6 mM MeHgOH.

b) Incubate at room temperature for 10 min.

c) Add 0.5 μl 0.15 M β-mercaptoethanol (1:100 dilution of 14 M stock) to inactivate MeHgOH.

d) Add formamide, hybridization buffer, and primer and proceed as for other reactions.

Heat at 68° for 10 min to denature.
Incubate at 48° for 45 min to anneal.

Following annealing, precipitate by adding:

300 μl ddH$_2$O
40 μl 4 M NaCl
1 ml EtOH

Precipitate, wash with 70% then 95% EtOH and dry.
Resuspend in 14.5 μl ddH$_2$O.

Add:

2 μl 10X reverse transcription buffer
4 μl 5 mM dNTP
(0.6 μl 500 ng/μl actinomycin)

1.5 μl reverse transcriptase

Incubate at 42° for 1 hr, add 0.5 μl 0.5 M EDTA to stop the reaction, analyze the reactions on an alkaline agarose gel (see cDNA section).

Following comparison of analytical reactions on alkaline (or urea-acrylamide) gels, reaction can be scaled up for preparative purposes.

Large scale reaction

(Include any modifications which were found to improve the reaction [i.e., MeHgOH, actinomycin]).

Annealing

deionized formamide	80 μl
10x hybridization buffer	10 μl
primer	5 μl
RNA	5 μl
	100μl

Anneal as for small scale reaction.

Primer Extension

Resuspend in 62.5 μg ddH$_2$O.

Add:
20 μl	5 mM dNTP
10 μl	10x reverse transcriptase (R.T.) buffer
7.5μl	R.T.
100 μl	

Incubate at 42° for 1 hr.
Remove 5 µl for analyzing on an alkaline agarose gel.
To the remainder add: 255 µl ddH$_2$O.
Phenol/SEVAG-extract, reextracting the interface.
Ether-extract.

Precipitate by adding:

40 µl	3 M sodium acetate
1 ml	EtOH

The cDNA can then be used to construct a cDNA library using the procedures detailed in the previous sections.

10x hybridization buffer: 0.4 M PIPES (pH 6.4)/4 M NaCl/10 mM EDTA

per 100 ml: 121 g PIPES
               8 ml 5 M NaOH
          23.4 g NaCl
            2 ml 0.5 M EDTA

Add PIPES and NaOH to <100 ml H$_2$O and stir to dissolve.
Add NaCl and EDTA.
Check pH and adjust if necessary.
Bring to volume.

*High-salt 10x reverse transcriptase buffer: 1 M KCl/0.1 M MgCl$_2$/0.04 M
NaPPi/4 mM DTT/0.5 M Tris·HCl (pH 8.3)*
per ml: 0.5 ml 2 M KCl
        0.05 ml 2 M MgCl$_2$
        0.02 ml 0.2 M DTT
        0.25 ml 2 M Tris·HCl (pH 8.3)
        0.18 ml ddH$_2$O

(Low-salt 10x R.T. is identical to this, except that no KCl is used.)

Prepare a stock of 0.04 M NaPPi.
Add 1/10 vol to reaction just before adding enzyme.

Subtractive Hybridization Techniques

INTRODUCTION

Subtractive hybridization (Alt et al. 1979) provides a powerful means of enriching for, and eventually cloning, genetic sequences that are preferentially expressed in one cell type and not another. This technology was employed by several groups in the mid-1970s (before the ready availability of modern cloning techniques) to purify specific cDNA sequences for use as hybridization probes. One of the first practical applications of this general method was the isolation of sequences derived from the retroviral *src* oncogene—which was known to be encoded by the RNA of one viral genome but was specifically absent from the genome of a related retrovirus (Stehelin et al. 1976). In other early experiments, subtractive hybridization was used to isolate cDNA sequences complementary to mRNAs overexpressed in cell lines that had been selected for resistance to the drug methotrexate; the overexpressed mRNA sequences were shown to encode the enzyme dihydrofolate reductase (DHFR), which is inhibited by methotrexate. With the DHFR-specific cDNA sequence purified by subtraction, it was demonstrated that overexpression of the DHFR mRNA resulted from amplification of the DHFR gene—the first demonstration of gene amplification (Alt et al. 1978).

Subsequently, subtractive hybridization technology has been used to isolate specific sequences differentially expressed in a variety of biological contexts. In particular the general method has been used to isolate genes specifically expressed by B and T lymphocyte cell lines (Alt et al. 1979, Mather et al. 1981, Hedrick et al. 1984, Davis et al. 1984)—including the elusive genes encoding the various subunits of the T cell antigen receptor. This chapter will focus on aspects of the subtractive hybridization technology required to clone differentially expressed genes and must be used in association with the preceding chapter on cDNA library construction.

The first step in utilizing subtractive techniques involves making single-stranded cDNA representing all of the RNA sequences expressed in a particular cell line (see figure 5.1 for a schematic representation of subtractive hybridization). Such radiolabeled cDNA from two different cell lines can be used, without the subtractive manipulations described below, to simultaneously probe a conventional cDNA library in order to define sequences differentially expressed in the two cell lines. Phage clones containing cDNA inserts representing sequences expressed in one of the cell lines and not the other will differentially hybridize to the cDNA probes from the two cell lines. However, this "differential screening" technique is limited—unmanipulated cDNA probes exhibit significant background hybridization (see below) and can only be used to isolate abundantly expressed sequences that can be identified above background hybridization. Subtractive techniques involve hybridizing the single-stranded cDNA from one cell line to an excess of RNA from a second cell line. In such a hybridization reaction, cDNA from the first line representing sequences expressed in both lines will form DNA:RNA hybrids with the RNA from the second cell line, whereas cDNA not repre-

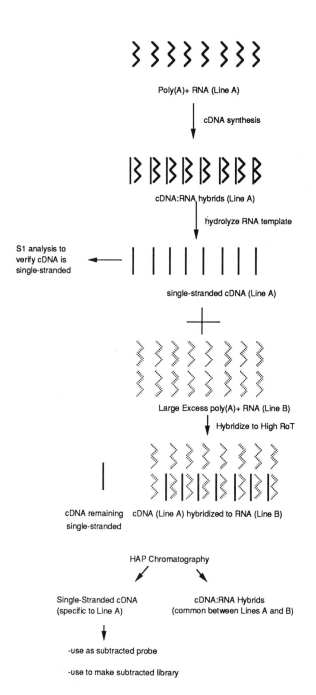

Figure 5.1. Schematic outline of subtractive hybridization procedures.

sented in the RNA of the second cell line will remain single-stranded (figure 5.1). The method also can be used to isolate cDNA sequences representing specific mRNAs that are expressed at a higher level in one cell line than another by limiting the excess of RNA used in the subtraction (Alt et al. 1978).

Chromatography over hydroxyapatite columns can separate the single- and double-stranded cDNA—thus dividing it into cDNA which is either specific to the first cell line or common to both cell lines. This cDNA can then be used to make "subtracted" cDNA libraries in which sequences specific to one cell line are greatly enriched, and also to make "subtracted" radiolabeled cDNA probes specific to a given cell line. Subtracted probes can be used to screen conventional cDNA libraries to clone the specifically expressed sequences; this method is much more sensitive than differential screening using nonsubtracted probes. The use of subtracted cDNA libraries (representing an enriched population of the cDNA clones desired) allows the screening of much smaller numbers of cDNA clones, which greatly aids in the plaque purification process, as will be discussed below. Additional techniques aimed at identifying cDNA clones representing low-abundance mRNAs will also be presented.

SYNTHESIZING FIRST-STRAND cDNA FOR PROBE PREPARATION AND SUBTRACTIVE LIBRARY CONSTRUCTION

The chapter on cDNA library construction details the synthesis of (and describes preparation and role of reagents used in the synthesis of) "HI" and "LO" specific activity first-strand cDNA. For use in subtracted cDNA *library* construction we usually make both and combine them in order to have both long, radio-resistant cDNA and a radiolabeled tracer to let us easily follow the cDNA during the following subtractive manipulations. For use in subtracted *probe* preparation, we make a "SUPERHOT" first-strand cDNA; although the cDNA made in this way is considerably shorter in length, it allows for the maximal amount of radiolabel incorporation.

When making cDNA probes we do not use radiolabelled TTP to avoid making radiolabeled copies of poly A stretches (tails) which can be over one hundred nucleotides in length; in these cases where nucleotide concentration is limiting supplementing the reaction with unlabeled TTP (to 500 μM) results in longer cDNA and greater net synthesis.

Table 5.1

	LO	HI	SUPERHOT
poly(A)$^+$ RNA (5 µg)	2.5	2.5	2.5
ddH$_2$O	8.0	4.4	0.0
Oligo(dT)$_{12\text{-}18}$ (1 mg/ml stock)	3.0	3.0	3.0
10x reverse transcriptase buffer	3.0	3.0	3.0
5 mM dNTPs (cold)	6.0	0.6	0.3
0.04 M sodium pyrophosphate	3.0	3.0	3.0
Actinomycin D (2 mg/ml in 50% EtOH)	1.5	1.5	1.5
[α-^{32}P] dCTP (12.5 µM at 800 Ci/mMol)	0.5	5.0	*
[ѳ-^{32}P] dGTP (12.5 µM at 800 Ci/mMol)	0.5	5.0	*
Reverse Transcriptase (about 20u/µl)	2.0	2.0	2.0

Incubate at 42–45° for 1–1.5 hr.

* For the SUPERHOT reaction we use 25 µl each of radiolabeled dATP, dCTP, and dGTP. This 75-µl volume is dried down to about 10 µl and added to the reaction, the total volume then being adjusted to 28 µl, prior to addition of the reverse transcriptase.

HYDROLYSIS OF RNA TEMPLATE TO PRODUCE SINGLE-STRANDED cDNA

Prior to subtractive hybridizations with heterologous RNA samples, the RNA template remaining in the above reaction (which is still hybridized to the cDNA) must be hydrolyzed to release single-stranded cDNA:

cDNA synthesis reaction	30 μl
ddH$_2$0	132 μl
1 N NaOH	18 μl

Incubate for 30 min at 68°.

Add 20 μl 1 M Tris·HCl (pH 8.0). (This will help buffer the HCl you are about to add, preventing big pH swings—acid plunge could depurinate your cDNA.)

Add titered amount of 1 N HCl slowly. (Add an amount you know will exactly neutralize the NaOH you added to a pH of 8.0 without the Tris present—titer the HCl and NaOH in trials that are spotted onto pH paper.)

Add carrier tRNA (10 μg) and run over a G-50 spin column to purify single-stranded cDNA from the unincorporated nucleotides. Expect 0.5–3 million Cherenkov counts for LO reactions, 10–30 million for HI reactions, and 100–300 million for SUPERHOT reactions.

The synthesized cDNA can now be assayed separately for the amount cDNA made and length (see cDNA chapter). At this point, it is also crucial to verify that the cDNA is now single-stranded, which is obviously required for the following subtractive manipulations. Assay for single-strandedness utilizes the single-strand specific nuclease S1 (see next section). The cDNA may not be single-stranded for two reasons—either the RNA hydrolysis step failed (only if done improperly) or the cDNA itself may contain "snap-backs." Snap-backs can form when the end of a cDNA molecule folds back and hybridizes to a preceding stretch of the same molecule (in a structure resembling a hairpin), resulting in a primer that reverse transcriptase can use to synthesize a second strand of cDNA that is complementary to and now covalently linked at its hairpin end to the first strand. Snap-backs can be distinguished from nonhydrolyzed DNA:RNA hybrids because only the former will still yield S1-resistant cDNA after boiling (because the cDNA strands simply snap back together upon cooling). Actinomycin D is usually effective in preventing snap-backs, but this activity can be decreased if Actinomycin D stock solutions are exposed to light or high temperatures for prolonged periods; if snap-backs are a problem (S1-resistant snap-back cDNA should not exceed 1–5% of the total cDNA), try a fresh stock solution of Actinomycin D.

When making subtracted libraries, the HI and LO cDNA's can be combined following verification that both synthesis reactions worked.

S1-NUCLEASE ASSAYS

S1-nuclease assays can be used to determine the extent to which radiolabeled cDNA is in a single- or double-stranded form. As described in the above section, this assay can be used to determine if the RNA template used to encode the cDNA has been hydrolyzed, and whether the newly synthesized cDNA has considerable snap-back properties. Furthermore, the same assay will be used to determine the extent of cDNA:RNA hybridization in hybridization reactions used to prepare or assay subtracted cDNA, as detailed below.

To perform the assay, small volumes (i.e., a few microliters) containing the radiolabeled cDNA sample (small numbers of counts sufficient for scintillation counting—i.e., 500 to 10,000 cpm—are used per sample) are added to 1.1 ml of S1 buffer:

1x S1 buffer

30 mM sodium acetate (pH 4.5)
3 mM $ZnSO_4$ or $ZnCl_2$
300 mM NaCl

10x S1 buffer

12.3 g sodium acetate
2.05 g $ZnCl_2$
87.5 g NaCl
_____

pH to 4.6 with acetic acid
Bring to 500 ml.

This buffer is conveniently prepared as a 10x stock. It is useful to prepare aliquots of 1x S1 buffer complete with 10 µg/ml denatured and sheared salmon sperm DNA (add 100 µl of 5 mg/ml stock to 50 ml) to standardize S1 reactions (see below).

Samples are vigorously mixed, vortexed, and may be frozen at this point for later processing.

Remove 0.5 ml x 2 from each sample and place into two tubes. (If it is not already in your stock, add 5 µg of denatured salmon sperm DNA to each and mix.)

Add an appropriate amount of S1 nuclease to one tube (see below).

Incubate both tubes for 30 min at 45° to digest.

Add 50 µg of salmon sperm DNA to each sample (to serve as carrier).

Precipitate nucleic acids by addition of an equal volume (0.5 ml) of 10% TCA, 1% Na pyrophosphate.

Let sit on ice for 10–15 min.

Collect precipitates on millipore filters and wash filters with multiple volumes of 5% TCA/0.5% NaPPi; collection and washes are conveniently done using the millipore vacuum filtration tub.

Filters are then counted in an appropriate scintillation fluid (e.g., Scintellene, Fisher).

Notes on S1-nuclease assay

1. *Presentation of data:* Hybrid formation is measured as the amount of TCA-precipitable radioactivity remaining after S1 treatment expressed as a percentage of the untreated control value. Endogenous S1 resistance (usually from 1% to 5% in cDNA samples–e.g., from snap-back, etc.) is subtracted from S1-treated and control samples before calculation of percent hybridization.

2. Both native and denatured salmon sperm DNA should, in theory, be added to S1 reaction. The denatured DNA serves to standardize the amount of substrate per amount of enzyme, and the native DNA serves to compete out any double-stranded activity the enzyme might have. In practice, we usually add only denatured DNA. The commercial salmon sperm DNA should be chloroform-extracted before use in the S1 reactions; the DNA used as carrier in the TCA precipitations need not be extracted. Both are prepared as 5 mg/ml stocks in H_2O, with gentle heating and stirring to dissolve. The DNA can be sheared by sonication, and denatured by boiling for 10 min; the DNA used to standardize the S1 reactions can then be chloroform-extracted, ethanol-precipitated, and redissolved.

3: *Titering the S1 nuclease* (Source: Boehringer-Mannheim, #818–330 [1 x 10^4 u]): The enzyme comes in glycerol buffer; for routine use, prepare a 10u/μl dilution of the S1 in S1 storage buffer (stored at -20°).

> *S1 storage buffer*
>
> 50% glycerol
> 20 mM sodium acetate (pH 4.5)
> 0.1 mM $ZnSO_4$
> 0.25 M NaCl

Of this dilution, one uses about 10 μl (100 u) per 0.5 ml assay (5 μg of denatured DNA). However, each batch of S1 must be titered. To titer, incubate 5 μg of denatured DNA, plus radioactive tracer DNA and various dilutions of S1 under conditions outlined above and measure TCA-precipitable cpm versus control sample (no S1). In two separate sets of reactions, the tracer should be single- or double-stranded to allow comparison of single- versus double-stranded activity of the S1 enzyme (although with a minimum excess of enzyme under the salt conditions used, there should be little double-stranded activity). An amount of S1 5-fold greater than the minimum amount needed to digest the single-stranded tracer completely (but lacking any double-stranded activity) is chosen. A native (double-stranded) and boiled/quick-chilled (single-stranded) nick-translated DNA fragment is conveniently used to titer the S1 for single- versus double-stranded activities of the enzyme.

4. TCA dilutions are conveniently made from 50% TCA/5% NaPyrophosphate stocks.

HYBRIDIZATION OF cDNA TO RNA

To obtain maximum understanding of the following section, the reader should be familiar with the theory of cDNA:RNA hybridization reactions driven by excess RNA. A convenient review of hybridization kinetics can be found in E. H. Davidson's textbook (1986). As described above, saturation hybridization of single-stranded cDNA from one cell line to a large excess of RNA from a second cell line should leave as single-stranded cDNA only those sequences not expressed in the second cell line. Two factors play major roles in determining how effective such hybridizations will be: the "RoT" achieved and the excess of RNA used. The RoT is a function of RNA concentration and time (concentration in moles of nucleotides per liter multiplied by time in seconds); hybridizations allowed to go to a RoT of several thousand can be considered to have gone to completion for even the least abundant classes of cellular mRNA sequences (Davidson 1986). The RoT per hour under the hybridization conditions to be described can be conveniently calculated by the following equation:

$$\text{RoT per hour} = 67.5 \times (\mu g \text{ RNA per } \mu l \text{ of hybridization mix})$$

While the RoT value indicates how far toward completion the hybridization reaction has gone, a sufficient excess of RNA to cDNA must still be provided. For example, cDNA represented in the added RNA will still remain single-stranded in a reaction that has gone to completion if the cDNA is actually in excess of the RNA. Routinely, a 5- to 10-fold excess of RNA to cDNA is used. Keep in mind that the "excess used" refers to the complexity of the cDNA, not to its amount; i.e., if you start with 5 μg RNA and make only 1 μg cDNA, its best to assume you have the equivalent of "5 μg of complexity" in this cDNA (i.e., you may have made shorter cDNA copies of all the RNA molecules rather than complete copies of only 1/5 of them). Thus a 5-fold excess in your hybridization mix would be 25 μg of RNA for this 1 μg of cDNA.

Hybridization reactions are carried out in the following Hybridization buffer (referred to as 1x H.B.):

1x H.B.

20 mM Tris·HCl (pH 7.7)
600 mM NaCl
2 mM EDTA
0.2% SDS
(0.5 $\mu g/\mu l$ carrier yeast tRNA, optional)

prepared as 1x, 2x, and 3x stocks (these often have to be heated to keep the SDS in solution).

For hybridization reactions the single-stranded cDNA is precipitated and dissolved in ddH$_2$O (make sure the counts have solubilized). Aliquots of the cDNA, 2x H.B. and the RNA (in H$_2$O) are then mixed in appropriate ratios. It is convenient to have more concentrated stocks of H.B. (i.e., 3x, 4x, and 5x) for more flexibility in setting up reactions. If an even more concentrated reaction is desired, the RNA and cDNA can be precipitated together and the pellet dissolved in a small volume of 1x hybridization buffer. A typical preparative reaction mix is:

5 μl cDNA in ddH$_2$O (5 μg "complexity")
15 μl 2x H.B.
10 μl poly(A)+ RNA in ddH$_2$O (30 μg total)

RoT (above reaction) = 67.5 x (0.66 μg/μl)/hr = 47/hr = 1128/day

RoT values can be modified by changing the amount of RNA added to a reaction, by changing the volume of the reaction, by changing the time of incubation, or any combination of the above.

Reactions are carried out at 68° in a microfuge tube. To prevent evaporation (and thus, concentration) reactions must be overlayed with mineral oil; tubes may be sealed securely by wrapping with parafilm (which may slightly melt). It is possible to boil overlayed reactions before starting the reaction (to ensure denaturation/solubilization of nucleic acids).

HAP CHROMATOGRAPHY

Subsequent to the hybridization reaction, HAP chromatography is used to separate cDNA that has hybridized to RNA from cDNA remaining single-stranded.

Preparing HAP slurry

1 g of HAP/ 5 ml of slurry in 0.1 M PB (0.5 M PB refers to an equimolar mix of 0.5 M monobasic and 0.5 M dibasic sodium phosphate; the pH of PB should be 6.8, and appropriate dilutions are usually made from the 0.5 M PB stock.)

Let sit 10 min and pour off fines; repeat; this may improve flow rates but is in practice not necessary.

Heat in boiling H$_2$O bath for 5 min.

The slurry can be stored for months (at least).

Setting up HAP column

Place plastic syringes in H_2O bath equilibrated to 60°, with needle passing through rubber stopper in bottom of bath.

Introduce cellulose acetate filter (cut to size with cork borer) into the bottom of a plastic 1–10-ml syringe (depending on column volume) and wet filter.

Add appropriate amount of HAP slurry to each column (with column closed) and let settle for 1 minute and open column; for most "subtractive" procedures which use relatively small amounts of DNA, a 0.5 ml bed of HAP in a 3- to 5-ml syringe is appropriate.

Wash each column with 5 or more volumes of 0.1 M PB (60°).

Loading HAP column

Make sample to 0.1 M PB with NaCl no greater than 0.3 M. (You may wish to use NaCl concentration of at least 0.15 M to ensure integrity of hybrids although this is not necessary for most applications.) Do this with solutions heated to 60°. It is useful to keep the 0.1, 0.12, and 0.5 M PB solutions in waterbath during the run. However, make up fresh stocks if this is done because the PO_4 gradually pyrolizes at the high temperature.

Usually the hybridization reaction (in a small volume <50 μl) sample is diluted >10-fold to a volume of 200–500 μl with 0.1 M PB for loading onto column.

Squirt onto column with vigor and pipette gently with column closed.

Let settle and then open column and collect effluent. For preparative procedures, sample should be passed over column several times.

Collect effluent, then continue to wash column with 0.1 M PB. The single-stranded DNA should be present in the effluent and the first few 0.1 M PB fractions. Wash until no more radioactivity comes off, then depending on the purpose wash with 0.12 M PB, again until no more radioactivity comes off. (This fraction may also contain single-stranded or partially duplex DNA which would contaminate the double-stranded fraction.) Finally, the double-stranded or hybrid DNA is eluted with 0.5 M PB. The exact concentrations of PB where ds and ss DNA are eluted may vary. This should be tested for each batch of HAP by S1 analyses of the DNA that comes off in the various fractions. If you are just interested in the single-stranded fraction it is unnecessary to collect the remaining fractions.

The fractions can be directly assayed for S1 resistance or used as a probe. However, other manipulations (i.e., further hybridizations, library construction) that utilize ethanol precipitations require removal of the PB salts, which form insoluble precipitates with ethanol. To do this, desired fractions off the HAP column are pooled and concentrated to about 100–200 μl using isobutanol extractions. This small volume is directly loaded onto a G-50 spin column (avoid loading any of the isobutanol [or any organic solvent] because this increases drying of the column and thus nonspecific "sticking" of the cDNA to the matrix; the isobutanol can be removed by doing an ether extraction), followed by loading 50–100 μl TE (with 10 μg carrier tRNA). The excluded volume is collected and can be precipitated for use in the next hybridization (or other step).

Notes on HAP chromatography

1. One g of DNA Grade BIO-GEL (BioRad Cat. # 130–0520) should bind at least 1 mg of DNA. However, the exact binding capacity should be tested for each batch of HAP. Usually, the presence of RNA does not interfere with binding of the DNA—but this should also be tested for each batch if large quantities of RNA are present. With the newer batches of HAP, the specifications are usually listed on the bottle. In addition, the concentration at which double- and single-stranded (or hybrid) DNA binds and elutes may vary from batch to batch—this is also usually listed on new bottles. In general, single-stranded DNA is eluted at 0.1 to 0.12 M and double-stranded from 0.2 to 0.5 M PB.

2. For processing samples that contain a very small amount of radioactive cDNA (e.g., for use as probes), it is useful to add about 3 μg of native and 3 μg of denatured salmon or herring sperm DNA (preferably sheared to an average size of 500–1000 bp); this amount of DNA can conveniently be processed on HAP columns of 0.2 to 0.5 ml. Carrier DNA is not included if the fractionated cDNA will be used for cloning purposes.

FURTHER SUBTRACTIONS, POSITIVE SELECTIONS, ENRICHMENT FOR LOW-ABUNDANCE SEQUENCES, AND SUBTRACTIVE STRATEGIES

The previous sections have outlined the methods for synthesizing radiolabeled cDNA and for performing a single subtraction on this cDNA. The single-stranded subtracted cDNA obtained in this way can be used in a variety of ways, with or without further subtractive hybridizations or positive selection steps. The cDNA can be used to make a subtracted cDNA library, as a probe to screen cDNA libraries (preferably if radiolabeled via the SUPER-HOT reaction), or as a probe in analytical RoT reactions to examine the specificity of the subtracted cDNA. Following sections will address the variety of uses for subtracted cDNA. We will now discuss the role and rationale of further positive and negative selections.

The subtracted cDNA can be subjected to additional subtractions. It seems that sequences often "sneak through" in a single subtraction; we usually find that two successive subtractions, each containing at least a 5-fold excess of RNA with respect to the complexity of the initial cDNA, are more effective than a single subtraction containing a 10-fold excess of RNA. The usefulness of a second subtraction depends on the amount of sneak-through as well as the extent to which the cell lines involved differ. For example, if 5% of the starting cDNA sneaks through a single subtraction and if the lines being compared are very similar (let's say they differ in only 0.5% of their RNA sequences), then only $0.5\%/(0.5\% + 5\%) = 10\%$ of a singly subtracted cDNA really is specific for sequences that differ between the two lines. A second subtraction (assuming the same amount of sneak-through) will increase the specificity of the subtracted cDNA to $10\%/(10\% + 5\%) = 67\%$. Alternatively, if the starting lines differ by 20%, then the increase in specificity of the cDNA will only jump from 80% to 93%.

A selection can also be done to enrich for sequences present at varying abundances. For example, if it is known that the desired sequence is present at low abundance within the subtracted cDNA fraction, hybridizations and chromatography can be performed to enrich for low-abundance sequences in the subtracted cDNA. This can routinely be done by hybridizing the cDNA back to the RNA from which it was derived for a relatively short RoT (of 50–100) at high excess (i.e., 5–10 fold) to eliminate high-abundance differentially expressed sequences present in the subtracted cDNA. Enrichment for low-abundance sequences is further discussed in the section on probe preparation and use.

Positive selections can also be used to further restrict the subtracted cDNA. For example, if it is known that line A expresses the particular sequence of interest whereas line B does not, cDNA from line A can be subtracted using RNA from line B. If line C also contains the desired sequence but is otherwise quite dissimilar to line A, the subtracted cDNA representing sequences in A and not B can then be hybridized to an excess of RNA from line C; only sequences shared between line A and C will form DNA:RNA hybrids. These positively selected hybrids can then be purified on HAP chromatography (see above); alternatively, the hybridization mix containing both single- and double-stranded cDNA can be used in cDNA library construction protocols that will only produce inserts from cDNA that is hybridized to RNA (see below).

The details of the subtractive reactions (e.g., cell lines chosen as sources of RNA for subtractions and positive selections, the RNA excess used, and the final RoT desired) are modified to fit particular cases. For example, if a sequence to be purified is absent in subtracted RNA, the excess of this RNA could be much greater than if it was present but at 10- to 100-fold lower abundance. We find that it is very instructive to do kinetic hybridization analyses of representative probes at each step, rather than doing "blind" subtractive reactions. Later we will present a sample subtraction (which can be very easily duplicated with any cell line that produces large amounts of a particular gene product). This type of analysis is useful to acquaint one with the technique and to test all of the components of the reaction.

For the various considerations pertaining to individual cases one can see several early publications dealing with the subject (see References).

MAKING A LIBRARY FROM SUBTRACTED cDNA

For producing subtracted cDNA libraries we start by combining single-stranded cDNA made using both HI and LO reaction conditions in order to have long, radio-resistant cDNA as well as a radiolabeled tracer to let us easily follow the cDNA during the various subtractive manipulations. This cDNA can be subjected to single or double subtractions, which can be followed by selection for low-abundance sequences as described earlier. The subtracted cDNA to be used in library construction will thus be in single-stranded form and isolated off a HAP column; it must be purified over a G-50 column and ethanol-precipitated as is routinely done for samples isolated over HAP. Library construction then requires making the cDNA double-stranded so that it can be ligated into the cloning vector. We will describe use of the nick-translation method for making double-stranded cDNA (see cDNA section 4), which requires that the cDNA be rehybridized to RNA. An alternative is the hairpin extension method. The latter method has the advantage of eliminating the additional RNA that is necessary for making the cDNA:RNA hybrids required for the nick-translation method. The advantage of the nick-translation method is that this final hybridization of the cDNA to RNA can be used as a positive selection step. The cDNA can either be hybridized back to RNA that was used as template for synthesizing the cDNA, or it can be hybridized to heterologous RNA that differs from the original RNA but that is known to contain the sequences that are to be isolated, further enriching for these sequences in the final cDNA library.

Final positive hybridization is done in a small volume with a large excess (>5- to 10-fold) to a high RoT (>2,000).

After hybridization is complete we dilute the reaction to 200 μl in TE, do one phenol/CHCl$_3$ extraction, and isolate cDNA:RNA hybrids through a G-50 spin column.

The hybridized cDNA sample (or actual aliquots from the hybridization reaction while it is still hybridizing) can be analyzed for % hybridization to verify cDNA to RNA hybridization, and then precipitated one time with NH$_4$Ac and used directly in the second strand reaction as described in the cDNA library section.

Effectiveness of second-strand synthesis can conveniently be analyzed by using combinations of S1 and RNase H assays on the purported second-strand as described in the cDNA library section.

After the second-strand synthesis we fill in the blunt ends (as described in cDNA section) but do not bother to methylate internal *Eco*R I sites given the already small size of the inserts (the manipulations done to this point leave you with a cDNA with an average size of 50–500 base pairs—see next section).

Then one phenol/CHCl$_3$ extraction, followed by NH$_4$Ac precipitation.

The double-stranded cDNA is now ready for linker ligation as described in the cDNA section.

LIGATION OF cDNA TO CLONING VECTORS

Aqueous hybridizations at 68° and HAP fractionations definitely nick cDNA sequences; however, we find the biggest size decrease occurs during the first hybridization with the size of the cDNA subsequently remaining constant at about 50–500 bp. Currently, we make size-selected libraries to avoid cloning smaller cDNAs. We have good success with size-selecting subtracted cDNA inserts (on ultrapure agarose and then electroeluting—see cDNA section). The size selection not only ensures removal of linkers but also of the large amount of small cDNA inserts present; we usually use 200–300 bp as the size cutoff so that we get a reasonable yield but also have clones with reasonable amounts of coding capacity. The cDNA can be cloned into any vector, with phage vectors being the vehicles of choice due to highest cloning efficiencies; the λ-Zap vectors from Stratagene are particularly convenient because plasmids containing inserts are quickly "zapped" out of the phage eliminating subcloning steps.

Subtracted cDNA libraries can also be transferred out of the original vector. Following amplification of the library, a conventional phage DNA isolation procedure can be performed to isolate microgram quantities of phage DNA containing the heterogeneous cDNA inserts representative of the library. These cDNA inserts can be isolated away from the vector as a smear on an ultrapure agarose gel, and then ligated into another vector (i.e., another phage or plasmid vector).

SUBTRACTIVE PROBES

Subtracted probes can be prepared using a rational strategy of subtractions and positive selections. The starting cDNA material is made using the SUPERHOT cDNA synthesis reaction outlined earlier. Regular cDNA probes can give high backgrounds when used for filter hybridizations, but doubly subtracted probes give low backgrounds and can be used for long exposures (see examples below). Doubly subtracted probes can also be hybridized back to RNA from which they were derived for short RoTs (i.e., RoT of 50–100) at high excess (i.e., 5–10x) and HAP-fractionated to eliminate (or enrich for) high-abundance differentially expressed sequences; a cDNA probe derived from the low-abundance fraction can be used to specifically identify lower abundance species. The probes can be used on Southern blots of cloned DNA sequences to verify that they work as desired. For example, a nonsubtracted cDNA probe derived from a pre-B cell line (which expresses medium levels of the Ig mu heavy chain mRNA and v-abl mRNA [both at about O.1%] and low levels of N-myc mRNA [<.001%]) will strongly identify IgM and v-abl cloned DNA fragments on a Southern blot, but hybridization to cloned N-myc fragments will not be above background (figure 5.2A). Such a probe doubly subtracted against a myeloma (which expresses IgM at a high level but not

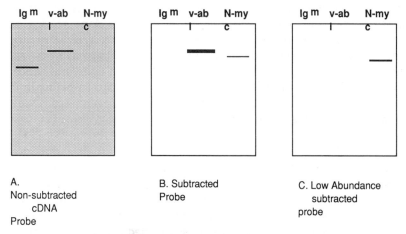

A.
Non-subtracted
cDNA
Probe

B. Subtracted
Probe

C. Low Abundance
subtracted
probe

Figure 5.2. Southern hybridization of cDNA probes on cloned genes to test specificity and efficacy of subtractive procedures.

v-abl or N-myc) will not identify a IgM fragment, still strongly identify the v-abl fragment, and now hybridization to the N-myc fragment will be evident due to the low background (figure 5.2B). Selection for low-abundance fraction of this subtracted probe will now only identify the N-myc fragment (figure 5.2C). A similar approach is employed to identify unknown differentially expressed clones. Based on the examples outlined above, the methodology can be used to select some of the least abundant sequences known.

When performing various subtractive experiments, it is useful to be able to follow sequences that are known to differ between the involved cell lines. However, in these cases the known sequences will also be cloned using the desired strategy; they can then be eliminated if they can be detected by hybridization to known probes. Because cDNA inserts in subtracted libraries are generally short in size, it is necessary to do such screening using probes that cover the entire mRNA transcript. It is also possible to eliminate known sequences from a subtracted probe, thus preventing their detection in a subtracted library. To do this, the cDNA being used as probe can be hybridized to plasmid DNA containing the sequences to be eliminated, as well as to the subtracting RNA. For plasmid subtractions 5–10 μg of plasmid cut with a frequent cutting restriction enzyme (i.e., *Hae* III or *Hinf* I) is included in the subtractive hybridization mix along with the subtracting RNA; cutting the plasmid allows it to be efficiently used in hybridizations with the RNA and speeds up the hybridization kinetics. Plasmid DNA cannot be included in subtractions to be used in library constructions because this DNA will eventually be cloned into the library.

SCREENING LIBRARIES AND IDENTIFYING CLONES OF INTEREST

Subtracted or nonsubtracted libraries can be screened with any combination of subtracted or nonsubtracted probes. If one is trying to clone sequences present in line A and not line B, it is usually worthwhile to screen a library made from line A with probes (either subtracted or nonsubtracted) from *both* lines A and B—thus desired phage clones will be identified by hybridization to the probe from line A but not by hybridization to the probe from line B. If sequences desired are present at high abundance, then conventional phage screening can be performed. That is, one can screen the initial library at high phage plaque density and then use (and reuse) the cDNA probe in plaque purification steps. However, for sequences not present at high abundance (which is often the case) conventional plaque purification methods will be too burdensome; signals obtained when screening plaques are very weak and require long (1–4 week) exposures. By this time probes have to be remade for the second round of screening, and signal intensity per plaque will actually be decreased on a plate containing many positive plaques (as the probe is diluted among many positive plaques). To avoid these problems, library screening is done in a modified manner:

Phage libraries are not plated densely, so that single plaques can be distinguished (maximum 5–10,000 on a large library plate). Screening subtracted libraries is obviously advantageous because this limits the number of plates that have to be screened due to enrichment of desired sequences. Filters can be hybridized back to back in hybridization bags to minimize the volume of hybridization buffer used.

Library screenings have to be exposed for 1–4 weeks. Subtracted probes are advantageous because they have much lower background than nonsubtracted cDNA probes, allowing weaker signals to appear above background; doubly subtracted probes have less background than singly subtracted probes and probes further enriched for low-abundance sequences have the lowest backgound of all. A proteinase K washing treatment of nitrocellulose filters is usually used because this generally reduces background on filters.

Differentially hybridizing plaques, displaying the desired pattern, are picked at the single plaque level.

No further screening of these plaques is done—the plaques are replated at low density (i.e., 50 plaques per small plate) and a single plaque is picked at random. This plaque will most likely represent a purified version of the original plaque picked; certain checks can be made to ensure and verify this:

The original library plates (which must be stored for weeks while filters are being exposed) must be plated and stored *very dry* and in the *cold* to minimize phage diffusion. We often dry plates before and after plating phage by putting them in a sterile hood (with the blower going) with the top off for about 30 min.

A blank spot on the original library plate is picked and plated together with the plaques of interest to verify limited diffusion of phage across the plate.

High titer phage lysates of these plaques are now prepared to be used in a slot-blot screening protocol which efficiently verifies the specificity of the phage inserts. A single plaque contains roughly 10^6 phage, whereas a high-titer phage lysate has 10^9 phage per ml. Screening 100 μl of a high-titer phage stock in a slot will yield a much stronger signal than a single plaque; exposure times for screening can be reduced from weeks to days.

Notes on Subtracted Probe Screenings: Conventional prehybridization/ hybridization buffers are used with the cDNA probes, using as many cpm/ml as possible. Filters are also washed conventionally, except that proteinase K background washes are prophylactically done to decrease background prior to extended autoradiographic exposure.

SLOT-BLOTTING PROTOCOL

This slot-blotting protocol has been optimized for use with Nytran membranes. Nitrocellulose membranes also work reasonably well; for nitrocellulose the formamide treatment below is not necessary for strong signals (straight phage lysate can be loaded), but treatment does seem to result in sharper slot bands, less slot leakage, and lower backgrounds.

per slot:

90 μl phage lysate
20 μl 1 M Tris·HCl (pH 8.0)
4 μl 0.5 M EDTA
115 μl 100% Formamide

_____

Heat for 10 min at 68°.
Cool on ice.
Spin for 5 min in a microfuge to pellet debris (which could clog slot).

Load onto well of slot-blotter (Schleicher and Schuell) without vacuum.
When all samples are loaded, turn on vacuum.
Wash slots with 200 μl 2x SSC.
Dry and bake membrane 30 min for Nytran, 1–2 hr for nitrocellulose.
Prehybridize, hybridize to appropriate probes conventionally (should use 1% SDS with the Nytran membrane).
Wash 3 x 20 min at 68° in 2x SSC/0.1% SDS.
Can do a proteinase K background wash (only useful for nitrocellulose blots) to further reduce background, followed by a final 2x SSC/ 0.1% SDS wash.
Expose for 1–7 days with an intensifying screen.

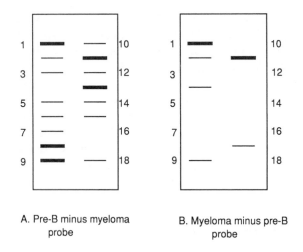

A. Pre-B minus myeloma
probe

B. Myeloma minus pre-B
probe

Figure 5.3. Hybridization of reciprocal subtracted probes to slot-blotted
DNA isolated from phages selected for specific hybridization to pre-B
specific subtracted probes.

Use of appropriate probes allows verification of specificity of cDNA inserts.
In the example presented in figure 5.3, initial phage were picked from a
subtracted cDNA library because they hybridized to a subtracted probe specific for immature pre-B cells but not to a probe specific for mature (plasma
cell stage) B cells. Figure 5.3(A and B) depicts slot-blot screening of these
phage with subtracted cDNA probes representing these two cell populations;
note that most phage contain inserts hybridizing to the subtracted probe
specific for the pre-B cells, and that the signal-to-background ratio was significantly improved using the subtracted probes.

QUICKLY PROBING cDNA INSERTS FOR SPECIFICITY ON RNA BLOTS

Use of the λ-ZAP vector (from Stratagene) greatly eases the process by which
probes can be prepared from phage clones of interest. The "zapping" process
(described at length in protocols available from Stratagene) eliminates tedious
subcloning procedures, allowing quick progression from phage clone to plasmid clone. Probes specific for the cloned inserts can then be easily prepared
by a variety of methods using plasmid DNA obtained by miniprep preparation. RNA probes can be made by using the conveniently located phage
promoters which border the cloned insert. Alternatively, DNA fragments can
be radiolabeled following isolation from restriction-cut plasmid minipreps

on low-melting-point (LMP) agarose gels; the LMP gel slice containing the DNA fragment can be soaked for 30 minutes in TE and then directly used, after melting, in a hexamer labeling reaction (try to use at least 10 nanograms per reaction). The polymerase chain reaction, using primers to amplify cloned inserts, can also be used to rapidly prepare probes from purified phage.

REFERENCES

Stehelin, B., R. Guntaka, H. Varmus, and J. M. Bishop, 1976, Purification of DNA complementary to nucleotide sequences required for neoplastic transformation of fibroblasts by avian sarcoma viruses, *J. Mol. Biol.* 101:349–365. This reference is one of the first descriptions of subtractive hybridization methods as applied in the isolation of cDNA sequences complementary to retroviral RNA sequences encoding the viral src oncogene. Detailed methods are included.

Alt, F. W., R. E. Kellems, J. R. Bertino, and R. T. Schimke, 1978, Selective multiplication of dihydrofolate reductase genes in methotrexate-resistant variants of cultured murine cells, *J. Biol. Chem.* 253, 1357–1370. This reference deals with the purification of cDNA sequences specific to RNA sequences (dHFR) that exist at increased abundance in a variant cell line by subtraction of RNA of a parental line in which they exist at approximately 100-fold lower abundance. The various steps (Rot analyses) are considered in detail.

Alt, F. W.,V. Enea, A. L. M. Bothwell, and D. Baltimore, 1979, Probes for specific mRNAs by subtractive hybridization. In *Eukaryotic Gene Regulation*, eds. Axel, R., T. Maniatis, and C. F. Fox, pp. 407–419 Academic Press. This paper describes the purification of cDNAs derived from relatively low (0.1%) to high (5%-10%) abundance, tissue-specific mRNAs (immunoglobulin heavy- and light-chain mRNAs). In this case, the subtracted RNA was usually devoid of the sequence to be enriched—thus, a large excess of subtractive RNA could be used. Few details of the methods are presented, but many general considerations are discussed.

Mather, E., F. Alt, A. Bothwell, D. Baltimore, and M. Koshland, 1981, Expression of J chain RNA in cell lines representing different stages of B lymphocyte differentiation, *Cell* 23: 369–378. This paper describes the use of subtractive-plus positive-differential hybridization techniques to purify a relatively low-abundance, tissue-specific sequence (J chain cDNA). This is the only example in which the two techniques were used simultaneously to purify a sequence.

Hedrick, S., D. Cohen, E. Nielsen, and M. Davis, 1984, Isolation of cDNA clones encoding T cell-specific membrane-associated proteins, *Nature* 308: 149–153. This paper describes the isolation of relatively low-abundance, tissue-specific sequences (cDNA sequences complementary to RNAs encoding one chain of the T cell receptor by subtractive hybridization and subtractive library methods). Few methods are presented.

Davis, M., D. Cohen, E. Nielsen, M. Steinmetz, W. Paul, and L. Hood, 1984, Cell-type-specific cDNA probes and the murine I region: The localization and orientation of A_a. *PNAS* 81: 2194–2198. This paper describes the derivation of cDNA libraries from subtracted cDNAs. Methods are presented in some detail.

Davidson, E. H., 1986, *Gene Activity in Early Development*, 3rd ed., Academic Press. Textbook detailing theoretical considerations concerning hybridization kinetics.

Transfection Procedures

INTRODUCTION

This section describes in detail several commonly used procedures for achieving DNA transfection. Protocols for the standard $CaPO_4$ and DEAE-dextran precipitations are especially good for adherent fibroblast lines but procedures for suspension cells are also given here. The efficiency of these transfection methods with lymphoid cells or other suspension cells was low. Many of these problems have largely been eliminated with the development of other methods. One of the most common methods is *electroporation*, which works well for many cell types and is very simple. *Protoplast fusion* is also useful for cells that are difficult to transfect. A newly developed technique called *lipofection* is very versatile and works on both suspension and adherent cells. In transient assays the lipofection works incredibly well. In contrast to most of the other methods the viability after this procedure is almost 100%. One of the most common systems for overexpression is the use of *gene amplification*. Procedures for the amplification of DNA sequences associated with DHFR genes in CHO cells or in many other cell lines are given.

The use of expression systems can be used for direct cloning. This is a large area and will be mentioned briefly. One of the most successful systems was developed by Seed (*PNAS* 84:3365–3369, 1987; *PNAS* 84:8573–8577, 1987). This method employs many of the methods described here. In this system a cDNA library is constructed by rather conventional means. The synthetic double-stranded DNA is inserted into the CDM8 expression vector using *Bst*X I linkers. The sequences in this vector are expressed at high levels in transiently transfected COS cells using DEAE dextran. The cDNA to be cloned must be expressed by itself on the cell surface. Cells expressing the antigen are selected by panning using the appropriate antibody. The plasmid DNA is isolated from these cells by Hirt extraction and then reintroduced into MC1061/p3 bacteria by a high-efficiency transformation. This enriched plasmid DNA is then reintroduced into COS cells using protoplast fusion. In subsequent cycles of panning and DNA transfer, protoplast fusion is used to accomplish the transfection. After three cycles individual DNA clones are isolated and tested for their ability to express the correct antigen.

One area that is not covered is the expression of genes that have already been cloned in the baculovirus system. The *baculovirus system* is a very useful eukaryotic expression system for attaining high levels of proteins that might be difficult to express in other systems. Basically the cDNA is subcloned into a plasmid downstream of the very strong late polyhedron promoter of the insect virus. This DNA is then recombined *in vivo* into a virus genome after co-transfection with viral DNA. The recombinant virus is then plaque-purified from the wild-type virus and then used to infect cells. Levels of expression are a few percent of cell protein. The methods for using that system are thoroughly covered in a manual written by Max Summers and Gale Smith is available from Dr. Summers at the Dept. of Entomology, Texas Agricultural Experiment Station and Texas A & M University, College Station, TX 77843.

The only comment we would have to add is that we found it necessary to do the plaque purification using nitrocellulose filter lifts and direct screening by hybridization. Searching for occlusion-negative cells especially early in the plaque purification was a very difficult task which was greatly simplified by screening for hybridization.

LIPOSOME-MEDIATED TRANSFECTION

A newly developed technique called *lipofection* is very versatile and can be used for both adherent and suspension cells. The DNA is entrapped with a synthetic cationic lipid that forms small liposomes. The viability of the cells postlipofection is almost 100%. In transient assays we find a 10- to 15-fold increase in levels of expression over DEAE dextran or $CaPO_4$ techniques. At present the compound N-[1-(2, 3-dioleyloxy)propyl]-N, N, N,-trimethylammonium chloride (DOTMA) is not commercially available but kits are available from BRL Life Technologies.

Protocol for adherent cells

1. The cells are used at 80%–90% confluency, which is about 3×10^5 cells per 35-mm culture dish grown in medium containing 5%–10% serum.

2. Rinse the cells twice with reduced serum medium (Opti-MEM^R from GIBCO).

3. For each 35-mm culture dish, dilute 1–5 µg of DNA in 0.5 ml of Opti-MEM^R. Dilute 10–15 µl of cationic liposome (lipofection reagent from BRL Life Technologies) in another 0.5 ml of Opti-MEM^R separately. The DNA and lipofectin are diluted separately to avoid precipitation.

4. Combine both the DNA and lipofection mixture and let it stand for 15 min at room temperature. You must use polystyrene tubes for this operation.

5. Apply the DNA/liposome complex to the monolayer culture dish and incubate the cells at 37° for 5–12 hr.

6. Following the transfection, add 3 ml of growth medium supplemented with 10%–20% serum. After this treat the cells normally.

Protocol for suspension cells

This procedure involves the use of a polyphenolic protein produced as Cell-Tak adhesive from BioPolymers, Inc. It is now distributed by Collaborative Research. It is available at a concentration of 1 mg/ml and is used at a concentration of 3.5 µg/cm^2 surface area. For example, a 35-mm culture dish has an area of 8.9 cm^2 which would need 30 µg of Cell-Tak (30 µl from the available stock). This reagent is expensive so one does need to use it carefully. Be sure to use enough because some experiments done with 1/3 the required amount were completely unsuccessful.

Preparation of the plates

1. Make a 0.1 M sodium bicarbonate solution at pH 6.5–8.0. Filter-sterilize the buffer.

2. Mix 30 μl of Cell-Tak in 1 ml of this buffer. Mix thoroughly and dispense within 10 min.

3. Layer this onto a 35-mm culture dish and incubate at 37° for at least 30 min. This is needed for adsorption.

4. The Cell-Tak comes out of solution as the pH is raised and adsorbs spontaneously to the first surface it contacts.

5. Pour off or aspirate the liquid and wash twice with sterile H_2O. This dish is now ready for use.

Lipofection

1. About 10–20 ml of suspension cells at about 3.5 x 10^5 cells/ml are collected by centrifugation in a clinical centrifuge.

2. Wash the cells twice with Opti-MEM^R. Resuspend the cells in 2 ml of Opti-MEM^R.

3. Layer the cells onto the 35-mm culture dish that was precoated with Cell-Tak and incubate for 30 min at 37°. The cells should be attached and can be confirmed by inspection under the microscope.

4. Remove the Opti-MEM^R medium.

5. Transfect them as described above with the DNA/liposome complex for 3–18 hr. The cells begin detaching within several hr. Suspend them in 30 ml of growth medium supplemented with 10%–20% serum and transfer to a culture flask.

REFERENCES

Felgner, P. L., T. R. Gadek, M. Holm, R. Roman, H. W. Chan, M. Wenz, J. P. Northrop, G. M. Ringold and M. Danielsen, 1987, *Proc. Nat. Acad. Sci. USA* 84:7413–7418.
A protocol for suspension cells which avoids the use of Cell-Tak has recently been described in *BRL FOCUS* 11:37–38 (1989). This method is simpler but doesn't work with some cell lines.

ELECTROPORATION

Background

Exposure to electrical pulses has been shown to effect the introduction of DNA into a wide variety of eukaryotic cell types, apparently by altering membrane porosity. This transfection process is affected by a number of variables which must be manipulated for peak efficiency. The easiest pulse waveform to generate (through simple capacitor discharge) is exponential decay, and this is also the most effective for cell transfection. The two important characteristics of this waveform for cell transfection are initial voltage and decay time. The initial voltage is essentially the voltage to which the capacitor bank is charged. The decay time, which is expressed as the resistance-capacitance time constant (τ), is defined as the time taken for the voltage to decline to $1/e$ (approximately 37%) of the initial voltage. τ in milliseconds (msec) is equivalent to the resistance in ohms multiplied by the capacitance in farads. Therefore, the length of the time constant is directly proportional to both the size of the capacitor and to the resistance through which it is discharged.

Most electroporation units provide a selection of capacitance values by which the time constant can be altered. Further control can be exerted by varying the resistance, which is inversely proportional to the ionic strength of the electroporation buffer. Thus, the resistance of Hepes-buffered sucrose is 5 times that of phosphate-buffered sucrose and 50 times that of phosphate-buffered saline, with parallel values for their respective time constants. A final factor to be considered is cuvette geometry. Resistance is directly proportional to the length of the path between electrodes and inversely proportional to the cross-sectional area (i.e., buffer volume). The voltage potential across the electrodes can be described as a gradient of field strength (E), expressed as volts/cm of interelectrode distance. Changes in either sample volume or cuvette size will therefore alter both the time constant and the effective voltage.

Setting up the test curve

The approach for any untested cell line is to empirically determine the optimal electroporation conditions by means of a transfection/killing curve. At the low end of the voltage-time constant spectrum, there will be no transfection. At the high end there will be complete cell death. The maximum yield of viable transfectants occurs at some point in between. Experimental data available in the literature for a number of cell lines provides a good starting range. In general it appears that adherent, fibroblastic cell lines have tough membranes and can be electroporated at high voltages (1000 to 2500 volts/0.4 cm and short time constants (0.1 to 0.5 msec, achieved by 0.25 to 25 μFD capacitance in PBS). Nonadherent lines, particularly lymphoid cells, are more fragile and require low voltages (100 to 400 volts/0.4 cm and long time constants (>10 msec, achieved by 960 μFD capacitance in PBS). In the former case, with high initial voltage and short time constants, the voltage dependance curve of transfection/killing efficiency becomes quite broad. Thus, the best approach for adherent cells is to select a single appropriate time constant (through choice of 0.25 to 25 μFD capacitance or a high-resistance buffer) and to vary the voltage in increments of 500 V. In the latter case, with lower initial voltage and longer time constants, the voltage dependence curve of transfection/killing efficiency becomes quite narrow. Thus, the best course for nonadherent cells is to select a single appropriate time constant (through choice of 960 μFD capacitance or a low-resistance buffer) and to vary the voltage in increments of 50 V or less.

In practice, we always use the low resistance HeBS buffer and establish optimal electroporation conditions using the selectable marker plasmid alone. For nonadherent cells, we use a capacitance of 960 μFD (aiming for a time constant of 10 ± 2 msec); for adherent cells we use a capacitance of 25 μFD (aiming for a time constant of 0.5 msec). We then vary the voltage from 150 to 400 V in 50-V increments for nonadherent cells or 1000 to 2500 V in 500-V increments for adherent cells. After 24 hr in bulk culture, viability is determined at each of the voltages. In general, conditions in which the viability at 24 hr is less than 50% can be expected to give optimal transfection efficiency. At 48 hr, viable cells are counted and plated out in 96 well plates at 10^3–10^4 cells per well in selective medium. At 2 weeks or more the percentage of wells with cell colonies growing is determined. If fewer than 30% of the wells are positive for growth the populations should be clonal. Published conditions for nonadherent cells using the ISCO 494 power supply can be approximately converted to use with this protocol (if the buffer and cuvette dimensions are comparable) by using 1/12th the voltage at 960 μFD capacitance.

Other variables affecting transfection frequency include the amount of DNA used, linearization of the plasmid and the use of carrier DNA. In general, the more DNA used, the greater the transfection frequency. In our standard protocol for the production of stable transformants we use 10–20 μg of each plasmid that has a selectable marker on it. For transient transfection studies 20 to 100 μg of supercoiled DNA is used. When cotransfecting a plasmid containing a gene of interest with another plasmid containing a selectable marker gene, we use 10–20 μg of plasmid with 1/10 or 1/20 the amount of the selectable plasmid. For a triple cotransfection of two genes of interest with a third plasmid containing a selectable marker, we increase this ratio to 1/40. In addition, some groups use 500 μg of carrier DNA and linearize their plasmids before transfection. We consider these two steps optional and generally do not use them.

Sample protocol for the production of stable transfectants

Materials

BioRad gene pulser with capacitance extender
Electroporation cuvettes with 0.4-cm interelectrode distance

Sterile 1x HeBS buffer (Hepes buffered saline)

20 mM Hepes (pH 7.05)
137 mM NaCl
5 mM KCl
0.7 mM Na_2HPO_4
6 mM dextrose

Filter-sterilize.
Geneticin (G418) from Sigma

Method (per sample)

1. Ethanol-precipitate 10–20 µg DNA of the plasmid containing the gene of interest. This concentrates the DNA and sterilizes it. If this plasmid does not contain a selectable marker gene, then cotransfect with 1–2 µg of pSV2-neo.

2. Resuspend the DNA in 0.8 ml 1x HeBS buffer and wait 1 hr for DNA to completely resuspend at room temperature.

3. Wash 1–4 x 10^7 cells which are growing in log phase with 1x HeBS buffer and resuspend these cells in the 0.8 ml of 1x HeBS which contains the DNA. Allow to sit at room temperature for 15 min.

4. Gently transfer the DNA/cell suspension to an electroporation cuvette and electroporate at appropriate voltage and 960 µFD capacitance. Record the time constant. Leave the mixture in the cuvette for 10 min at room temperature.

5. Transfer the cells with a sterile pasteur pipette to bulk culture in media containing 10% FCS.

6. Count the number of viable cells at 12–24 hr.

7. At 48 hr, again count number of viable cells and collect the cells by centrifugation. Resuspend them in selective media at a concentration of 10^4–10^5 cells/ml. Plate 100 µl of cells (10^3–10^4) with multichannel pipette into individual wells of a 96-well plate.

8. After 10 days add an additional 100 µl of selective media to each well.

9. After 2 to 6 weeks you will see colonies on the bottom of positive wells and the media in these wells may turn yellow. If less than 30% of the wells are positive then by Poisson analysis the positive wells are clonal. Pick the cells out of these wells with the pipetteman and expand them in selective media in 24-well plates followed by T-25 and T-75 flasks. Freeze aliquots of the cells in liquid nitrogen in 10% DMSO containing media as soon as possible and collect cells for Northern or FACS analysis concurrently.

Note: Recently conditions have been established for several human lymphoid and myeloid lines that have been difficult to transfect (see Doffinger et al. *Nucl. Acids Res.* 16:11840 (1988). Below are electroporation conditions for selected cells of interest (in HeBS or PBS Buffer).

Adherent Cells

	Voltage (V)	*Capacitance (µFD)*
CHO	280	960
L	900	25
HeLa	300	960
ES	800	3
	or 240	960

Nonadherent Cells

J558L	250	960
SP2	250	960
A20	350	960
P3x63Ag8	250	960
BW5147	325	960
R1.1	300	960
HPB-ALL	250	960
Jurkat	250	960
Molt 4	250	960
JM	250	960

REFERENCES

Shigekawa, K., and W. J. Dower *BioTechniques* 6:742–751 (1988). This is a very good review of current experience.
Potter, H., et al. *Proc. Nat. Acad. Sci. USA* 81:7161 (1984).
Toneguzzo, F., et al. *Mol. Cell Biol.* 6:703 (1986).
Smithies, O., et al. *Nature* 317:230 (1985).

CALCIUM PHOSPHATE TRANSFECTION OF CELLS

1. One day prior to transfection seed adherent cells at about 1×10^6 per T-75 flask.

2. Dilute 100 ng to 1 µg of plasmid DNA (supercoiled or linear) into 500 µl of TE buffer (1 mM Tris·HCl [pH 7.9], 1 mM EDTA) containing 20 µg of carrier DNA (target cell or salmon sperm DNA) and 0.25 M $CaCl_2$ (from a 2.5 M stock solution).

3. Shake DNA-$CaCl_2$ dropwise into an equal volume of 2x HeBS.
    2x HeBS

    280 mM NaCl
    1.5 mM NaH_2PO_4
    50 mM Hepes (pH 7.10 [within 0.05])
    Let sit 30 min to 1 hr at room temperature.

4. Wash cells once with 10 ml medium before transfection. Dilute DNA-$CaCl_2$ precipitate with 3 ml of medium and add to cells. Incubate at 37° for 6–8 hr. Rock occasionally.

5. Aspirate and add 10 ml medium to rinse cells and pour off. Repeat once. Add 20 ml fresh medium containing 50 µg/ml gentamycin and incubate 24 hr at 37°.

6. Replace medium with selective medium–after 24 hr for HAT, 48 hr for G418. Allow cells to grow for 10–14 days before picking clones.

Notes

1. In some cases, higher levels of transfection may be achieved if, 4 to 6 hr after the addition of DNA, the cells are subjected to a 3-min shock with 4% DMSO in medium at room temperature or 10%–15% glycerol in medium at 37°. Dilute immediately after the shock with 10 ml of PBS (DMSO and glycerol are toxic). Pour off, wash two more times with PBS, then replace with regular medium.

2. For transient assays in L cells one can plate 2×10^6 cells per T-75 flask and use 10 µg of plasmid DNA. Otherwise the transfection protocol is the same. The cells are then harvested by scraping at 48 hr (see CAT assay protocol).

3. For suspension cells such as Abelson-MuLV transformants use $3–5 \times 10^7$ cells per experiment. Place the cells in a 50-ml conical tube and spin down gently. Aspirate the medium and wash in serum-free medium.

At this time, the cells can be aliquoted into individual 15-ml conical tubes for each transfection. Spin down the cells, aspirate the medium and resuspend the cells in the $CaPO_4$ precipitate. Make sure to resuspend thoroughly. Let it stand for 15 min at room temperature, then add 10 ml of complete medium and place in the CO_2 incubator. After 4 hr, spin down in the clinical centrifuge, wash in serum-free medium, then distribute into complete medium for plating. Usually the distribution of 3×10^7 cells into four 24-well plates (100 ml of medium at 1 ml/well) will ensure the clonality of the transformants that will arise in some wells. For myelomas use fewer cells per experiment—usually 10^6 cells per transfection is appropriate.

4. Conditions have been found by Chen and Okayama (*Mol. Cell. Biol.* 7:2745–2752, 1987) which have further optimized the transfection efficiencies.

PROTOPLAST FUSION TRANSFECTION

This technique achieves the transfer of plasmid DNA from bacteria into the mammalian cell by PEG-mediated fusion of bacterial spheroplasts with the mammalian cells. The procedures described here were optimized for DH1 bacteria. Any bacterial strain should work but the conditions for generating spheroplasts will vary from strain to strain. It is wise to characterize one strain and then use it for all final constructions that might be used with this procedure. This technique is used to introduce plasmid DNA into cells that are difficult to transfect or when it is more convenient to reintroduce DNA without going through a plasmid DNA preparation (e.g., the Seed procedures using the CDM8 vector). For a period of several hours it is a rather demanding procedure but it works well. Electroporation is much simpler than protoplast fusion but it is sometimes difficult to find just the right conditions for transfection. For protoplast fusion the biggest variable seems to be the survival of the mammalian cells to the procedure. This can be overcome to a certain extent by adding more cells.

Protocol

Protoplast preparation (see abbreviations at the end of the protocol)

1. Grow DH-1 cells (containing the Amp^R plasmid to be expressed) in 25 ml of L broth containing ampicillin (50 µg/ml) to A_{600} approximately 0.75 (about 5×10^8 cells/ml).

2. Add CAM to the bacterial culture to a final concentration of 250 µg/ml.

3. Incubate at 37° for 12 to 16 hr.

4. Harvest the cells by centrifugation for 20 min at 4° at 3 krpm in a JA-10 rotor.

5. Aspirate off the supernatant and resuspend the cells in 1.25 ml of cold ST.

6. Add 250 µl of lysozyme (5 mg/ml in T250) and incubate 5 min at 4°.

7. Add 500 µl of cold EDTA and incubate 5 min at 4°.

8. Add 500 µl of cold T50 and transfer to a 37° water bath for 10 min.

9. Dilute slowly over a period of 20 min with 10 ml of warm DSM.

10. Incubate 10 min at room temperature.

Cell fusion

1. Harvest 2–5 x 10^6 cells by centrifugation in a clinical centrifuge. Cells such as J558L (a murine plasmacytoma) or L cells transform and survive well so we generally use 2 x 10^6 cells. Another B lymphoid cell doesn't transfect as efficiently so we use 5 x 10^6 cells to start the transfection.

2. Add 5 ml of the protoplast suspension to the cell pellet and mix.

3. Transfer to a 60-mm Falcon tissue culture dish.

4. Centrifuge at 1.8 krpm in a JA-10 rotor for 10 min at room temperature.

5. Aspirate the supernatant from the cell layer carefully.

6. Add 1.5 ml of 50% PEG that has been prewarmed to 37°.

7. Centrifuge the dishes in the JA-10 buckets for 60 sec without the brake.

8. Add 5 ml of prewarmed DMEM to the dish.

9. Swirl and decant into a 50-ml conical tube.

10. Repeat steps 8 and 9 twice and pool the washes in the same 50-ml conical tube.

11. Recover the cells at 1 krpm in the JA-10 rotor for 10 min.

12. Resuspend the cells in 2 ml of CM (DMEM/10% FCS/antibiotics).

13. Determine the cell density.

14. Plate in 96-well plates at 10^4 (J558L or L cells) or 2 x 10^3 (A20 cells) cells per well.

15. Initiate selection after 48 hr (i.e., neomycin, mycophenolic acid).

Comments

1. During the preparation of protoplast steps 4 through 8 should be carried out at 4°. Extended incubation (step 4) and rapid dilution (step 9) of lysozyme-treated cells will severely decrease the yield of protoplasts.

2. The adherence of cells to plastic dishes (step 4, cell fusion) is variable with different lines. Careful aspiration of supernatants following centrifugation (step 5) usually results in about 50% cell recovery. Optimal cell plating densities (step 14) and selective drug concentrations (step 15) also vary with different cell lines; J558L, L cells, or A20 cells transfected with pSV2neo are selectable with G418 at 2 mg/ml.

Reagents (All sterile)

Chloramphenicol; 62.5 mg/ml	(CAM)
20% sucrose, 50 mM Tris·HCl (pH 8.0)	(ST)
250 mM Tris·HCl (pH 8.0)	(T250)
250 mM EDTA (pH 8.0)	(EDTA)
50 mM Tris·HCl (pH 8.0)	(T50)
DMEM, 10% sucrose, 10 mM $MgCl_2$	(DSM)
Polyethylene glycol (1:1 in DMEM)	(PEG)

DEAE-DEXTRAN TRANSFECTION OF COS CELLS

1. Plate COS cells at 10^6 cells/10 cm plate (or 3×10^5 cells/3.5-cm plate).

2. About a day later the cells should be at 50%–70% confluent. Wash the cells with PBS. Then add in 2 ml (1 ml for the smaller dish) of PBS (500 μg/ml DEAE-dextran + 10 μg plasmid DNA). Incubate for 30 min at 37°. The cells will round up. Remove the DEAE-dextran-containing solution and wash very gently with PBS (optional).

3. Add 5 ml (2 ml for the smaller dish) of DMEM containing 5% FCS + 100 μM chloroquine and incubate for 3 hr at 37°. An optional step is to give the cells a DMSO shock using 10% DMSO in regular medium for 2.5 min at 37°.

4. Wash the cells twice with PBS and incubate in normal medium for 40 hr.

5. Two to three days after the DNA was exposed to the cells harvest the cells for immune precipitation or immunofluorescence assay.

   COS cells in culture are grown in DMEM containing 5% FBS, in 5% CO_2 at 37°. To subculture the cells wash them with PBS and add 7–8 ml trypsin/EDTA at room temperature for 8–10 min. Remove the trypsin/EDTA solution by spinning in a clinical centrifuge and resuspend the cells in regular medium. For subculturing at 2–3 day intervals split the cells 1:4, for 4–5 day intervals split them 1:8.

AMPLIFICATION OF DHFR GENES FOR HIGH-LEVEL EXPRESSION

The amplification of dihydrofolate reductase (DHFR) in DHFR-deficient CHO cells has been used to amplify an associated gene to achieve high levels of expression. Selection for increased expression of the introduced DHFR gene is accomplished using the folate antagonist methotrexate. Initial selection can begin at 5 to 20 nM and be gradually increased to 200 μM methotrexate. This selection in CHO is done with the wild-type DHFR gene. There is also a mutant of DHFR which can be used as a dominant selectable marker in many cell types (Simonsen and Levinson *PNAS* 80:2495–2499, 1983; Horwich et al. *J. Cell Biol.* 100:1515–1521, 1985). The initial selection at 200 nM results in some gene amplification and also selects completely against any untransfected cells. Subsequent cycles of selection at increased levels again results in gene amplification. In either scheme the DHFR gene could be introduced by cotransfection or be on the DHFR-containing plasmid. The method of choice would most likely be electroporation although $CaPO_4$ does work well for CHO cells.

Electroporate cells using 20 μg of the plasmid containing the gene of interest, 1–2 μg of the DHFR gene if it is a cotransfection and 380 μg of carrier DNA. Optimally, the gene to be expressed is subcloned into the DHFR vector and 50 μg of the linearized plasmid DNA could be used plus 350 μg of carrier DNA. The electroporation conditions are 960 μFD and 280 V for CHO cells. Other cell types will have their special conditions.

For CHO cells

1. Plate the cells in α+ medium and incubate until the cells become confluent. This should take at least 2 days.

2. Trypsinize the cells and replate them in α-medium at a 1:15 split. Replace the α- medium every 4–5 days. After about 2 weeks colonies should appear. If individual clones are desired it is best not to disturb the culture dishes too much. Individual clones can be picked using standard procedures or bulk cultures can be maintained.

3. To initiate the amplification in methotrexate a culture should be split 1:6 and exposed to 5, 20, or 50 nM methotrexate in α- medium. After a few weeks the cells should have adjusted and an appropriate culture can be selected for further selections.

4. Subsequent 4-to-10-fold amplification steps may be carried out. Plate out a 1:6 split of cells in the higher concentration of drug. Each time the amount of drug is increased the cells will grow more slowly and spread out more. When the cells have been passaged such that their morphol-

ogy returns to normal, they can be passaged at the regular interval (1:15 every 3 days) and the amount of drug may be increased. An upper limit for effective selection is about 200 μM. Be careful especially during the long-term maintenance periods because CHO cells are very sensitive to overgrowth.

α- medium

α- medium (from GIBCO)
10% dialyzed fetal calf serum (can be purchased from GIBCO)
4 mM glutamine

α+ medium

α- medium
10% fetal calf serum
4 mM glutamine
10 μg/ml thymidine (convenient stock solution-100x)
10 μg/ml adenosine (stock-100x)
10 μg/ml deoxyadenosine (stock-400x)

For many cell types

1. After electroporation the cells are plated in their normal growth medium for two days.

2. Selection can then be applied using 200 nM methotrexate and 4 μg/ml folic acid in the normal medium containing dialyzed serum.

3. After the cells have survived the selection (usually 2 weeks) subsequent increases in methotrexate levels can be accomplished in 4-to-10-fold steps. Depending on the growth rate of individual cells types it may take 2–4 weeks to complete a cycle of selection.

Comments

1. Methotrexate is available in a very convenient concentrated liquid stock from Calbiochem or as a solid from Sigma. The shelf life of the liquid stock solution at room temperature is at least two years. Handle it with gloves because it is carcinogenic.

2. The presense of deoxyribonucleosides and ribonucleosides in certain media such as Click's can eliminate the selection by DHFR. In this case make up media using DMEM plus other necessary ingredients.

INTRODUCTION OF FOREIGN DNA INTO CELLS VIA RETROVIRAL VECTORS

Retroviral infection can be used as an alternative to DNA transfection for the introduction of foreign genetic material into cells. This approach has several advantages:

1. Infection of several cell types which are refractory to transfection.

2. High gene transfer efficiency, which can be as high as 100% (as compared to <1% with transfection). As a result, cells present in low numbers, such as bone marrow stem cells, can be genetically manipulated.

3. Ability to study the effects of introduced genes in total cell populations and not only in relatively rare transfectants, in which undesired secondary events might have occurred during the selection process. Despite its attractiveness, use of retroviral vectors can be limited by several potential problems:

   a) *Requirement for actively replicating cells.* Retroviruses must integrate into the cellular genome for proper transduction and expression of viral (and transduced) genes. This can occur only in actively replicating cells. Thus, cells which are not cycling will not be effectively infected. Recently, other viral vectors have been developed for the transduction of genes into noncycling cells, such as neurons (Geller and Breakefield *Science* 241:1667, 1988).

   b) *Variability in expression levels of foreign genes.* Several factors can affect expression of the transduced genes:

   1) Distinct DNA fragments, even when inserted at the same site in a retroviral vector, can be expressed differently and can have various effects on viral titer. Furthermore, the nucleotide sequence of the DNA fragment to be inserted is not a good indicator of expressibility of the gene. However, DNA segments which contain internal splicing donor-acceptor sites (even if normal splicing events can occur) as well as poly A addition sites (already provided by the viral LTR) are less likely to be expressed correctly.

   2) The promoter driving transcription of the inserted gene might not be active in the particular cell type chosen for the experiment.

   3) Insertion of the retrovirus in its proviral form can occur in a region of the genome which is transcriptionally silent. For this reason individual cellular clones should be screened for high expression. This problem does not arise if bulk populations of infected cells are studied. However, if high expression of the inserted gene is toxic to cells, high

expressing cells would be selected against. An example of this problem and a way to partially circumvent it had been recently described (Huang et al. *Science* 242:1563, 1988).

Retroviral vectors which transduce an independent selectable marker together with the gene of interest allow selection of pure populations of cells infected with the recombinant virus. Double infection of cells and their subsequent selection are made possible by the use of vectors carrying two different antibiotic resistance genes, such as those encoding resistance to G418 and hygromycin (Yang et al. *Mol. Cell Biol.* 7:3923, 1987; Hartman and Mulligan *PNAS* 85:8047, 1988). Another marker, the bacterial β-galactosidase gene, allows the easy detection of virally-infected cells not only in culture but also in the animal, by a simple chromogenic assay (Price et al. *PNAS* 84:156, 1987). Expression of the selectable marker and the gene of interest can be driven by the same promoter, the viral Long Terminal Repeat (LTR), generating two transcripts by internal splicing (Cepko et al. *Cell* 37:1053, 1984). Alternatively, expression of the two genes can be independent, by use of an internal promoter as well as the viral LTR and deletion of splice donor-acceptor signals (Korman et al. *PNAS* 84:2150, 1987). (Some caution should be applied in the use of these selectable markers, since reports exist about possible interference in the expression of two different genes transduced by the same retrovirus (Emerman and Temin *Mol. Cell Biol.* 6:792, 1986). This, however, has not been the general experience of several other laboratories.)

Recombinant retroviruses are usually defective and the necessary trans-acting functions can be supplied in two ways:

1. Rescue by helper virus. This approach offers the advantage of production of viruses at high titer but because of the associated helper, viral spread cannot be controlled by limiting it to the original, infected cell population. In order to obtain a favorable ratio of recombinant to helper virus, cotransfection with plasmid DNA corresponding to both helper and vector seems to work better than transfecting cells with only vector DNA and rescuing the recombinant virus later, by superinfection with helper virus.

2. Use of "packaging cell lines" which carry integrated in their genome a proviral copy of a helper virus crippled in its packaging signal (Mann et al. *Cell* 33:153, 1983; Miller and Buttimore *Mol. Cell Biol.* 6: 2895, 1986). In this way, all necessary viral gene products are produced, but the endogenous viral RNA cannot be packaged and released as infectious virus. Subsequent transfection of these cells with a recombinant construct which contains all the necessary cis-acting signals, results in the packaging and release of the corresponding RNA as infectious recombinant virus, free of helper. The released virus can be used for one round of infection, but cannot spread further. This provides an important ad-

vantage for studies where it is important to limit infection to the initially exposed cells, even if the yield of recombinant virus can be less than that recovered in the presence of helper. Even by use of "packaging cell lines," it is possible that helper virus is generated via recombination of the resident "crippled" provirus with the transfected construct or with some other endogenous retroviral sequence. For this reason it is important to check for the presence of helper in the viral preparations as described below. To minimize this problem, new packaging lines have been recently developed where the proviral helper genome has been integrated as two separate DNA fragments (Miller and Buttimore [1986]). In this way, recombination events recreating a full length viral genome should be exceptionally rare. "Packaging cell lines" are available for the production of both ecotropic and amphotropic viruses, which can be used, respectively, to infect rodent cells or cells of a large variety of origins, including human.

Methods

1. Plasmid DNA corresponding to the engineered vector can be transfected into normal NIH3T3 cells together with helper virus plasmid DNA or, alternatively, can be transfected into "packaging cells." The standard calcium-phosphate technique can be used, with either pure plasmid DNA (10–20 mg/plate) or plasmid DNA (0.1–1 mg/plate) plus carrier salmon sperm DNA (32 mg/plate). Transfected clones can then be selected with the appropriate antibiotic as described in the previous section.

2. It is important to screen several independent clones for viral production since there is a substantial variability in the titer of virus released by the various producers. We routinely test 10 clones from each transfection. Medium is removed from dishes and, after one wash with PBS-, cloning cylinders are applied around individual colonies. Effective sealing is provided by using cloning cylinders which have their lower edge covered by a light coat of vacuum grease. About 200 μl of trypsin-EDTA solution are then applied into each cylinder. Cells are detached by vigorous pipetting a few minutes later, transferred directly to a 60 mm plate, and grown to confluence in selective medium containing the appropriate antibiotic. Freshly confluent cultures are then tested for viral production by replacing the antibiotic-containing medium with normal medium and continuing the incubation for another 18 hr. Virus is then collected (see below) and cells are frozen until further testing.

3. Virus (i.e., 12–18 hr supernatant medium) is collected from cells and passed through a 0.45 μm filter to remove contaminating cells and de-

bris. Filters with smaller pores should not be used, since virus could be filtered out. The virus should be placed immediately in ice, since it is very thermolabile (half life of 30 min at 37°, but a few hr at 0°). It can be used immediately to infect other cells or it can be stored frozen at -70° for long periods of time (up to one year). In this case, the virus can be thawed rapidly at 37° and placed immediately in ice.

4. Infection is done by adding virus (straight or at various dilutions) to cells in the presence of polybrene (8 µg/ml; this is the concentration that is usually used but it could be toxic for certain cells and might have to be reduced to 2–4 µg/ml which can also be effective). Incubation is for 2 hr at 37°. The virus is then removed and replaced with fresh medium. Cells are allowed to grow for 24–48 hr and then can be split into selective medium.

5. An alternative to this procedure which is often used to enhance chances of infection is cocultivation of target cells with viral producer cells which have been pretreated with mitomycin C in order to prevent their replication. Treatment is done by exposing cells to mitomycin C (0.5–1 mg/ml in medium) for 2 hr and refeeding with fresh medium for another 24 hr. Target adherent cells can then be plated on subconfluent cultures of treated producers or, in the case of cells growing in suspension, simply added to confluent cultures of the producers. The producers themselves can be trypsinized and replated after mitomycin treatment and can also be frozen for subsequent use.

ISOLATION OF TRANSFECTANTS

Selection of transfectants

Monolayers
Add selective medium 2–3 days after transfection, and change every 3 days thereafter. Positive clones should appear after 2 weeks. Clones can be isolated by picking with glass cloning cylinders, or by subcloning the population by limiting dilution.

Suspension cells (lymphocytes)
After 2 or 3 days, add an equal volume of 2x selective medium to each well (already containing 1 ml nonselective medium) containing cells. Change the medium with 1x selective medium at least every 3 days. Positive clones should appear between 10 days and 3 weeks after the cells have been placed in selection.

For tk selection, use HAT medium (see below). For G418 (neo) and mycophenolic acid (gpt) selections, see below.

SELECTION OF DRUG-RESISTANT VARIANTS

A stepwise protocol of gradual selection has proven fruitful for the selection of drug-resistant variants of A-MuLV transformed cell lines. Begin by placing the cells in medium containing enough of the drug to kill about 90 percent of the wild-type cells. This is usually a concentration of 100-to-200-fold less than that in which a resistant variant will ultimately be selected and passaged. For example, tk-selection requires a bromodeoxyuridine (BUdR) concentration of 10^{-4} M. Begin the selection of a variant at about 5×10^{-7} M. Adjust this concentration according to the cell line, and increase by 2-to-5-fold whenever the cells are growing relatively well. It is often helpful to maintain backup plates at a lower concentration during the selection in case the concentration of the drug is increased too fast. For selection of a tk-variant, 2–3 months are usually required to obtain a population of cells that grows well in 10^{-4} M BUdR. It may be helpful to bring the BUdR concentration up to 5×10^{-4} M to decrease the "background" of cells that survive plating into HAT medium.

Solutions

HAT

Littlefield (lymphocytes):
100x aminopterin = 3.82 mg/200 ml (in 0.01 N NaOH)

100x HT = 272.2 mg hypoxanthine
77.65 mg thymidine
Per 200 ml in 0.01 N NaOH. Store frozen.

HAT

Axel (for L cells):
200x hypoxanthine 0.3 g
        Aminopterin 20 mg
        Thymidine 103 mg
        Per 100 ml in 0.05 N NaOH. Store frozen.

BUdR

100x = 0.3 g of 5-Bromo-2'deoxyuridine/100 ml H_2O (approx. 10^{-2} M, so that 1x = 10^{-4} M)
Store frozen.

G418

Make up stock in medium minus serum. First dissolve 1 g G418 (Geneticin) in 100 ml of medium and filter-sterilize the solution. This is a 10x solution for most purposes. A 10x dilution into regular medium will make a solution at 1 mg/ml. Store at 4°.

For each cell line, titrate a kill-curve because resistance is variable. Different batches may be of different strengths, and so each bottle may require titration.

HT

Transition Medium—Use hypoxanthine and thymidine made up as above. Littlefield concentration has been sufficient for all cell types tested so far.

gpt selection

100x xanthine & hypoxanthine:
25 mg/ml xanthine (28.6 mg/ml of Na Salt)
1.5 mg/ml hypoxanthine)
Make in 0.3 N NaOH.

1000x Mycophenolic Acid = 2 mg/ml. Make up in base.

To make gpt selection medium, add hypoxanthine and xanthine and neutralize medium with 0.3 N HCl. Add both slowly and in increments to avoid wide swings in pH. It is possible to adjust the pH of the H and X before addition to medium, but then it tends to precipitate in the cold. For Abelson lines, mycophenolic acid is often added to a concentration of 2 μg/ml, but kill-curves should be performed on each cell line. Always add 1x glutamine to this medium.

DAP

2.6 diamino purine—used for APRT selection: 100x = 2.5 x 10⁻² M. Add base to get it into solution.

glutamine

100x stock is 1.5 g/100 ml (15 mg/ml). Store frozen. In H_2O, this is good for only 2–4 weeks at 4°.

gentamycin

For gentamycin sulfate, make 100–200x stock at 1.6 g/100 ml (16 mg/ml). With gentamycin base, use 10 mg/ml stock.

Freezing medium

5%–10% DMSO in tissue culture medium 20% fetal calf serum

Complete RPMI medium

RPMI plus 10% fetal calf serum, 50 μM 2-mercaptoethanol, and 1x Pen/Strep or gentamycin, if needed.

Helpful Hints

Contamination. For contamination with yeast, if it is necessary to save the cell line, plate in either fungizone or nystatin. Nystatin (Gibco) seems most versatile for lymphocytes. Be very careful handling contaminated material, and treat all plates, media, etc. with wescodyne.

Trypsinization. Warm trypsin before use. Wash cells in PBS, then add 1 ml of trypsin to each plate. If the trypsin is prewarmed, there is no need to place the cells in the incubator, where the CO_2 actually inhibits the trypsin. Leave the trypsin on long enough so that the cells come off easily, then take up in the trypsin.

Analysis of DNA-Protein Interactions

NUCLEAR EXTRACT PREPARATION

This procedure is designed to extract nuclear proteins from tissue culture cells. The cell membrane of most cells will break fairly easily if the cells are allowed to swell in a hypotonic buffer (buffer A) while most nuclei will remain intact. The intact nuclei can then be separated from the cell lysate by centrifugation. Resuspending the pelleted nuclei in a hypertonic buffer (buffer C) allows them to be easily broken and gives a crude nuclear extract with relatively little contamination from cytoplasmic proteins. The conditions described below are for suspension cells; modifications may be necessary for adherent cells or cells that are especially difficult to lyse. Cells can be harvested from T-flasks when they are at a density of 1–2 x 10^6 cells/ml. Cells grown in roller bottles can be up to 3 x 10^6 cells/ml. The cells should be healthy and, ideally be at least 90% viable by Trypan Blue exclusion. An estimate of the total number of cells to be harvested should be made by counting a representative sample. Rotors and centrifuges should be prechilled to 4°. This protocol is based upon the procedure of Dignam et al. in *Nucl. Acids Res.* 11:1475–1489 (1983).

1. Harvest the cells and pour them into centrifuge bottles.

2. Collect the cells by centrifugation. Generally at 320 g. av. for 10 min at 4°, e.g., 1700 rpm in a Beckman JA-10 rotor.

3. Carefully pour off and discard the supernatant. In large scale preparations, it is possible to leave the pellet in the bottle, add fresh sources of cells to the bottle and centrifuge again as in step 2. This can be continued for several cycles.

4. Resuspend the cell pellet in PBS at 4°. Use at least five times the volume of PBS as the volume of the cell pellet. As an example J558L lymphoid cells yield approximately 1 ml of packed cell volume for every 6 x 10^8 cells.

5. Centrifuge the resuspended cells as in step 2.

6. Carefully aspirate off the supernatant and discard it.

7. In the same bottle, resuspend the pellet in five times the cell pellet volume of buffer A.

8. Incubate on ice for 10 min, allowing the cells to swell in the hypotonic buffer.

9. Centrifuge the resuspended cells as in step 2.

10. Carefully aspirate off the supernatant. Note that some of the cytosolic proteins may have leaked from the cells. If these are of interest, you may wish to save this supernatant.

11. Resuspend the cell pellet in 2 volumes of buffer A.

12. Break the cell membranes by homogenizing in a Dounce homogenizer using ten strokes with the "B" pestle. The nuclei should remain intact.

13. Pour the suspension into centrifuge bottles and spin at 25,000 g. av. for 20 min, e.g., 15 krpm in a Beckman JA-17 rotor.

14. Pour off the supernatant. Save if you also want the cytosolic extract. See step 15a below.

15. Remove the pelleted nuclei onto a weigh boat or other convenient surface. Cut the pellet into tiny pieces using a razor blade or other sharp blade.

16. Suspend in buffer C (3 ml per 10^9 initial cells). Break the nuclei with ten strokes in a Dounce homogenizer with the "B" pestle. This treatment will lyse the nuclei in the hypertonic buffer.

17. Pour the homogenate into centrifuge bottles. Attach the bottles to a rotation device and mix them by rotation for one hour at 4°.

18. Centrifuge at 15.5 krpm for 30 min at 4°.

19. Dialyze the supernatant vs. buffer D100 overnight.

20. Remove any precipitate by centrifuging 15.5 krpm (or more), for 30 min at 4 °.

21. The supernatant, designated crude nuclear extract (CNE) may be aliquoted and stored at -80° until needed. The protein concentration should be about 6–8 mg/ml and at least 15 mg of protein per 10^9 cells.

The cytosolic extract from step 14 can be prepared for use as follows:

15a. Add 0.11 volumes of buffer B to the supernatant.

16a. Centrifuge for one hr at 100,000 g. av. (e.g., 40 krpm in a Beckman Ti50.2 rotor). Discard the pellet.

17a. Dialyze the supernatant vs Buffer D100 overnight.

18a. Remove any precipitate by centrifuging at 40 krpm for 1 hr at 4°.

19a. This supernatant, designated the S100 fraction, may also be aliquoted and stored at -80° until needed.

Buffers

All buffers should be chilled at 4°.

Stock solutions

1 M DTT can be stored frozen in small aliquots.

0.1 M PMSF dissolved in 100% ethanol and stored at -20°. Note that PMSF is not very stable in aqueous solution.

Buffer A

10 mM Hepes (pH 7.9 at 4°)
1.5 mM $MgCl_2$
10 mM KCl
0.5 mM DTT–added fresh from the stock just prior to use

Buffer B

0.3 M Hepes (pH 7.9)
1.4 M KCl
0.03 M $MgCl_2$

Buffer C

20 mM Hepes (pH 7.9)
25% glycerol (by volume)
0.42 M NaCl
1.5 mM $MgCl_2$
0.2 mM EDTA
0.5 mM PMSF and 0.5 mM DTT (add fresh just prior to use)

D100

20 mM Hepes (pH 7.9)
20% glycerol (by volume)
100 mM KCl
0.2 mM EDTA
0.5 mM PMSF and 0.5 mM DTT (add fresh just prior to use)

MOBILITY SHIFT ASSAY: DNA-BINDING PROTEIN GELS

Sample preparation

Gel mix for 4% acrylamide native gels

5 ml	10x DBB-1
5 ml	40% acrylamide
3.7 ml	2% bisacrylamide
36 ml	ddH$_2$O

Combine and degas (optional) before continuing, add the following just prior to pouring:

320 μl	10% ammonium persulfate (freshly made)
20 μl	TEMED

It takes about 1 hr to completely polymerize the gel and then the gel must be preelectrophoresed. Prepoured gels can be stored several days if immersed in 1x DBB-1 buffer; room temperature is fine, 4° is better.

Sample mix

2 μl 5x DBB-2 buffer
7 μl sample and any additions
1 μl labeled probe
10 μl total (load 5 μl on gel)

The 7 μl for sample plus additives may include competing DNA, competing protein, or salt(0.4 M KCl reduces nonspecific binding to the probe). Mix the sample ingredients in a microfuge tube. Upon adding the final ingredient, use the pipette tip to gently mix. Do not vortex. A quick spin in a microfuge is OK. Allow at least 5 min for incubation at room temperature.

Running the gel: set-up

Set up gel in a gel box equipped to circulate buffer between the chambers. The 1x DBB-1 (not DBB-2) should be used. Connect peristaltic pump to pump the buffer from bottom to top chambers (best using 2 heads). Make sure all bubbles are removed from the bottom of the gel. Also rinse out the wells to remove any residual TEMED. Electrophorese towards the positive electrode (red).

Preelectrophoresis

Preelectrophorese the gel by running it for at least one hour at the voltage to be used during the actual run (see below). This is done to drive out the TEMED. The preelectrophoresis can be done for extended periods, or the gel can be left set up for a day or two after pre-electrophoresis. In that case, replace the buffer with fresh buffer prior to use.

Electrophoresis

There is no dye in the sample mix. Tracking dye (0.25% BPB, 0.25% XC, 15% Ficoll 400) can be added to one or more lanes either before or after loading sample. We usually add a small amount of dye (o.s.-1 μl) to each well, run the gel until the dye is just into the gel, then load the samples. This marks the wells, making it easy to see the wells to load them, and serves as a tracking dye during the run. Bromophenol blue runs approximately with an 80-base pair probe.

Running

Once the samples are loaded, they should be run at a voltage that does not induce significant heat (this is a native gel). The gels are about 2 mm thick. The following voltages work well:

Size of gel plate (ht x wd in cm)	Voltage	Time
14 x 19	110	90 min
20 x 26	220	120 min
20 x 19	220	120 min

After completion of the run, remove the gel from the gel box, remove one of the glass plates, wrap the gel in saran wrap and place it at -70° for autoradiography.

10x DBB-1 buffer

60.57 g Tris base
285.27 g glycine
7.45 g disodium EDTA

Bring to 2 L with ddH$_2$O; pH should be approximately 8.5–8.6.

5x DBB-2 buffer

50 mM Tris·HCl (pH 7.5)
250 mM NaCl
5 mM DTT (optional, see note)
5 mM EDTA
25% glycerol

Can be stored aliquoted and frozen. *Note on DTT:* DTT interferes with the binding of some proteins and should be omitted for those assays.

It is also possible to use TBE as the buffer system:

10x TBE

121 g   Tris base
62 g   boric acid
7.2 g   EDTA disodium

Add ddH$_2$O to 1 L.

Make a 50% polyacrylamide stock:

240 g acrylamide
10 g bis acrylamide

Add ddH$_2$O to 500 ml.

For a 4% gel:

20 ml   50% acrylamide solution
25 ml   TBE
5 ml   glycerol
1.5 ml   10% ammonium persulfate
150 μl   TEMED

The running buffer is 1x TBE. Electrophorese at 20–40 volts/cm of the length of the gel.

RENATURATION OF DNA-BINDING PROTEINS FROM AN SDS GEL

1. Perform the KCl shadowing to localize the protein of interest and cut slices immediately from the SDS gel. Resuspend in 300 μl Hargress buffer (O.1% SDS, 50 mM Tris·HCl[pH 7.9], 0.1 mM EDTA, 5 mM DTT, 0.15 M NaCl). If there are small amounts of protein then, elution into buffer containing BSA at 100 μg/ml should be performed. If the protein seems to elute without chopping the gel, don't do it (otherwise see *Cell* 49:741, 1987, and *Science* 234:45, 1986). Elute at room temperature for about 3 hr while shaking on a vortex mixer.

2. Precipitate the protein with 5 vol of cold acetone at -20° and centrifuge in a microfuge for 30 min at 4°. Use 100 μg of carrier BSA if small amounts of proteins are involved and not added previously.

3. Wash the protein pellet with 80% acetone. Air-dry or dry on the speed vac.

4. Resuspend in 100 μl of the guanidine·HCl/TM buffer and incubate 30 min at room temperature.

5. Layer onto a spun column equilibrated in the TM buffer which contains 0.1% NP40 and 0.1 M KCl. Leave the renatured protein at 4°.

TM buffer

50 mM Tris·HCl (pH 7.9)
12.5 mM $MgCl_2$
1 mM EDTA
1 mM DTT
20% glycerol

Guanidine-HCl/TM buffer is TM buffer plus

0.1 M KCl
0.1% NP-40
6 M guanidine·HCl

FOOTPRINTING METHODS

Methylation interference

This is a relatively simple method of footprinting the sites on DNA which interact with DNA-binding proteins. The DNA fragment of interest is partially methylated and is then run on a gel retardation assay. The bands of interest are cut from the gel, cleaved by a reaction that cuts primarily at the methylated residues and analyzed on a denaturing gel used for sequence analysis. If methylation of a particular nucleotide (G and to a lesser extent A residues are methylated) interferes with DNA binding to the protein, then that residue will be underrepresented on the sequencing gel by comparison to a control sample. Remember that the DNA probe must be labeled at one end only (ordinarily for a gel retardation assay it can be labeled at both ends, if desired). You may wish to construct separate probes labelled at each end. If you label only one strand, make sure that there will be G (or A) residues in the region of interest. The site of protein-DNA interaction may be only 10–20 bp.

Preparing the probe

1. Label the DNA fragment either by kinasing or more commonly by filling in radioactive nucleotides using the Klenow polymerase reaction (see section 11).

2. After heat-inactivating the Klenow enzyme perform the second restriction enzyme cleavage.

3. Phenol-extract and EtOH-precipitate the reaction products. Resuspend the reaction products in 200 μl DMS buffer (see section 11).

4. Add 1 μl dimethyl sulfate to the reaction at room temperature for 3–5 min.

5. Stop the reaction using 50 μl of the G stop solution. Ethanol-precipitate the reaction products. Discard the EtOH supernatant in the 5 N NaOH waste.

6. Purify the DNA fragments on an acrylamide gel and elute the appropriate end-labeled fragment.

Mobility shift assay

The mobility shift assay is performed as described optimizing for the amount of bound species. The bound and free DNA species are eluted from the gel and EtOH-precipitated.

Recovering the samples

Options: The simplest way to recover samples is to soak-elute the cut band. Unfortunately, additional materials may soak out of the gel slice which can interfere with the subsequent analysis. The use of a charged DEAE membrane (NA45 from Schleicher and Schuell, see the section 9 on the preparation of these membranes) gives clean samples which footprint well. There are several ways to use these membranes.

a) Band interception in agarose. Pour an agarose gel and cut a slot in the gel large enough to insert the gel slice. Cut another slit just ahead of the inserted slice and place a strip of DEAE membrane in the slit. Electrophorese the gel until the probe has been run onto the DEAE membrane. Remove the membrane and rinse it in NET buffer (0.15 M NaCl, 0.1 mM EDTA, 20 mM Tris·HCl[pH 8]). Leave the strip in NET buffer until ready to elute the sample from the strip. Do not let the strip dry out.

b) The use of a commercial electroeluter. The IBI device (Model UE4) elutes DNA into a salt barrier. It can be used as designed, but a superior method is to cut strips of DEAE membrane, placing them in front of the barrier chamber and electroeluting onto the membrane much like with the agarose gel. This is simpler than the agarose gel method. The electroelution methods all give recoveries of better than 90%.

c) Soak elution onto the membrane. Put the gel slices in microfuge tubes, add 500 µl NET buffer and add a strip of prepared DEAE membrane (3 mm x 15 mm is a good size). Heat the tubes at 65° overnight, mixing several times, and make certain that both membrane and gel slice are immersed. Recoveries are lower by this method than by electroelution (typically 40%—70%), but this is much easier if a large number of bands have been cut.

DNA fragments are eluted from the membranes and processed as follows:

1. Rinse the membranes with bound probe in NET buffer (never let them dry), then place them in fresh microfuge tubes. Screw cap microfuge tubes are recommended since the samples will be heated later. Add 400 µl of high salt NET (1 M NaCl, 0.1 mM EDTA, 20 mM Tris·HCl [pH 8]) buffer. Incubate at 65° at least 4 hr or overnight, mixing several times making sure that the membrane remains immersed.

2. Remove the membrane from the tube. Typically, 80%–90% is recovered in the buffer. Unless there is a large amount of DNA in the sample it is best to add 0.3–1 µg of carrier DNA to each tube. Mix an incubate on dry ice or -70° for at least 30 min, then spin in a chilled microfuge for 30 min. Discard the liquid and allow the pellet to dry.

3. Resuspend the DNA in 100 μl of 1 M piperidine. Heat to 90° for 30 min. This cleaves the DNA at the methylated bases.

4. The piperidine must be completely removed or it will interfere with the sequencing gel. Freeze the samples and lyophilize overnight. Resuspend in 50 μl ddH$_2$O, freeze and lyophilize. Resuspend in 40 μl, freeze and lyophilize. Resuspend in 20 μl ddH$_2$O, freeze and lyophilize. If the piperidine is not completely removed it will leave a powdery residue. Make sure this residue is completely gone.

5. Resuspend the samples in formamide loading buffer (90% v/v deionized formamide, 1 mM EDTA, 0.05% xylene cyanol). Run on a sequencing gel with bromophenol blue as a marker in an empty well. A single 40 cm long gel works well for most probes. These gels vary, of course, from normal sequencing gels since there is only 1 lane per sample and the G residues and to a lesser extent A residues will be prominent. One or more of the Maxam/Gilbert sequencing reactions can be performed on untreated probe to give unambiguous sequence identification. Comparisons of different samples are easiest if equivalent amounts of radioactivity have been loaded in each lane.

DNase I partial digestion

This method examines the site of protein-DNA interaction by determining the region of DNA that is more resistant to partial DNase I digestion. The DNA is fractionated on a sequencing gel so the DNA fragment must be labeled only at one terminus. Conditions are determined such that a single nick per DNA molecule is made. The protein-DNA binding reaction is set up and then digested with DNase I. The reaction is terminated using EDTA. The mobility shift assay is used to obtain a source of the digested DNA-protein complex. DNA molecules in the free band have been nicked by DNase I but would show no evidence of specific protein-DNA interaction. The DNA in the bound and free bands is eluted and electrophoresed in a sequencing gel usually adjacent to a sample of the same DNA fragment that has been subjected to the A + G Maxam-Gilbert reactions.

1. For the titration of the appropriate amount of DNase I you will need to set up approximately 6 reactions: the DNA fragment with and without protein, the complete binding reaction without DNase I, and then at least 3 different amounts of DNase I. Start using 1 μl of DNase I at about 50 μg/ml and then 5- to 10-fold dilutions below that. Set up the DNA binding assay in 20 μl using conditions previously determined that show optimal activity.

2. Add 20 μl of 0.01 M $MgCl_2$ to all reactions except the two controls with and without protein.

3. Add 1 μl of each of the dilutions of DNase I to a reaction at room temperature. After a standard amount of time, generally 1 min, add 1 μl of 0.5 M EDTA and place the tube on ice.

4. Have a gel ready and run the samples.

5. The best sample is one in which the highest amount of DNase I was used and gave the expected pattern of gel retardation.

6. Excise the free and bound DNA fragments and place in a microfuge tube. The NA45 DEAE elution procedure is recommended. It is also possible to elute the DNA by soaking in a high-salt buffer followed by organic extraction. Because no subsequent procedures are performed on the DNA the following method gives DNA that is generally pure enough to give good footprints. Crush the gel and add about 0.5 ml of elution buffer (0.5 M ammonium acetate, 0.1 M EDTA, 0.1% SDS, 10 μg/ml proteinase K and 5 μg/ml carrier tRNA). Place at 37° overnight.

7. Remove the solution and extract with phenol: chloroform (1:1) and again with phenol until the aqueous phase is clear.

8. EtOH-precipitate and rinse the pellet with 70% EtOH and dry.

9. Electrophorese on an appropriate sequencing gel to resolve the region of interest. Run an equal number of cpm in adjacent lanes of the free and bound species and an A + G ladder.

Orthophenanthroline copper nuclease

This protocol begins by assuming that the conditions for optimizing the DNA-protein complex in a 4% or 6% native gel have been determined and performed.

1. Dismantle the gel and submerge in 200 ml of 10 mM Tris·HCl (pH 8.0). One of the glass plates can be used to handle the gel but the gel should not remain attached to the plate.

2. Four solutions must be prepared and ready for use:
    a) 20 ml 100% EtOH containing 116 mg neocuproine.
    b) 20 ml H_2O containing 100 μl 3-mercaptopropionic acid (MPA).
    c) 1 ml 9 mM $CuSO_4$ in H_2O (mol. wt. = 250).
    d) 1 ml 40 mM 1,10 phenanthroline (OP) = 7.2 mg/ml.

3. Mix solutions *c* and *d* and wait 1 min as it turns blue. Then add 18 ml of H_2O to this mixture. Then add to the gel.

4. Initiate the reaction using solution *b* which will turn brown. Allow the solutions to mix but don't shake the gel during the incubation.

5. After 7–10 min, terminate the reaction by adding solution *a* which will turn yellow.

6. After 2 min rinse with H_2O.

7. Process for autoradiography as usual. This would normally be an exposure at 4°.

8. Excise the DNA-protein complexes and the unbound DNA. Elute by soaking (see DNase I protocol) or electroelution using NA45 DEAE membranes. Electrophorese samples on a sequencing gel (see section 11).

Reagents can be obtained from Aldrich:
    1,10 phenanthroline (Cat. no. 13,137–7)
    Neocuproine or 2,9 dimethyl 1,10 phenanthroline (#12,190–8)
    3-mercaptopropionic acid (#M580–1)

ELUTION OF PROTEINS FROM SDS-PAGE GELS FOR AMINO ACID SEQUENCING

For gas phase sequencing one needs to prepare at least 50 pmol of protein and preferably 300 pmol or more. It is possible to purify the protein band from an SDS-PAGE gel using either KCl shadowing or a brief Coomassie staining of the gel to identify the protein band.

Coomassie staining

1. After the gel has been run immerse it in 30% isopropanol, 10% acetic acid containing Coomassie blue for 15 min at room temperature.

2. Destain the gel using 16.5% methanol, 5% methanol for 1 hr at room temperature.

3. Identify the band and excise it with a razor. Rinse it 6–7 times with H_2O until the pH is between 6 and 7.

4. Electroelute into a small volume for 8–9 hr at 40 V. If elution is performed at room temperature use 0.05 M NH_4CO_3, 0.1% SDS or if it is done at 4° use 0.05 M Tris·HCl (pH 7), 0.1% SDS.

5. Add at least 9 volumes of EtOH and place at -70° for 30 min. Bring the tube to room temperature and then spin in a microfuge for 30 min. Air-dry.

KCl shadowing

1. Immerse the gel in ice cold 0.2 M KCl, 1 mM DTT for several minutes.

2. Identify the band and excise with a razor. It may be necessary to shine a light on the gel at an angle to see bands. This method is not very sensitive but it is good for proteins that have not been denatured.

CAT (CHLORAMPHENICOL ACETYL TRANSFERASE) ASSAYS

Harvesting cells

1. After the transfection procedure, cells should be harvested by scraping the cells from the plastic surface and pelleting in a clinical centrifuge. The cells should be washed once in PBS.

2. Resuspend cells in 100 ml lysis buffer (0.15 M NaCl, 0.01 M Tris·HCl [pH 7.9], 1.5 mM MgCl$_2$, 0.65% NP-40) in a microfuge tube.

3. Spin 5 min at 4° in a microfuge and remove supernatant and save for CAT assays at -20°. Measure the protein in the lysate using the OD$_{280}$ or Bradford assay.

Enzyme assay

4. The reaction is performed in a final volume of 150 µl:

70 µl	1 M Tris·HCl (pH 7.8)
1–2 µl	^{14}C chloramphenicol (about 50 mCi/mmol)
20 µl	4 mM acetyl CoA
55 µl	extract + ddH$_2$O (typically 30 µl of extract is used)

5. Incubate 60 min at 37°.

6. Extract chloramphenicol with 1 ml of ethyl acetate by vortexing for a few sec.

7. Separate phases by a brief spin at room temperature and take the top phase.

8. Dry down in a speed vac. This solvent is very volatile and the drying occurs quickly.

9. Resuspend samples in 30 ml ethyl acetate and spot on a TLC plate. Dry with a hair dryer.

10. Develop TLC in chloroform:methanol (95:5) by ascending chromatography.

11. Let the plate dry for a few minutes. Expose for autoradiography.

Notes

1. Cells can be plated at a density of 1×10^5/ml in 20 ml in a T-75 flask two days prior to the lipofection, calcium phosphate or DEAE dextran transfection. After 2 days, they should be harvested in about 3×10^7/ml. Use 0.5 ml for a transfection or about 1.5×10^7 cells.

2. Freeze-thawing can be used to lyse cells. For fibroblasts, 3 cycles of freeze-thawing work, but lymphoid cells need 10 cycles. First freeze in dry-ice ethanol for 5 min and then put at 37° for 5 min. Vortex and repeat the cycle. After the cycles are finished, do a clearing spin in a microfuge for 5 min at 4°. Use 30–50 ml lysate per assay. The original volume for the freeze-thaw procedure is 100 ml.

3. The sodium salt of acetyl CoA is used. The chemical is unstable so it should be made fresh or aliquoted and stored at -20° for periods up to two weeks.

4. Pipette the ethyl acetate using a glass pipette only. The extractions may be done in 1.5 ml microfuge tubes.

5. The TLC plates can be bought from Baker (Baker Flex; 2738-E10).

6. The solvent front moves rapidly and usually 30–45 min are sufficient to migrate 7–10 cm, which is adequate.

PROTEIN QUANTITATION BY BRADFORD ASSAY

This is a very simple method for determining amounts of protein in a solution in the range of 1 to 10 μg.

1. Generate a series of dilutions of BSA in 100 μl of 0.15 M NaCl such that the range from 1 to 10 μg is covered. Be sure to include 2 tubes with no added protein.

2. Add 1 ml of Coomassie blue and mix well.

3. After 2–3 min at room temperature measure the OD_{595} and plot the absorbance readings. Then generate a known plot of absorbance vs. protein concentration.

4. Repeat the procedure on your unknown sample and determine the concentration from the plot.

TCA PRECIPITATION OF NUCLEIC ACIDS

1. To approximately 0.3 ml of a reaction, add 0.5 ml of 0.08 M NaPPi (sodium pyrophosphate), and 0.05 ml of 4 mg/ml yeast RNA and mix.

2. Add 0.5 ml of 25% TCA (trichloroacetic acid), vortex, and let sit on ice for 10 min or more.

3. Filter through 0.45 micron HAWP Millipore membrane filters.

4. Wash the filter using (2x 5 ml) cold 5% TCA.

5. If ^{32}P was used one can count Cherenkov radiation using the ^{3}H channel with no addition of counting fluid. Alternatively, a toluene-based fluid or Aquasol may be used.

REFERENCE

Baltimore, D., A. S. Huang, and M. Stampfer, *Proc. Nat. Acad. Sci. USA* 66:572–576 (1970).

PROTEIN GELS (SDS)

1.   Preparing the gel

SDS gels are usually run with two parts to the gel. The lower part, or running gel, is where the main separation occurs. The upper part, or stacking gel, contains the wells for loading the sample. The stacking gel has a lower acrylamide concentration than the running gel as well as lower buffer strength and pH. When the samples reach the interface between the two parts of the gel they back up, or "stack" into a relatively thin layer at the interface before entering the running gel. It is this property which gives fairly sharp bands even when the wells are filled with sample.

a) The running gel

The running gel can be of any workable concentration (roughly 5%-25% acrylamide, most commonly 7.5%-20%), low acrylamide concentrations separate high-molecular-weight proteins best, high acrylamide concentrations give generally sharper bands as well as separating lower-molecular-weight proteins. For any given acrylamide concentration there is a minimum protein size for which everything smaller than that runs together at the electrophoretic front. For small proteins, e.g., 10,000 kDa or less, a gel of at least 12.5% to 15% acrylamide should be used; this will, however, leave large proteins(100,000 kDa or more) bunched together at the top of the gel. A 7.5% acrylamide gel will give better separation of large proteins but the small proteins will run together at the bottom of the gel. An acrylamide concentration should be chosen to give the best separation for the proteins of interest. Note that it is possible to pour gels as a gradient (e.g., 20% at the bottom to 7.5% at the top) to maximize the range of separation but reproducibility of such gels is difficult.

b) Gel mixture for running gel

	7.5% gel	10% gel	12.5% gel	15% gel
40% acrylamide stock	7.0 ml	9.3 ml	11.7 ml	14.0 ml
2% bisacrylamide stock	3.7 ml	5.0 ml	6.2 ml	7.5 ml
2 M Tris·HCl (pH 8.8)	7.0 ml	7.0 ml	7.0 ml	7.0 ml
ddH$_2$O	19.1 ml	15.5 ml	11.9 ml	8.3 ml

Combine and degas this mixture. Add the following and mix just prior to pouring.

	7.5% gel	10% gel	12.5% gel	15% gel
10% SDS	375 μl	375 μl	375 μl	375 μl
10% ammonium persul- fate (freshly prepared)	250 μl	250 μl	250 μl	250 μl
TEMED	6.3 μl	6.3 μl	6.3 μl	6.3μl

c) **Pouring the running gel**

There must be space between the top of the running gel and the bottom of the wells for the samples to "stack." One centimeter is usually adequate, but more space can give tighter bands, especially if the sample volume is large. Choose the comb you plan to use and mark the gel plates 1 cm below the point the comb will reach. Pour the running gel up to this point.

d) **Overlaying the running gel**

Carefully overlay the gel with 1–2 ml of another liquid. This serves two purposes: it produces a level interface at the top of the gel and it excludes atmospheric oxygen. A 1:1 mix of isobutanol and water works well. Alternatively the buffer components can be used (a mixture of 9.35 ml 2 M Tris·HCl(pH 8.8), 0.5 ml 10% SDS, 40.15 ml ddH$_2$O). Add the overlay carefully from the side so that it does not mix with the acrylamide solution. If you are using the Tris, it should be removed as soon as the gel is polymerized (about 45 min) to prevent polymerization of the dilute acrylamide that has been mixed into or diffused into the overlay. When freshly poured, a line will be visible between the gel mix and overlay. This line will disappear. When it reappears the gel is polymerized. Fresh overlay can be added to keep the gel moist until use. Carefully remove all of the overlay just prior to pouring the stacking gel.

e) **Gel mixture for the stacking gel**

The following gives a 6.3% acrylamide concentration. It can be reduced to 5% if desired.

3.0 ml 40% acrylamide
1.6 ml 2% bisacrylamide
4.0 ml 0.625 M Tris·HCl (pH 6.8)
10.2 ml ddH$_2$O

Combine and degas this mixture. Just prior to pouring add the following:

200 μl 10% SDS
240 μl 10% ammonium persulfate, freshly made
7.5 μl TEMED

f) Pouring the stacking gel

We use notched gel plates and tape off the notch (Scotch magic transparent tape) so that it will hold liquid. Pour gel mixture to cover the bottom of the notch, then put the comb in place. When polymerized (about 45 min) remove the comb, the tape and cut away the excess gel down to the notch.

2.   Preparing the samples

a) Amount of sample to prepare

If staining will be done using Coomassie blue stain, then 10 to 30 μg per lane of protein will be needed for crude samples to be easily seen. One to two mg of a single protein species is enough. These numbers will vary depending on how wide the lanes are and how pure the sample is. Silver staining requires only about 10% as much protein as Coomassie blue (or less) but different proteins stain with different intensities with silver. The sensitivity is about 10–30 ng of protein in a single band. Other protein stains which are occasionally used (e.g., Stains-All, Amido black, etc.) are usually somewhat less sensitive than Coomassie blue and require more protein.

b) Sample volume

Generally the smaller the better for sample volume as long as it is enough to evenly cover the bottom of the well (5–10 μl is good). It is possible to fill the wells completely full (or even fill the wells, run that into the gel, then fill them again) to get enough protein, but the final gel will be progressively fuzzier with larger volumes. Under most circumstances it is desirable to concentrate dilute samples or precipitate them (e.g., with 20% TCA) and redissolve them in sample buffer. Salts, glycerol, and other buffer components should be kept to a minimum because excess amounts can cause spreading of the lanes and other aberrations in the way the gel runs.

c) Sample buffer

Protein samples can be mixed directly 1:1 with the sample buffer. Alternatively, precipitated, or lyophilized samples can be dissolved directly in the buffer.

Sample Buffer (25 ml)

4% SDS	1 g
62.5 mM Tris·HCl (pH 6.8)	2.5 ml of 0.625 M Tris·HCl (pH 6.8)
10% glyerol	2.5 ml
0.02% bromophenol blue	5 mg
8 M urea	12 g
	Add ddH$_2$O to 25 ml.

Store this frozen in 1-ml aliquots and add 2-mercaptoethanol to 5% just prior to use (50 ml/ml). The urea is necessary for DNA-binding proteins but is optional for other proteins.

d) Final preparation of samples

Gels run best if all samples are the same volume and concentration. For prettier gels, take all samples to the same volume and fill any unused wells with the same amount of sample buffer.

e) Boiling samples

Protein samples should be boiled for 2 min prior to loading. Allow them to cool prior to loading.

3. Loading and running the gel

a) Gel buffer

3 g Tris base
14.4 g glycine
1 g SDS Adjust to 1 L with ddH$_2$O

b) Setting up

When you are ready to load the gel, set the gel up in the gel box and fill both top and bottom chambers with the gel buffer. Remove all air bubbles from the bottom of the gel and rinse out the wells with buffer.

c) Loading the samples

Use a thin pipette tip or Hamilton syringe or other liquid transfer device that can reach between the glass plates to the bottom of the wells. Carefully layer the samples on the bottom of the wells. The glycerol in the sample buffer makes the samples dense enough to remain at the bottom of the wells.

d) Running the gel

Connect the electrodes with the positive pole at the bottom of the gel. For 20 cm x 19 cm plates, the gel is typically run at 75 volts until the samples are in the gel, then at 125 volts until the dye reaches the running gel, and at 200–250 volts until the gel is done. Proper running conditions vary with the size of the gel and the acrylamide concentration but the current should not be enough to heat the gel.

e) Finishing the run

When the Bromophenol blue dye in the samples approaches the bottom of the gel (the dye runs near the same point as the smallest protein) turn off the gel and remove the gel plates. The gel plates can be pried apart with a spatula or knife. The gel will remain stuck to one of the plates. The gel should be transferred to a flat-bottom container large enough for the gel to lie flat. Hold the gel plate with the gel stuck to it over the container with the gel down. Use the spatula to gently peel the gel from the plate starting from the highest corner. The gel should peel off in one piece and fall into the container ready to be stained.

Notes

(1) Degassing the gel mixes may be regarded as optional, but oxygen interferes with acrylamide polymerization. If the gel mix is not thoroughly degassed the polymerized gel will run as though it had a lower acrylamide concentration. Twenty minutes under the house vacuum is usually enough.

(2) The gel should be used as soon as possible after it has finished polymerizing so that the buffers in the two layers do not mix. However, the running gel can be poured the previous day as long as it is kept cool and not allowed to dry out.

(3) Acrylamide is very toxic. It is a cumulative neurotoxin and may also be a carcinogen. It should always be handled very carefully. The acrylamide powder is especially dangerous because it can be inhaled, so a mask should be worn while weighing it out and gloves should always be worn when handling acrylamide. If splashed with acrylamide it washes off easily with water. Because powdered acrylamide is so toxic we make up stock solutions and store them in the dark at 4°. UV light can polymerize acrylamide. A stock at room temperature in glass will very slowly polymerize in the bottle. We make a 40% acrylamide stock. Some labs prefer 30%, but the final ratio of acrylamide to bisacrylamide should remain approximately 37.5 to 1. If you go through solutions rapidly it is OK to mix the acrylamide and bisacrylamide in a single container. Different brands

of acrylamide vary in quality. We filter the solution through a 0.2 μm filter. Other treatments such as passage through a column of mixed bed resin will remove impurities that may cause artifacts.

(4) These instructions are for full-size gels (most commonly 20 cm x 19 cm x 0.1 cm). They should be generally applicable to most sizes of gel plates, although minigels require a higher acrylamide concentration than the full-size gels do to give a comparable separation range.

4. Staining the gel

a) Coomassie blue gel staining

(1) *Preparing the gel stain*
0.2% Coomassie blue R250
20% methanol
10% glacial acetic acid

To make 1 L, dissolve 2 g of dye in 200 ml of methanol and leave stirring at least 1 hr, then add 700 ml of ddH$_2$O and 100 ml glacial acetic acid. The dye will not dissolve well if the acid is added at the beginning. If significant amounts of undissolved dye remain it is desirable to filter the solution.

(2) *Staining the gel*
As soon as the gel has been run and been placed in a container for staining, pour in enough of the stain solution to cover the gel. The methanol and acetic acid precipitate the proteins, fixing them in place, and the Coomassie blue binds tightly to the protein. Allow the gel to stand in this solution for 30–60 min with gentle shaking. Though it is not wise to leave the gel in this stain for extended periods (some dye may slowly precipitate making the gel difficult to fully destain) the gel may not be completely stained at this point. A secondary stain with less dye and less alcohol is used by some, but we use the simpler approach of removing about 90%–95% of the stain mix and pouring in gel destain. The gel may be left overnight like this.

(3) *Destaining*
The destaining solution is 10% methanol and 10% acetic acid in ddH$_2$O. Repeated changes of the destaining solution over a period of hours with gentle shaking will slowly remove all the dye except that bound to protein. Alternatively, a wad of laboratory wipes or soft paper towels can be immersed in the destaining solution. The

paper will absorb the dye from the solution, eliminating the need for repeated changes of solution.

b) *Other staining procedures*

Coomassie blue staining is probably the most commonly used staining technique: it is reasonably sensitive and gives a reasonable indication of relative quantities of protein because, for most proteins, the intensity of the stained band is proportional to the amount of protein. There are now alternatives to Coomassie blue staining that are considerably more sensitive, although different proteins may not stain with equal efficiency in these metal-based stains. Commercial kits are now available for silver staining, and Kodak offers a kit using a nickel-based chemistry. To use the Kodak Kodavue kit two changes should be made in the sample buffer: urea should be omitted altogether, and the bromophenol blue tracking dye should not be added to the samples until after they have been boiled. We use the BioRad silver stain kit as per the manufacturer's directions with the exception that we make up the developer solution fresh in small quantities just prior to use–16 grams of developer in 500 ml of ddH$_2$O, stirred constantly until it is fully dissolved (15–60 min).

Several other dyes such as Stains-All and Amido black are occasionally used to stain gels. While they may be useful in certain specialized cases, for most purposes Coomassie blue staining will give superior results. Proteins can be visualized on an unfixed gel by immersing the gel in ice-cold buffer of 0.2 M KCl, 1 mM DTT for several minutes. This method has very low sensitivity but may be good enough, if you look very closely, to identify and cut a very prominent individual band from a gel without having to denature a protein first.

This isolated protein can then be soak-eluted, and protein sequencing can be performed. There is a new type of negative staining kit for proteins–the stain precipitates in the gel in the absence of protein leaving blank bands where the protein is present. If the kit works as advertised it should be useful for recovering native proteins from the gel because no fixation process is involved. For instance, individual bands could be visualized and cut from the gel or the gel could be stained then subjected to Western blot transfer with the staining pattern left behind on the gel as a permanent record.

5. Drying gels

Two different methods are commonly used for gel drying. The gel can be dried on filter paper which gives more support to the gel but is opaque. This procedure is used if autoradiography is planned. A second procedure is to dry the gel between two sheets of cellophane which leaves the dried gel transparent.

a) Drying on paper using a gel dryer

This method requires a gel dryer which holds the gel flat, heats it, and applies a vacuum simultaneously. A separate pump is usually used to provide the vacuum and a moisture trap should be between the dryer and the pump to protect the pump. A dry-ice/ethanol cold trap is used.

(1) Preparing the gel

If the gel is a Coomassie-stained SDS gel, the gel should be fully destained, as residual Coomassie blue dye will appear darker after drying. If the gel contains urea, that also must be soaked out of the gel before drying. Cut a sheet of heavy filter paper (3MM) larger than the gel to be dried. Thoroughly wet the paper. If the paper is dry the gel will stick very tightly to it and be difficult to reposition as necessary. Pick up the gel and place it on the wetted paper being careful to get it smooth with no air bubbles between the paper and the gel. Place plastic wrap over the top of the gel to keep the gel from sticking to the gel dryer. No plastic should be over the back of the paper. If the gel is radioactive place a second sheet of dry filter paper under the first one to protect the dryer from contamination.

(2) Setting up

Place the gel sandwich (paper/gel/plastic wrap) in the gel dryer with the paper down flat on the support surface, i.e., paper side towards the vacuum. Close the dryer, making sure that gaskets, rubber seal, etc. are all properly positioned to seal under the vacuum. Turn on the vacuum source and make sure that the apparatus seals properly and there are no leaks. It is important that any necessary adjustments are made at this point. If the vacuum seal is broken on a partially dried gel the gel will usually break into pieces.

(3)   Drying

Drying time depends on a number of factors, such as the size of the gel, the quantity of the vacuum, and how much heat is applied. A typical set-up should thoroughly dry a full-sized gel (e.g. 19 cm x 20 cm) at moderate heat in 1–2 hr. High heat will dry the gel faster but can cause it to curl more severely later. The gel will not dry well without heating. On most driers, the outline of the paper and the outline of the gel are visible through the rubber sheet that seals off the apparatus— if the outlines are hard to see they should be fairly easy to feel. When the gel is dry, the outline of the paper remains but the edge of the gel can no longer be felt. It is helpful if a bit of extra time is allowed as a safety margin.

b)   **Drying between cellophane**

Using this method requires a drying frame. The ones we use have one piece which is a sheet of stiff plastic, 24.5-cm square, and a second piece with the same outer dimensions but with the central 20 cm square cut out. If the plastic is clear, then the gel can be clearly seen while drying.

(1)   Preparing of the gel

After the gel is stained and fully destained, glycerol should be added to the destaining solution to 2%–3% (or water with 2%–3% glycerol can be used) and the gel allowed to equilibrate in this for up to 1 hr prior to stretching between the cellophane sheets.

(2)   The cellophane

Bio-Rad cellophane (Cat. no. 165–0963) is used although any good quality cellophane should work. The cellophane should be thoroughly wetted by immersion in water prior to use: two sheets at least as large as the frame per gel.

(3)   Set-up

Place the solid frame piece flat and wet it with water. Lay a sheet of cellophane over the frame being careful that no air bubbles are trapped between the two. Wet the cellophane with additional water from a squirt bottle. Carefully pick the gel out of the destaining tray and place it on the wetted cellophane (gels of high acrylamide percentage are usually sturdy enough to hold together if picked up from one edge; very low percentage gels may benefit from being lifted on a thin flexible sheet of plastic used like a large spatula). After centering the gel, wet its surface and edges from the squirt bottle and carefully lay the second sheet of cellophane on top. All of the wetting of surfaces is to make it easier to avoid trapping air bubbles which, if large can cause the cellophane sheets to peel apart later. When everything is in place, put the second part of the frame on top so that the gel is completely exposed through the cut-out section. Clamp the entire apparatus together with clamps at each corner and in the middle of each side.

(4)   Drying
The gel will be fully dried after one to three days at room temperature depending on air humidity, temperature, etc. In winter the humidity may be so low in heated buildings that the slight shrinking of the cellophane which accompanies drying, if allowed to continue too long, can lead to the cellophane breaking apart from stress. Therefore, as soon as the gel is dry the clamps should be removed. If the gel is removed from the frame at this point the cellophane that extends beyond the edges of the gel will tend to curl. This can be eliminated by trimming off the excess cellophane. Alternatively the cellophane can be loosened from the frame to release the stress, then put back together for a few more days (or otherwise held securely flattened) to leave the sheet intact. The sheet can then have holes punched in it for insertion in a binder, can be written on to identify the gel, etc.

Manipulation of Plasmids

BACTERIAL TRANSFORMATION BY ELECTROPORATION

Electroporation is so superior to other methods of transformation that it becomes routine once it is established in a lab. The efficiencies routinely obtained are in the range of 10^9 transformants/μg and higher. It does require the purchase of an electroporation device that is suitable. The cuvettes used are half the width of the cuvettes used for mammalian cell electroporation. The larger cuvettes do work but with greatly reduced efficiency.

There are a few comments worth making to prevent annoying problems. The procedure is so efficient that one can pick up small amounts of DNA from at least two known sources—the tubes used to prepare the bacteria cells and the microfuge tubes used for ligations. Be sure to use clean autoclaved bottles or tubes to prepare the cells. If one obtains a very small number of transformants be especially careful to adequately characterize transformant plasmid DNAs. The chances are greater that a given plasmid might actually be a contaminant. The cuvettes are reusable although many labs use them disposably. Rinse them with sterile H_2O immediately after use and then with 95% EtOH. Cleaning them before they dry should prevent them from collecting cell debris. It is advisable to use a cuvette washer for this purpose. Although it is not recommended by the supplier we place the dry tubes under a UV light for 10–15 min to further sterilize the cuvettes.

As mentioned in the protocol, the electroporation is very sensitive to the presence of salt in the ligation reactions. We routinely add 100 μl of 0.3 M sodium acetate and 250 μl EtOH and precipitate the ligated DNAs. After two subsequent rinses with 70% EtOH the DNA is resuspended in 5 μl TE and half of it is used in the electroporation. Finally, the number of cells in each electroporation is higher than the number usually used in $CaCl_2$ transformations. As a consequence, we have increased the amount of ampicillin in the plates to 100 μg/ml.

Preparation of cells

1. Grow an overnight culture of bacteria.

2. Make a 1:10 or 1:100 dilution into L broth the next day. A 250-ml culture of cells will ultimately yield 500 μl of cells that will be used in 40-μl aliquots for transformations. This is a 500-fold concentration of the cells.

3. Grow the cell to $OD_{600} = 0.6$ to 0.75.

4. Chill the sterile centrifuge tubes and rotor that will be used to harvest the cells. Large rotors should be cooled in the centrifuge.

5. Pour the cells into the centrifuge tubes and chill on ice for 15 min.

6. Centrifuge at 4 krpm for 15 min at 4°. Pour off the supernatant and resuspend the cells in about 10 ml of ice-cold ddH$_2$O. Add more ice-cold ddH$_2$O to bring the volume up to the original 250 ml.

7. Repeat the centrifugation step, pour off the supernatant and resuspend the cells in 5 ml of ice-cold 10% glycerol and place in a sterile screw-cap centrifuge tube.

8. Centrifuge for 10 min at 4 krpm at 4°.

9. Pour off the supernatant and add 500 μl of ice cold 10% glycerol. Store in 90-μl or 135-μl aliquots in sterilized microfuge tubes at -70°. Use 40 μl of cells per transformation.

Electroporation

1. Chill the 0.2-cm cuvettes on ice.

2. Have sterile tubes ready that can be placed in a shaker after the electro-poration at room temperature, one for each sample.

3. Thaw the bacterial cells on ice. This takes about 10 min. Use 40 μl per transformation.

4. Turn on the electroporator and allow to warm up for a few minutes. We use a BioRad Gene Pulser.

5. Connect the pulser unit to the pulse controller with the electrodes and the pulse controller to the sample chamber.

6. Set the capacitor at 25 μFD and the resistance at 200 ohms.

7. Press the "set volts" pad, then "raise volts" pad for a voltage of 2.5 kV.

8. Aliquot 40 μl of cells into the chilled cuvettes.

9. Add 1–2 μl of DNA to each aliquot of cells in the cuvette. Gently tap the cuvette so that cells fall to the bottom of the cuvette and no bubbles form. Let the cuvette sit on ice for 5 min.

10. Wipe the cuvette completely dry and place it in the cuvette holder making sure the holder is also dry. Place the holder in the slide of the sample chamber.

11. Push the slide into the chamber until the cuvette makes a firm contact with the electrodes.

12. Press and hold both red buttons on the gene pulser unit. The front panel will flash *ChG*. A beep signals the delivery of the pulse. After the beep, release the buttons. Occasionally there may be an electric arc across the inside of the cuvette. These electroporations work but less efficiently. In our experience this is due to adding too much volume (probably salt) from a ligation reaction. If 2 or more μl are used with 40 μl of cells there is a greater problem with discharging than if one uses 1 μl. Cooling the cuvette on ice after adding the DNA and wiping it dry again helps. In practice the discharge problem can be minimized and the sample concentrated by EtOH precipitating the ligation reaction and resuspending it in a very small volume of TE.

13. Immediately (as quickly as possible but certainly less than 30 sec) add 1 ml of SOC medium with a pipetteman. Using a sterile pasteur pipette mix the cells and SOC medium. Transfer the solution from the cuvette to the previously labeled sterile test tubes and place in a shaking incubator at 37° for 1 hr.

14. Plate 200 μl or dilutions of the cells per plate. With such high efficiencies it is occasionally necessary to plate fewer cells to be able to pick single colonies.

15. Check the time constant and actual volts after each electroporation by pressing appropriate pads on the gene pulser. The time constant should be between 3.0 and 5.0. If the time constant is below 2 you will usually get transformants but often 100-fold fewer than when higher time constants are achieved.

SOC medium

per liter	final concentration
20 g Bacto tryptone	2%
5 g yeast extract	0.5%
2.5 ml 4 M NaCl	10 mM
2.5 ml 1 M KCl	2.5 mM

Mix the above in 970 ml of H_2O and autoclave. Then add the following ingredients which have been filtered through a 0.2 μm sterile filter unit. The $MgSO_4$ and $MgCl_2$ can be mixed prior to sterile filtration or added separately. A 2 M stock containing both reagents is convenient, in which case one would add 10 ml per liter.

10 ml 1 M $MgSO_4$	10 mM $MgSO_4$
10 ml 1 M $MgCl_2$	10 mM $MgCl_2$
10 ml 2 M glucose	20 mM glucose

BACTERIAL TRANSFORMATION WITH CALCIUM CHLORIDE

This procedure is a standard one which requires no special reagents or equipment. For some purposes having frozen aliquots of competent bacterial prepared in this manner is very convenient. The efficiencies generally obtained with this procedure are 10^5 to 2×10^6 transformants/μg of supercoiled DNA. However this method is put aside once one has become accustomed to the much higher efficiencies of bacterial transformation by electroporation.

1. Grow a 100-ml culture of bacteria to an approximate density of $OD_{590} =$ 0.3 to 0.5.

2. Chill on ice for 10 min.

3. Centrifuge to pellet the bacteria for 10 min at 4°.

4. Resuspend in 30 ml of ice-cold 50 mM $CaCl_2$, 10 mM Tris·HCl (pH 8.0) and incubate for 30 min on ice. Use filter-sterilized solutions and sterile pipettes to avoid contaminating bacteria.

5. Centrifuge as above.

6. Resuspend in 4 ml of cold $CaCl_2$/Tris solution. Add 15% sucrose to this solution if you wish to aliquot cells and freeze at -70°.

7. Use immediately or let sit on ice up to one day before using. Longer times up to 4 days will work but with reduced efficiency.

8. Combine 0.3 ml of competent cells with up to 10 μl of plasmid DNA or ligation mixture and incubate 30 min on ice.

9. Incubate at 37° for 5 min or at 42° for 2 min.

10. Add 1 ml of L broth and incubate for 45–60 min at 37°.

11. Spread 0.1–0.2 ml per plate using a glass rod or plate in 3 ml of top agar. For ampicillin plates should be 35 μg/ml, for tetracycline 15 μg/ml and if X-gal selection is being used 50–100 μl (of a 20 mg/ml stock made in dimethyl formamide) can be added per plate before or after the plate is poured or in the top agar. For transformations in which X-gal selection is being used after overnight growth at 37° the plates may be placed at room temperature or in the cold to facilitate the blue color development.

REFERENCE

Dagert, M., and S. D. Ehrlich *Gene* 6:23–28 (1978).

BACTERIAL TRANSFORMATION WITH HIGH EFFICIENCY

This protocol can yield transformation efficiencies and competent cells can be stored frozen. Frozen competent bacteria prepared by similar procedures are commercially available.

Reagents

SOB medium

2% Bacto tryptone
0.5% yeast extract
10 mM NaCl
2.5 mM KCl
10 mM $MgCl_2$
10 mM $MgSO_4$

Prepare without Mg, autoclave, then add Mg from filter-sterilized stock that is 1 M in $MgCl_2$ and $MgSO_4$.

SOC medium

Add glucose from sterile stock (2 M) to SOB to a final concentration of 20 mM.

LM plates

1% Bacto tryptone
0.5 % yeast extract
10 mM NaCl
10 mM $MgSO_4 \cdot 7H_2O$
1.5 % Bacto agar

Use antibiotics at 35 μg/ml, except tetracycline (17 μg/ml).

FSB (frozen storage buffer)

10 mM KAc
100 mM KCl
45 mM $MnCl \cdot 4H_2O$
10 mM $CaCl_2 \cdot 2H_2O$
3mM HA $CoCl_3$
10% redistilled glycerol (BRL # 5514)

Adjust the pH of a 1 M KAc stock to 7.0, filter, and store frozen. Adjust the pH of the final solution to 6.4 with 0.1 N HCl, filter, and store at 4°. The pH will drift to 6.1–6.2, then stabilize.

DMSO

Store in 550-µl aliquots at -20°.

DTT

The stock is 2.25 M, 40 mM potassium acetate (pH 6.0). Filter and aliquot (0.5 µl), and store at -20°.

Transformation protocol

1. Pick a single bacterial colony from a plate using a toothpick and disperse it in 1 ml SOB by vortexing. Inoculate a prerinsed flask that is 3%–10% filled with SOB. The numbers in parentheses will refer to a (100 ml) bacterial culture in a 1–3 L flask. Incubate at 37° shaking at 275 rpm until it reaches an OD_{550} = 0.45 to 0.55 (2–2.5 hr). Pour the fluid into 50-ml conical tubes and place on ice for 10–15 min.

2. Spin 2.5 krpm 10 min at 4°. Resuspend in 1/3 volume of FSB (33 ml) by gentle vortexing and place on ice for 10–15 min. Spin again at 2.5 krpm for 10 min at 4°. Resuspend in FSB at 1/12.5 original vol of culture (8 ml).

3. Add DMSO to 3.5% (0.28 ml), swirl and place on ice for 5 min. Add the same amount of DMSO again (0.28 ml), then incubate on ice for 5 min. Aliquot 210-µl samples into chilled polypropylene tubes (Falcon 2059). The 100-ml starting volume of cells should give enough competent cells for 40 transformations.

4. Add DNA (in <10 µl; 10 pg to 1 ng for intact plasmids), swirl and leave on ice for 30 min. Heat-shock at 42° for 90 sec and put on ice for 1–2 min. If other types of tubes are used, recalibrate time of heat shock. Add 800 µl SOC at room temperature, and incubate at 37°, 225 rpm, 1 hr. Spread an aliquot on an LM plate (dilute in SOB if necessary).

Storage of cells

1. Transformed cells—short-term—can be stored overnight at 4° after 37° incubation. Long-term—dilute 1:1 with 40% glycerol/60% SOB, chill on ice, freeze on dry ice, and place at -70°.

2. Competent cells—Aliquot cells and freeze on dry ice or in liquid N_2, and store at -70°. To use later, thaw in air at room temperature until it is just liquified, then place on ice for 10 min. Add DNA and proceed as above.

REFERENCE

Hanahan, D., *J. Mol. Biol.* 166:557 (1983).

COLONY SCREENING WITH RADIOLABELED PROBES

This procedure is used to screen transformants for the presence of a particular DNA sequence. This is especially useful if the desired transformant is at a low frequency in the population. It can save doing a large number of minipreps or identify a plasmid subclone if the size of the insert is unknown.

Make duplicate plates: one for screening, one for picking.

1. Place nitrocellulose filter onto plate, wetting first across the middle, then towards the sides. Make orientation stabs with needle and ink.

2. Lift the filter off, turn *colony-side-up,* and place onto 2–3 ml of 0.5 N NaOH on plastic wrap. Alternatively place a sheet of 3MM paper on top of a sheet of saran wrap and wet it with 0.5 N NaOH or the subsequent solutions. Lay the filter on top of the soaked 3MM paper. Be careful not to allow fluid on the top of the filter because it will smear the bacterial colonies. Leave for 5–7 min.

3. Dry colony-side-up on paper towel 2–3 min or if using the 3MM paper transfer to the next solution.

4. Place onto 2–3 ml of 1 M Tris·HCl (pH 7.5) on plastic wrap or 3MM paper soaked with 1 M Tris·HCl (pH 7.5) for 2–3 min.

5. Dab onto paper towel to remove excess liquid, then place onto 2–3 ml of fresh 1 M Tris for 2–3 min.

6. Place onto 2–3 ml of 6x SSC on plastic wrap or soaked 3MM paper for 2–3 min.

7. Dry completely.

8. Bake in a vacuum oven at 80° for 90–120 min before hybridizing.

RAPID PLASMID MINIPREP (ALKALINE LYSIS)

This is our preferred procedure but variations upon it exist.

1. Harvest 1.5 ml of cells with a 30-sec spin in the microfuge. Repeat to collect the total of 3 ml. Add the second 1.5 ml on top of the first cell pellet.

2. Resuspend cells in 0.2 ml of GET buffer and place on ice.
    An optional step is to add 20 µl of 10 mg/ml freshly dissolved lysozyme in GET buffer and incubate on ice for 30 min. In practice we rarely use it but for some strains such as those used in M13 cloning it may help.

3. Add 0.4 ml Alkaline-SDS solution, mix well and leave on ice 5 min.

4. Add 0.3 ml ice-cold KAc solution, mix well and leave another 5 min on ice.

5. Microfuge at 4° for 15 min. All subsequent microfuge centrifugations are at room temperature.

6. Pipette out the supernatant and place in a second tube.

7. Add isopropanol, mix, and place at -70° for 10 min. Do a 15-min microfuge spin.

8. Rinse pellet with cold 70% EtOH and dry (air or vacuum). Do not dislodge the pellet.

9. Add 100 ml TNE containing 10 mg/ml RNase A and incubate 60 min at 37°.

10. Add 500 µl EtOH and place at -70° for 10 min.

11. Spin 10 min in microfuge.

12. Rinse pellet with 70% EtOH and dry.

13. Resuspend in 50 ml ddH$_2$O and do a 10-min microfuge spin at room temperature. There seems to be a variable amount of insoluble supercoiled plasmid DNA that is resistant to cleavage with restriction enzymes. One occasionally sees ghost bands at the position of supercoiled DNA in all digests of miniprep DNAs. This step removes most of that material.

14. Use 5–10 μl of DNA above any pelleted material per assay.

Solutions

GET   50 mM glucose
10 mM EDTA
25 mM Tris·HCl (pH 8.0)

Alkaline SDS 0.2 N NaOH
1% SDS
Prepare fresh and store at room temperature.

KAc   3 M KAc, pH 4.8
(29.4 g KAc, 11.5 ml glacial acetic acid, ddH$_2$O to 100 ml)

TNE   50 mM Tris·HCl (pH 8.0)
150 mM NaCl
1 mM EDTA

RAPID PLASMID MINIPREP (BOILING METHOD)

1. Grow 1.5 ml overnight culture. Spin for 30 sec in a microfuge tube.

2. Wash with 1 ml of cold TE. Spin.

3. Resuspend in 200 μl cold STET buffer.

4. Add 20 μl of 10 mg/ml lysozyme prepared fresh in water or TE.

5. Incubate at room temperature for 10 min.

6. Place the tube in the heating block set at 95° for 2 min or in a boiling water bath.

7. Quickly spin for 15 min.

8. Transfer the supernatant to a new tube containing 10 μl of 1 M Tris·HCl (pH 8).

9. Phenol-extract once. Ether-extract twice, removing the cloudy interface after the first extraction. This step is optional but should facilitate cleavage by restriction enzymes.

10. Precipitate with 2 volumes of isopropanol (no salt). Freeze on dry ice. Spin for 15 min in the cold. Wash with 95% EtOH. Dry.

11. Resuspend in 100 μl TE. Cut 5 μl. (*Note:* It is often possible to distinguish wild-type vs. recombinant supercoiled plasmid by running undigested preps.)

STET buffer

8% sucrose	8 g
5% Triton X-100	5 ml (10%)
20 mM EDTA	4 ml (0.5 M)
50 mM Tris·HCl (pH 8)	5 ml (1 M)
	Bring to 100 ml with ddH$_2$O

PREPARATION OF PLASMID DNA ON CsCl GRADIENTS

1. Grow *E. coli* bearing a plasmid under selection to saturation. A volume of 250 ml is convenient. One can also grow the cells to an approximate OD_{590} of 0.7 and amplify the plasmid by adding chloramphenicol to the culture (1 ml of 300 mg/ml chloramphenicol suspended in 95% ethanol per L of culture). Let the cells amplify for 4–6 hrs.

2. Harvest the cells by centrifugation for 20 min at 4° at 8 krpm in the JA-10 rotor. Discard supernatant and drain fluid from the tubes briefly.

3. Resuspend the cells from the 250-ml culture with 4 ml of cold 25% sucrose, 0.05 M Tris·HCl (pH 8.0) and place in a polyallomer SW41 tube. Keep the cells on ice through these procedures.

4. Add 0.3 ml of a freshly prepared lysozyme solution (30 mg/ml in 0.25 M Tris·HCl [pH 8.0]), mix thoroughly after placing parafilm on the tube, and let sit on ice 10–30 min.

5. Add 0.7 ml of 0.5 M EDTA (pH 8.0), mix thoroughly, and let sit on ice 10–30 min.

6. Add plasmid detergent solution approximately equal to the total aqueous volume which should fill the tube. Mix well and let sit on ice 10–30 min. The preparation may be stored at -20° at this point if convenient.

7. Centrifuge for 90 min at 4° at 36 krpm. If the solution is very viscous longer centrifugation times (3 hr) may be needed to pellet the chromosomal DNA.

8. Pour the supernatant into a 15-ml graduated conical plastic tube. Add 1 g solid CsCl/ml of supernatant. Dissolve by placing at 37° and mixing periodically.

9. Place the solution in two quick-seal polyallomer tubes for the Ti-50 or Ti-70 fixed-angle rotor leaving room for about 0.3 ml of ethidium bromide solution (10 mg/ml in H_2O) at the top. If the volume of supernatant is not sufficient to fill the tubes one can add a solution of cesium chloride:water (1:1) or use smaller tubes with inserts.

10. Centrifuge for 24–36 hrs at 25° at 45 krpm or 55 krpm in the Ti-70 rotor.

11. Two bands of DNA should be apparent after the exposure to UV light. The top band has some *E. coli* DNA and form-II plasmid DNA (nicked circles). The bottom band is the form-I supercoiled plasmid DNA. To

remove the plasmid DNA place the tube in a clamp on a ring stand and puncture the top of the tube with an 18- or 20-gauge needle. Then using a 3- or 5-ml syringe, insert the needle about a centimeter below the form-I band and remove the band. From this size tube the DNA band can be removed in about 2 ml.

12. From 250 ml of cells one obtains a total of about 1–20 mg of plasmid DNA. This DNA can be transferred to a 12-ml quick-seal tube, topped up with CsC1-H$_2$O and rebanded in the fixed angle 70-Ti rotor for 24–36 hrs at 25° at 55 krpm. This concentrates the DNA and further purifies it. The rebanded DNA can be removed in about 1.5–2 ml.

13. The ethidium bromide is removed by successive extraction with iso-propanol saturated with CsC1. The isopropanol can be about 90% iso-propanol and 10% H$_2$O. Mark the initial volume of form-I DNA on the glass tube. Add approximately an equal volume of isopropanol solution, vortex vigorously for 10 sec, and place in a rack to allow the phases to separate. Remove and discard the upper phase containing ethidium bromide. Repeat the extraction at least 5 times. The soluble ethidium is removed after about 3 extractions but the bound ethidium requires more extractions for removal. Each extraction removes some H$_2$O so after about 3 extractions you may add ddH$_2$O to the original volume using the mark on the tube. Do *not* add more volume when adding water than was originally in the tube. A consequence can be that the less dense CsCl solution containing your plasmid DNA will mix with the iso-propanol solution resulting in a single phase. If this does happen one can retrieve the sample by adding back more CsCl:H$_2$O (1:1) solution and reextracting with the isopropanol solution.

14. Dialyze the extracted plasmid DNA in 0.01 M Tris·HCl (pH 7.6), 0.001 M EDTA with at least two changes of buffer. The plasmid may be concentrated by ethanol precipitation only after dialysis. Contaminants in the CsCl when precipitated with the DNA occasionally render it resistant to restriction endonuclease cleavage.

Plasmid Detergent Solution

Final Concentration	*per L*
0.063 M EDTA	125 ml 0.5 M EDTA
0.05 M Tris·HC1 (pH 8.0)	50 ml 1 M Tris·HC1 (pH 8.0)
0.4% sodium desoxycholate	4 g sodium desoxycholate
1% NP-40	10 ml NP-40
	ddH$_2$O to 1 L

Note: The plasmid detergent solution can also be made by substituting a final concentration of 0.5% Triton X-100 for the sodium desoxycholate and NP-40.

LARGE-SCALE PLASMID PREPARATION BY ALKALINE LYSIS

This procedure is in part a scaled-up version of the alkaline lysis miniprep procedure. It gives good yields of plasmids that typically give low yields presumably due to low copy number per cell (e.g., pBR322 and cosmids).

1. Grow 750-ml culture of cells containing desired plasmid to saturation.

2. Collect the cells by centrifugation and resuspend in 10 ml of GET buffer (50 mM glucose, 10 mM EDTA, 25 mM Tris·HCl [pH 8.0]) and place on ice.

3. Add 5 mg of lysozyme dissolved in 0.5 ml of 0.25 M Tris·HCl (pH 8.0). Let sit on ice for at least 15 min.

4. Add 30 ml alkaline-SDS solution (0.2 N NaOH, 1% SDS, freshly prepared). Mix well and leave on ice for 5 min.

5. Neutralize with 23 ml of 3 M sodium acetate (pH 4.8). Mix well and leave on ice at least 30 min.

6. Centrifuge for 30 min at 8 krpm at 4° in a Sorvall or Beckman centrifuge. One could also use an SW28 rotor but it is not necessary. One nice feature about this method is that it can eliminate the ultracentrifugation step at this point. Pour off the supernatant into a separate centrifuge tube. Sometimes it helps to pour the supernatant through gauze to filter out particles that don't remain on the centrifuge tube.

7. Add 45 ml of isopropanol, let sit for 5 min at room temperature and then centrifuge again in the Sorvall centrifuge for 20 min at 8 krpm.

8. Pour off the isopropanol and let it drain well .

9. Resuspend the pellet in 8 ml of TE and add an equal weight of solid CsCl to the new volume of the solution; add ethidium bromide and additional (1:1) CsCl:H_2O solution to fill up the centrifuge tube; and band to equilibrium as described in the preparation of plasmid DNA on CsCl gradients.

STRATEGIES FOR PLASMID SUBCLONING

The final manipulation to accomplish a subcloning experiment is usually the combination of 0.1–0.5 μg each of the vector DNA and insert DNA in a 10-μl ligation reaction and subsequently transformation of bacteria. Individual transformants are then analyzed using minipreps of plasmid DNA for plasmids that possess the predicted structure. There are a number of considerations in deciding on a particular vector, the best restriction sites to use, and the method of preparation of the DNA components.

Perhaps the simplest type of subcloning is the transfer of DNA from a vector that lacks the selectable marker that is on the recipient vector. An example of this would be the subcloning of DNA in a bacteriophage into a plasmid. Commonly one might want to subclone the *Eco*R I, *Bam*H I or *Hind* III fragments from a phage into a plasmid. The recipient plasmid needs to have the appropriate restriction sites in a nonessential region and amplify well to produce large amounts of plasmid DNA. If one wishes to make RNA probes the plasmid should have the SP6 or T7 polymerase sites near a polylinker site. The pUC18 or pUC19 plasmids, the pGEM3 or pGEM4 plasmids, or pSP64 or pSP65 plasmids are very useful for many subcloning purposes. The presence of the polylinker is very useful in multistep constructions and eliminates the need in many circumstances for the use of synthetic linkers to create special restriction sites.

The vector may be dephosphorylated at the site of restriction enzyme cleavage in which case recircularization of the plasmid is prevented and thus its ability to transform bacteria. The CIP'd vector DNA (dephosphorylated using calf intestine phosphatase) will transform after an insert DNA is successfully ligated via the phosphates on the insert DNA. The ability of CIP'd vector to transform bacteria is usually about 0.01%–0.1% of the frequency with which supercoiled plasmid DNA transforms cells. This is probably due to some low level of partial restriction-enzyme digestion or incomplete dephosphorylation. One hopes to see a stimulation of the total number of transformants when insert is added to vector as compared with the vector alone. One can still have the desired recombinants and see no stimulation. Substances are acquired during the preparation of inserts that are often inhibitory to bacterial ligation or transformation.

The vector can be prepared by adding the appropriate restriction enzyme and adding 1 unit of CIP for the last 30 min of the digest. We have found that this is also sufficient to dephosphorylate blunt-ended DNAs or 3' overhangs. In many circumstances the entire phage DNA might be digested with the desired enzyme, the DNA phenol-extracted, ethanol-precipitated, and resuspended in a small volume of TE. An appropriate amount of the total digest may be used. If there are many DNA fragments produced by the particular enzyme, you might wish to gel-purify the fragment if you know its size. Alternatively, the individual transformants may be screened by hybridization for the desired clone.

It is sometimes advisable to use vectors that have not been treated with CIP but which use X-gal selection for the visual identification of new recombinants (e.g., pUC19). The efficiency of generating clones is higher when the vector is not CIP'd. This is especially useful for subcloning very large DNAs (e.g., 15–20 kb genomic *Sal* I fragments from EMBL3 phages) that are more difficult to subclone. It is also a good idea to leave the phosphates on vectors and inserts when performing blunt-end ligations.

The most common constructions involve the transfer of DNA fragments from one plasmid to another, both of which have the same selectable marker (usually *Amp*). It is often simplest to just gel-purify the insert and ligate in the presence of the new vector. One can avoid gel purification in some cases by first inactivating the source of insert DNA by cleavage with a restriction enzyme that doesn't cut the insert but does cleave the plasmid DNA and then treating the DNA with CIP. After heating, phenol extraction, and ethanol precipitation one can digest using the restriction enzyme to achieve the subcloning. The entire digest can then be ligated into the appropriately digested recipient vector DNA. Analysis of the subclones can then be used to select the appropriate subclone.

Because it is possible to ligate blunt-ended DNAs one can fuse ends into the polylinker sites and have useful cloning sites nearby. Blunt ends may be produced by enzymes such as *Pvu* II, *Hinc* II, and *Sma* I or may be produced very easily by filling in a 5' overhang using the Klenow polymerase. These termini are reliably produced. It is also possible to remove 3' overhangs using the exonucleolytic activity of T4 DNA polymerase or mung-bean nuclease.

Cloning of oligonucleotides

To have a continuous source of a synthesized nucleotide sequence one usually clones the sequence into a plasmid. Such sequences may be used as probes or linkers in particular plasmid constructions. In most cases it is desirable not to have oligomeric structures of the synthetic sequence. Some procedures suggest phosphorylating oligonucleotides prior to cloning but we use them without 5' terminal phosphates just as they are synthesized. Because the oligonucleotides lack phosphates it is impossible to clone multimers of the sequences. The ligation reaction uses the 5' terminal phosphates provided by the cloning vector. If one uses a 50-to 100-fold molar excess of the double-stranded oligonucleotides over the vector one can successfully achieve insertion of the synthetic sequence even when the vector is not gel-purified. Longer oligonucleotides up to 100 bases in length are sometimes found in only a few percent of the transformants. In this case if it is not readily identified by the analysis of miniprep DNAs, one can screen the colonies on nitrocellulose filter lifts using one of the two synthesized strands as a probe after labeling with [32]P γ-ATP and polynucleotide kinase.

1. Plan to set up a ligation using about 0.1 pmol of vector (about 0.2 μg of pUC19) and about 10 pmol of double-strands (about 0.15 μg of each strand if it is about 50 bp in length). Do not try to increase the efficiency by adding 10-fold more vector. At very high DNA concentrations plasmids containing multiple vector molecules can be formed with odd structures. Anneal the 2 oligonucleotides in 0.1 M NaCl, 10 mM Tris·HCl (pH 7.4) in 6 μl for about 15 min at 65°, then 15 min at 56°, and finally place at 42° until you are ready to assemble the ligation reaction.

2. Set up the ligation reaction using the vector at about 0.1 μg/μl in TE that has been digested using the appropriate restriction enzymes, phenol-extracted, and ethanol-precipitated.

   6 μl annealed oligos
   2 μl vector
   1 μl 10x ligase mix
   1 μl T4 DNA ligase

   Incubate for at least 2 hr at 17° if the termini have complementary overhangs. If it is a blunt-end ligation incubate at room temperature for at least 6 hr.

3. After transformation of bacteria, individual minipreps can be tested for insertion of the synthetic sequence by alteration of restriction digestion patterns or if necessary hybridization with kinased oligos. In many cases it is a good idea to examine the actual DNA sequence of the new insert before much further experimentation has been performed.

An Example of a Plasmid Construction

The goal is to create a chimeric cDNA for expression in stably transformed mammalian cells. The first 3/4 of the cDNA are to be derived from clone A which is initially in a phage. The next segment is synthesized and a third segment is derived from the 3' end of another cDNA that is in another plasmid. After all of that construction the new cDNA will be transferred to the appropriate cDNA expression vector.

1. The cDNA that was inserted into the phage DNA using *Eco*R I linkers is first subcloned into the *Eco*R I site of pUC19. The insert goes into the *Eco*R I site in pUC19 randomly in one of two orientations. For this construction the polylinker sequence needs to be at the 3' end of the cDNA clone. We wish to make use of these polylinker sites in subsequent steps. The other consideration in deciding on the direction of assembly (5' vs. 3') of the DNA segments is that the 3' fragment must be gel-purified because a frequently cutting enzyme is to be used. "Fre-

quently cutting enzyme" refers to an enzyme that recognizes a commonly occurring tetra or pentanucleotide sequence. Thus, it is not possible to easily build this construction in the 3' to 5' direction. The EcoR I subclone having the desired orientation is identified by analyzing minipreps.

2. A double-stranded synthetic oligo about 80 bp is synthesized and blunt-end ligated into the Hinc II cleaved pUC19 subclone produced in step 1. The Hinc II enzyme cuts at the desired place in the cDNA clone and in the pUC19 polylinker. The oligonucleotide was made such that the Hinc II sites are still present in the new plasmid and a BamH I site in the oligo is now the site of insertion for the next fragment. The oligo maintained the desired protein sequence but 1 bp was also changed to eliminate an unwanted Hind III site. The transformants having the oligo inserted in the correct orientation are identified. The presence of all new restriction-enzyme sites that should be in the oligo are checked.

3. The plasmid made in step 2 is treated with BamH I plus CIP to be used as the vector in the next step. A fragment from the 3' end of the second cDNA is prepared by complete digestion using BstY I. The BstY I site has the GATC overhang and is thus compatible with the BamH I site. The source of the insert DNA was chosen from another EcoR I subclone in the polylinker sequence in pSP65. The BstY I cleaves the polylinker at the BamH I site leaving the EcoR I site on the fragment to be subcloned. The correct orientation should be identified by EcoR I digestion. This construction should be EcoR I excisable and thus ready for the next step.

4. The EcoR I insert needs to be inserted into the Xho I site in the cDNA expression vector. This could be accomplished by either of 2 methods. The simpler procedure is to perform a blunt-end ligation using gel-purified insert and Xho I cut vector. Both the vector and EcoR I insert must be made blunt (filled-in) using Klenow polymerase. Alternatively, one could use Xho I linkers to clone the blunt-end EcoR I fragment into the Xho I site in the expression vector. A subclone having the desired orientation must be identified.

Nucleic Acid Probes

AGAROSE GELS

Agarose gels are the most commonly used gels for molecular cloning experiments. For most analytical purposes the use of type-II low-endosmotic agarose is adequate. Ultrapure agarose is good for gels that will be used to electroelute DNA fragments or even for Northern or Southern blots. A special low-melting point (LMP) agarose can be very useful for DNA fragment purification. For making radiolabeled probes by hexamer labeling the liquified fragments can be used directly in the enzymatic reaction.

The fractionation of DNA molecules using conventional electrophoresis is usually done in horizontal gels that are 3–5 mm thick. The separation is a function of the agarose concentration and the size of the DNA molecules. Agarose gels are very sensitive to the differences in DNA conformation present in circular DNAs. The terms *form-I* (supercoiled DNA), *form-II* (nicked circles), and *form-III* (linear DNAs) are derived from the mobilities exhibited in sucrose gradients. The form-I DNA migrated the fastest down the gradients whereas the form-III was the slowest. In agarose gels the linear molecules migrate as a function of their molecular weight. That is, over much of the fraction range of the gel the log of the molecular weight versus the migration gives a linear plot. Form-I DNA moves much faster and form-II DNA slower than the linear form-III DNA molecules. As an example, pUC19 linear DNA is 2.7 kb; the supercoils of pUC19 run at about 1.6 kb, and the nicked circles at about 3 kb.

The fractionation range of DNA varies according to the following concentrations of agarose:

5–60 kb	0.35%
2–20 kb	0.7%
0.6–8 kb	1%
0.5–6 kb	1.2%
0.2–4 kb	1.4%
0.1–2 kb	2%

These numbers are estimates and should be considered useful guides. The 0.35%—0.7% gels might be used to analyze partial digests for cosmid or phage libraries or Southern blots. Gels between 1% and 1.4% are the most commonly used for many purposes. The highest useful concentration is about 2% and would be used primarily to distinguish fragments between 100–500 bp.

Pouring agarose gels is very simple. Agarose is added to a 1x buffer solution and microwaved. Be sure not to overheat the solution. The agarose may break down and the gel can become very soft. All of the agarose particles should be dissolved. After cooling the solution to less than 70° it is poured directly into the gel former. It is common to add ethidium bromide to a final concentration of 0.5 μg/ml after the solution has been microwaved. A gel can be examined during the electrophoresis run or immediately after the run. Alternatively, one can stain the gel using the same amount of ethidium bromide in the running buffer after the BPB and XC dyes have migrated to an appropriate position. The gel may also be run in a buffer containing ethidium bromide. The gel is usually ready after about 30 min and does not need any electrophoresis prior to loading the samples.

For most nondenaturing gels the Tris-acetate buffer is preferable. The buffer should be recirculated especially for long runs or runs at higher voltages. For shorter runs it isn't essential. Tris-borate and Tris-phosphate solutions are better buffers. However, elution of DNA from Tris-borate gels is less efficient and ethanol precipitations from DNAs eluted from Tris-phosphate gels contain considerable amounts of phosphate.

Denaturing gels can be used for analyzing either RNA or DNA. Details concerning the use of glyoxal and formaldehyde gels for Northern blots are given in section 2. For analysis of single-stranded DNA one can use alkaline agarose gels—usually 1% gels. The running buffer is 30 mN NaOH, 1 mM EDTA. There are two ways to cast the gels in order to avoid exposing the agarose to NaOH at high temperature. The gel solution can be microwaved in H_2O and a 5x or 10x NaOH/EDTA solution added after the solution has cooled. Alternatively, the gel can be cast in 30 mM NaCl, 1 mM EDTA but soaked in the alkaline running buffer for 30 min prior to electrophoresis.

There may be certain rare cases when it is necessary to use a very strong denaturing agent, methyl mercuric hydroxide. Other methods should be tried first because this compound is poisonous and all manipulations should be performed in a chemical fume hood. A procedure is given below:

1. An agarose gel (1%–1.4%) is cast in NE buffer (0.05 M boric acid, 0.005 M $Na_2B_4O_7 \cdot 10\ H_2O$, 0.01 M sodium sulfate, 0.001 M EDTA [pH 8.19]). The agarose is dissolved by heating in NE buffer and then 0.5 ml per 100 ml of gel solution of MeHgOH is added and the gel poured. The stock solution is 1 M so the gel is 0.005 M MeHgOH. The electrophoresis is performed using NE buffer. The gels should be run relatively fast (3–5 hr) so they should draw about 100 mA.

2. The RNA sample in ddH_2O is treated with MeHgOH (at 5 mM) for 15 min at room temperature just prior to layering the gel.

3. An equal volume of 2x-NE buffer containing BPB dye and 5 mM MeHgOH is mixed with the treated sample and applied to the gel.

4. Dismantle the gel and soak in about 200 ml of 0.05 N NaOH, 0.005 M β-mercaptoethanol (about 80 µl/200ml), 2 µg ethidium bromide for 40 min at room temperature with gentle shaking. This removes the MeHgOH and nicks the large RNAs to facilitate the transfer.

5. Neutralize the gel with washes (3 x 5 min) in 0.2 M potassium phosphate (pH 6.5) containing 0.007 M iodoacetic acid. For 1 L, mix 100 ml of 1 M KH_2PO_4, 100 ml of 1 M K_2HPO_4, 800 ml ddH_2O and 1.3 g iodoacetic acid. The gel may be photographed at this point.

6. Wash the gel twice in the desired transfer and assemble a transfer as described in section 2.

PREPARATIVE ACRYLAMIDE GELS

5% Gel (60 ml)		8% Gel (60 ml)	
1 M TBE	6 ml	1 M TBE	6 ml
40% acrylamide	7.5 ml	40% acrylamide	12 ml
2% bisacrylamide	5 ml	2% bisacrylamide	8 ml
ddH$_2$0	40.5 ml	ddH$_2$0	33 ml
10% ammonium		10% ammonium	
persulfate	1 ml	persulfate	1 ml
TEMED	30 μl	TEMED	30 μl

These gels (about 2-mm thick) are commonly used for the preparation of both unlabeled and radiolabeled DNA fragments. The volumes given are for gels 30-cm long and 15-cm wide. A 5% gel takes about 800 volt-hr and an 8% gel about 1000 volt-hr to run. They can be run at 60–100 V overnight or 200–500 V in a shorter time. At higher voltages heating occurs which can crack the glass plates that are usually about 3–5 mm thick.

1. Mix the components minus the TEMED and place on a magnetic stir plate.

2. Just before pouring the gel add the TEMED to the stirring solution. The gel should be allowed to polymerize 60 min prior to use. Prerunning this gel is not necessary.

PURIFICATION OF DNA FRAGMENTS FROM AGAROSE AND POLYACRYLAMIDE GELS

1. Load restricted DNA sample (10 to 500 μg) on gel into appropriately sized slots to minimize the area of band to be excised.

2. Electrophorese at low voltage (1 to 5 V/cm) until maximum resolution is attained.

3. Stain the gel with ethidium bromide (10 μg/ml) and locate desired fragment with long-wave UV illuminator.

4. Excise area of gel containing fragment with a razor blade and trim off excess.

5. Transfer the gel slice to dialysis tubing and add about 0.3 ml of 1/2 x TBE.

6. Electroelute the DNA from the gel piece into the dialysis tube for 30 min to 3 hr at 100 V using 1/2 x TBE as the electrophoresis buffer. Monitor the progress by long-wave UV.

7. Reverse electrode polarity for 10 sec at 200 V to remove DNA from the dialysis bag wall. Massage the bag to disperse DNA from the front wall on the tube.

8. Collect solution from dialysis bag and wash gel slice/bag with 1/2 x TBE and pool the washes. For many procedures it is adequate to proceed to step 11 and just precipitate the DNA.

9. Adsorb electroeluted DNA over a Whatman DE-52 cellulose column (0.5 ml packed volume) preequilibrated in TE100 (10 mM Tris·HCl [pH 7.9], 1 mM EDTA, 100 mM NaCl)—discard the eluate.

10. Elute DNA from the column (after flushing it dry with a pipette bulb) with 0.5 ml of 10 mM Tris·HCl [pH 7.9], 1 mM EDTA, 1 M NaCl (TE1000); repeat with another 0.5 ml to remove remaining DNA.

11. Add 2 vol of ethanol, and allow the DNA to precipitate at -70° for 10 min.

12. Collect DNA pellet by centrifugation, wash with 70% ethanol, and resuspend in appropriate buffer.

Comments

1. We routinely use autoclaved buffers (TE100 and TE1000) and agarose (BioRad: ultra pure DNA grade) for these procedures. Exposure of gels to shortwave UV can damage and degrade DNA: a hand-held long-wave illuminator is sufficient to localize a band of interest.

2. If the DNA fragment is excised from an acrylamide gel the piece is usually small and the precipitation can easily be done in a microfuge tube.

3. Fragments eluted from agarose gels are sometimes eluted in larger volumes and the DNA is not as pure as it is when eluted from acrylamide. Purification on DE-52 is a quick step and the DNA is good for any purpose.

4. DNA fragments less than 250 bp can be soaked out of the gel. This is less work than setting up electroelution and is especially good if a large number of samples are being processed. Submerge the gel slice in soak-elution buffer (0.3 M NaCl in TE) and incubate at 37° for at least 6 hr. Remove that solution and replace it with more of the soak-elution buffer and let it sit for several hr at 37°. If the DNA is radiolabeled one can monitor the elution with a Geiger counter. For fragments between 300–600 bp up to 50% of the DNA can be eluted.

ELUTION OF DNA FROM AGAROSE WITH GLASS POWDER

This procedure is based on the initial observations of Vogelstein and Gillespie (*PNAS* 76:615–619, 1979). It is useful to obtain pure DNA fragments for further enzymatic manipulations or subcloning and is very rapid. It can also be used to remove dNTPs, organic solvents, or other unknown molecules from samples of DNA. A kit termed "GENECLEAN" has been assembled by BIO 101 Inc. in La Jolla, California, which appears to be very similar to this method.

Reagents

Silica 325 mesh

Prepare by resuspending 25 ml powder in 500 ml H_2O and stir one hour. Let settle for 1 hour and centrifuge. Resuspend pellet in 100–200 ml H_2O. Add citric acid to 50% and bring close to boil (in hood). Wash 4 times with H_2O and store as a 50% slurry in H_2O. From 250 ml powder there are about 20 g of fines.

NaI Solution (Sigma)

Mix 90.8 g NaI plus 1.5g Na_2SO_3 in 10 ml H_2O and filter through a Whatman #1 or 0.45 μm Nalgene filter. Add 0.5 g Na_2SO_3. The solution should be saturated. Store in the dark at 4°.

Ethanol wash solution

50% EtOH plus 0.1 M NaCl, 0.01 M Tris·HCl (pH 7.5), 0.001 M EDTA. Store at -20°.

Elution buffer is TE

0.01 M Tris·HCl (pH 7.5), 0.001 M EDTA

Procedure

1. Grind up gel and dissolve in 2 ml/g NaI solution for 30 to 60 min at 37°.

2. Shake glass slurry until all powder is in suspension. Add an aliquot to the dissolved gel and let the DNA adsorb to glass at 0° for 1–2 hrs. About 20 μl of slurry is enough for 15 μg DNA in 2 ml total volume.

3. Spin 60 sec in a microfuge. Wash the pellet with 10 volumes of NaI solution at 0°–4°. Resuspend with a pipette and then spin in a microfuge.

4. Wash twice with 10 volumes of cold EtOH wash solution.

5. Elute by resuspending the pellet in 2–3 volumes of TE, incubate 30 min at 37°, and centrifuge.

6. Repeat the elution and pool the 2 supernatants and EtOH-precipitate.

ELUTION OF DNA USING NA45 DEAE MEMBRANES

This method of elution of DNA yields very clean DNA for any subsequent procedure. It is useful for eluting DNA out of agarose gels or acrylamide gels. It is especially useful for footprinting DNA-protein binding sites primarily because the samples are so pure. The membranes are available from Schleicher and Schuell.

Preparation of the membrane

1. Soak the membrane in 10 mM EDTA (pH 7.6) for 10 min at room temperature. The membranes are available in various sizes of circles, strips, and sheets.

2. Replace the solution with 0.5 N NaOH for 5 min at room temperature.

3. Replace the solution with several changes of ddH$_2$O and store at 4°.

Binding and elution of the DNA

1. Binding the DNA is accomplished by electrophoresing the DNA into a strip of membrane which is inserted into a gel. For agarose gels identify the DNA by ethidium bromide staining, make an incision below the desired DNA fragment, and insert a piece of the prepared membrane. If the DNA has been separated in polyacrylamide, excise the region of the gel containing the DNA fragment. Cut a well in an agarose gel and place the piece of acrylamide into it. Add agarose around the acrylamide and insert the NA45 membrane such that the DNA can be electrophoresed into the membrane.

2. Electrophorese the DNA into the membrane. This can be monitored using ethidium staining.

3. Remove the membrane from the gel and place it in 0.15 M NaCl, 0.1 mM EDTA, 20 mM Tris·HCl (pH 8). Vortex or shake it to remove any fragments of the gel. The membrane can be eluted immediately or stored at 4° in the same buffer. Don't let the membrane become dry.

4. Place the strip in elution buffer (1 M NaCl, 0.1 mM EDTA, 20 mM Tris·HCl [pH 8]) such that the strip can be covered after a quick spin in the microfuge (approximately 200 μl).

5. Incubate for 20–45 min at 55°–68° with periodic mixing.

6. Remove the solution and rinse the membrane with another 50–100 μl of elution buffer.

7. EtOH-precipitate the DNA. Reprecipitate if there is a significant amount of salt in the precipitate.

Comments

1. The capacity of these membranes for DNA is high (about 20 μg/cm²).

2. For large DNAs that are several kb in size the salt in the elution buffer can be raised to 2.5 M.

3. The membrane may also be used to elute RNA from gels. In this case elute using 1.8 M sodium acetate (pH 7.4), 2 mM EDTA, 0.2% SDS in 55% formamide. Heat at 65° for 8 min. The formamide should inhibit RNase activity. Wash the filter with an additional 50–100 μl of elution buffer. Dilute the solution with 2 volumes of H_2O and EtOH-precipitate. It may be wise to add carrier RNA to ensure recovery of the desired RNA.

NICK TRANSLATION: METHOD 1

1. Thaw the labeled dNTPs about 20 min before using.
    Assemble a reaction mixture containing the following:

5 μl of each [α-^{32}P]dNTP (Sp.Act. 800 Ci/mmol)	20 μl
1.25 μl of a 50 μM of all 4 dNTPs	1.25 μl
10x nick-translation buffer	3 μl
DNA (about 200 ng)	4 μl

    Preincubate for about 15 min at 15° and then add:

DNase I (Worthington) dilution	1 μl
DNA polymerase I	1 μl

2. Incubate the nick-translation reaction for 1 hr at 15°.

3. Then add 6 μl of 5x stop (2.0% SDS, 50 mM EDTA).

4. Add 10 μg tRNA.

5. Bring volume up to 100 μl with ddH$_2$O.

6. Phenol-extract once.

7. Unincorporated triphosphates are removed by running the above mixture over a spin column.

    10x Nick Translation Buffer (kept at 4°)

0.5 M Tris·HCl (pH 7.5)	2.5 ml 2 M
0.05 M MgCl$_2$	0.5 ml 1 M
0.01 M β-mercaptoethanol	70 μl stock
500 μg/ml BSA	0.5 ml 10 mg/ml
	ddH$_2$O to 10 ml

Comments

1. Each cold nucleotide is 1.25/30 x 50 μM = 2 μM final concentration. One can do reaction of half of the above protocol to save reagents with no difficulty. Usually one obtains 20–30 million Cherenkov counts per half nick-translation reaction. 50 μCi of each labeled nucleotide is used. Because the specific activity is 800 Ci/mmol, the final concentration of each labeled nucleotide is approximately 2 μM.

2. We use a titrated dilution of a 0.5 mg/ml DNase I stock.We currently use a 1/250 dilution of a 0.5 mg/ml DNase I stock (Worthington). Dilutions are made in 10 mM sodium acetate (pH 4.5).

3. Using this procedure all 4 labeled dNTPs are mixed with a low concentration of unlabeled dNTPs. This guards against a given lot of 1 or more of the radiolabels' being defective. Another variation of this scheme is to use some of the dNTPs labeled and the others unlabeled. For instance, one might use 5 µl each of labeled dCTP and dATP and 5 µl each of a 0.2 mM stock of unlabeled dGTP and TTP.

Titrating DNase I

The DNase I is from Worthington, code DPFF.

1. Make stock DNase of 5 mg/ml in DNase storage buffer: 0.15 M NaCl in 50% glycerol.

2. Make 10^{-3}, 10^{-4}, 10^{-5} dilutions into 10 mM sodium acetate (pH 4.5).

3. Do a nick translation using pBR322 or an equivalent DNA sample as usual using 25–50 µCi of one [α-^{32}P] triphosphate and twice the amount of cold triphosphates, using 1 and 5 µl of the above DNase I dilutions.

4. Spot an aliquot of each nick translation onto DE-81 paper in duplicate. Wash 6 times in 0.5 M Na_2HPO_4 for 5 min each. Wash twice in H_2O for 1 min each. Wash twice in 95% EtOH for 1 min each. Dry and count. Include an aliquot of the triphosphate label only (the same amount as used in single nick translation) for determination of background radioactivity. To determine % incorporation, count an aliquot of reaction without washing. A level of 30% incorporation is a good probe. Higher levels of incorporation may result in DNA fragments that are too short to be good probes.

$$\% \text{ incorporation} = \frac{(\text{washed nick translation}) - (\text{washed dNTPs})}{(\text{unwashed dNTPs})}$$

5. Analyze an aliquot of each reaction on a 1% alkaline agarose gel (run labeled DNA size markers) to make sure size of 200–500 bp (see cDNA section for alkaline gels).

NICK TRANSLATION WITH HIGH-SPECIFIC-ACTIVITY dNTP: METHOD 2

This procedure is especially good for purified DNA inserts:

Dry down:
      20 µl dATP   3000 Ci/mmol
      20 µl dCTP   10 mCi/ml, aqueous
      2.5 µM final concentration

Add:
      2.5 µl dGTP   50 mM cold stocks
      2.5 µl dTTP   5 mM final concentra-
      2.5 µl 10 x NT salts   tion
      250 ng DNA

Bring up to:
      22.7 µl with ddH$_2$O

Add:
      1.3 µl 10^{-4} dilution of DNase I stock (1 mg/ml) in ddH$_2$O
      1 µl DNA polymerase I (10 units/µl)

      25 µl reaction

Incubate at 14°.
Desalt over Sephadex G-50 in 0.1 x SSC
                           0.1% SDS
                           2.5 mM EDTA

10 x NT salts	*DNase I Stock*
500 mM Tris·HCl (pH7.8)	Make DNase I powder 1 mg/ml
50 mM MgCl$_2$	in 10 mM Tris·HCl(pH 7.5)
100 mM β-mercaptoethanol	3 mM Mg acetate
500 µg/ml bovine serum albumin	10 mM NaCl
(DNA grade)	50% glycerol
Store at -20° in 1-ml aliquots.	Store at -20° in 1-ml aliquots.

Comments

1. We have found it convenient to vary the reaction time rather than DNase concentration when working with fragments of different sizes. While the digestion time which offers both optimum specific activity

and optimum denatured probe size must be determined empirically, the following guidelines are generally applicable:

1 to 1.5 kb for 1.5 hr
4–6 kb for 2–2.5 hr
8–10 kb for 3 hr

2. Performing half-reactions using this procedure works well and conserves radiolabel.

HYBRIDIZATION USING FORMAMIDE/DEXTRAN SULFATE

Prehybridization

	Stock	Final Conc	10 ml	15 ml	50 ml
Formamide	100%	50%	5 ml	7.5 ml	25 ml
SSCPE	20x	5x	2.5 ml	3.75 ml	12.5 ml
Denhardt's	50x	5x	1.0 ml	1.5 ml	5.0 ml
Salmon sperm DNA	5 mg/ml	500 μg/ml	1.0 ml	1.5 ml	5.0 ml
SDS	10%	0.1%	0.1 ml	0.15 ml	0.5 ml
ddH$_2$O			0.4 ml	0.6 ml	2.0 ml

Use 15–20 ml of solution per blot.
Prehybridize at 42° at least one hr.

Hybridization

	Stock	Final Conc	10 ml	15 ml	50 ml
Formamide	100%	50%	5 ml	7.5 ml	25 ml
SSCPE	20x	5x	2.5 ml	3.75 ml	12.5 ml
Denhardt's	50x	1x	0.2 ml	0.3 ml	1.0 ml
Salmon sperm DNA	5 mg/ml	100 μg/ml	0.2 ml	0.3 ml	1.0 ml
Dextran sulfate	50%	10%	2 ml	3 ml	10 ml

Boil probe for 5 min before adding to hybridization buffer. Use 10–20 ml buffer per blot. Use approximately 10[6] Cherenkov counts per ml buffer.

Hybridize at 42° for at least 6 hr (2 hr hybridization works fine for cloned DNAs, including filters containing phage).

Wash

1. Squeeze out hybridization solution and save. It can be reused by boiling for 5 min. Cool on ice before adding to filters.

2. Rinse filters with 2x SSC, 0.1% SDS at room temperature for 5 min to remove formamide.

3. Wash 3–4 times with 2x SSC, 0.1% SDS at 68° for about 15 min each. Judge background with Geiger counter. To reduce background, a proteinase K wash can also be done. For 100 ml, add 5 ml 1% SDS, 20 mg proteinase K in 95 ml PK buffer. Wash 1 hr at 37° (this can be done in a hybridization bag).

4. Rinse with 0.2x SSC at room temperature to lower the salt concentration.

Solutions used for prehybridization and hybridization

Dextran sulfate

1. 50% dextran sulfate (Pharmacia) in ddH$_2$O

2. Heat to 68° to dissolve.

Salmon sperm DNA (5 mg/ml)

1. Add DNA (2.5 g for 500 ml) to sterile TE at room temperature.

2. Stir with heating to dissolve.

3. Sonicate (at 7–10 rating using large tip for 7 min or until proper viscosity).

4. Put in water bath and let boil for 15 min.
   Cool on ice.

50x Denhardt's

	500 ml
1% bovine serum albumin	5 g
1% polyvinylpyrrolidone	5 g
1% ficoll	5 g
0.1% sodium azide	0.5 g
	+ Sterile ddH$_2$O

Filter through 0.45 μm Nalgene filter at room temperature. Freeze in 100-ml aliquots.

An alternate procedure for making 100x Denhardt's is to prepare a separate 6% stock of BSA, polyvinylpyrrolidone, and ficoll. Each of these ingredients dissolves well by itself. By mixing equal volumes of the three reagents one achieves a 2% stock of each in the final solution. This mixture does not need to be filtered and does not precipitate over time.

HYBRIDIZATION USING BSA/SDS (CHURCH AND GILBERT)

1. Prehybridize blot for 30 min at 65° using a minimal amount of solution.

2. Add the probe at 1–10 x 10^6 cpm/ml and hybridize overnight at 65°.

3. After two quick 2–3 min rinses in buffer A, wash 2 x 20 min at 65° in buffer A and 4 x 20 min at 65° in buffer B.

4. For rehybridization, the blot can be stripwashed in 0.1% SDS, 0.1x SSC at 95° for 2–4 x 15 min.

Materials

Hybridization buffer

	10 ml	Final
Bovine serum albumin (fraction V)	0.1 g	1%
SDS	0.7 g	7%
1 M phosphate buffer (pH 6.8)	5 ml	0.5 M
0.5 M EDTA (pH 8.0)	20 μl	1 mM

Mixing of the components is most easily achieved if added to a minimal (4 ml) of H_2O in the above order and then brought to a final volume.

Wash A

	1 L	Final
BSA	5 g	0.5%
SDS	50 g	5%
1 M phosphate buffer	40 ml	40 mM
0.5 M EDTA	2 ml	1 mM

Wash B

	2 L	Final
SDS	20 g	1%
1 M phosphate buffer	80 ml	40 mM
0.5 M EDTA	4 ml	1 mM

REFERENCE

Church, G. M., and W. Gilbert *Proc. Nat. Acad. Sci. USA* 81: 1991 (1984).

HYBRIDIZATION USING AQUEOUS CONDITIONS

Aqueous hybridization

	per 100 ml
4xSSC	20 ml of 20x SSC
5x Denhardt's	5 ml of 100x Denhardt's
0.1% SDS	1 ml of 10% SDS
0.1% NaPPi	1 ml of 10% NaPPi
10% dextran sulfate	20 ml of 50% dextran sulfate
100–200 µg/ml denatured	
carrier DNA	1–2 ml of 10 mg/ml stock solution

The use of dextran sulfate is optional. It can increase the signal several-fold but sometimes can increase the background especially if there are plasmid vector sequences in the probe. High background can also be a problem if the solution is overheated or if there is particulate matter in the solution of dextran sulfate. In the latter case filtering the solution can help.

Prehybridize at 65° for at least 3 hr. Add the probe using 1 x 10⁶ cpm/ml and hybridize overnight (16–20 hr). Wash with a solution containing 2x SSC, 0.1% SDS, and 0.1% sodium pyrophosphate for 4 x 20 min at 65°.

For hybridization using oligonucleotides the aqueous conditions listed above are fine but the SSC is generally increased to 6x SSC. For oligonucleotides that are to be used as probes that have some mismatches (probes based on protein sequence) these conditions are also good. As a rule, for oligonucleotides less than 40 bases we use 37°–42°. For longer oligonucleotides, increasing the temperature of the hybridization and washing to 50°–56° can increase the hybridization signal. Unless the oligonucleotides are very long (greater than 70 bases) the use of formamide hybridization conditions is discouraged.

RADIOLABELING BY RANDOM HEXAMER EXTENSION

Probes made using this procedure have many advantages. The specific activities achieved are very high. The amount of DNA used for each preparation is less than one typically uses for nick translation. A preparation of a DNA fragment can be used to synthesize more probes by this method.

Buffers: *TM* 250 mM Tris·HCl (pH 8.0)
       25 mM MgCl$_2$
       50 mM 2-mercaptoethanol
    OL 90 U/ml oligos (random hexamers-Pharmacia) in 10 mM
       Tris·HCl (pH 7.5), mM EDTA
    LS 156 μl 1 M HEPES (pH 6.6)
       156 μl DTM (78 μl 0.200 μM
       dATP, dTTP, dGTP + 78 μl 2x TM)

1. Denature the template by mixing 1.5 μl DNA (50–100 ng) plus 11 μl H$_2$O and boiling for 3 min. Then plunge in ice.

2. Then add: 11.4 μl LS
      1.0 μl BSA (Pharmacia—10 μg/ml)
      5.0 μl [α^{32}P] dCTP (3000 Ci/mmol)
      1.0 μl Klenow polymerase

  Incubate at room temperature for 2–4 hr.

3. Phenol:chloroform (1:1) extract, add 5 μg tRNA,and purify on a spin column.

Comments

1. These probes are handled in the same manner as nick-translated probes.

2. A new nonradioactive hexamer labeling procedure has been developed by Boehringer-Mannheim which appears to have a sensitivity very similar to radiolabeled probes.

REFERENCE

Feinberg, A. P., and B. Vogelstein *Analyt. Biochem.* 132:6 (1983).

SP6 RNA PROBES

1. The SP6 plasmid should be linearized as near to the 3' end of the insert as possible, preferably at a site within the polylinker. Digest a few μg of plasmid DNA with an appropriate restriction enzyme. After the digestion do two phenol extractions and two extractions with an excess of ether. Precipitate the DNA with EtOH and resuspend at 1 μg/μl in DEP-treated H_2O.

   Note: RNA inhibits the SP6 reaction—either use double-banded plasmid preparations or ammonium acetate-precipitated DNA to get rid of free nucleotides.

2. The radiolabeled nucleotide used in these reactions is rUTP. The final UTP concentration desired is 12.5 μM. The vanadyl complex is from Promega Biotech. The SP6 polymerase and human placenta RNase inhibitor (RNasin) are from Boehringer-Mannheim or Promega.

^{32}P Probes

1. Add in order at *room temperature* (important—DNA will precipitate if cold):

   4 μl 5x buffer (200 mM Tris·HCl [pH7.5], 30 mM $MgCl_2$, 10 mM spermidine)
   2 μl 1 M DTT
   5 μl [α-^{32}P] UTP
   1.1 μl rNTP mix (A, C, G each 10 mM, U at 400 μM)
   0.8 μl RNasin (40 u/μl)

   Add 1 μg DNA and bring to 19 μl with DEP-treated H_2O.

2. Add 1 μl SP6 polymerase, incubate 60 min at 30°.

3. Add 1 μl 10 mM UTP
        1 μl RNasin
        0.5–1 μl SP6 Polymerase

   Incubate 40 min more at 30°.
   Incubations appear to give longer RNA transcripts when done at 30° but incubations can be done for 40 min and then 30 min at 37°.

4. Digest the DNA template by adding 2 units (2 μl) of RNase-free DNase (Promega or Worthington) for 15 min at 37°.

5. Bring volume up to 50 μl with TNE (DEPC-treated TE containing 0.1 M NaCl). Save 1 μl for an estimation of total incorporation. Extract with 1x phenol/SEVAG.

6. To separate unincorporated from incorporated nucleotides, the reaction mixture should be run over a G-50 spin column. Count an aliquot. Expect 60%–90% incorporation.

    Blots hybridized with SP6 probes should be incubated at 60°, using the same prehybridization and hybridization buffers used for nick-translated probes.

    Wash: 3x for 60 min each, 0.05x SSC, 0.1% SDS, 68°

    (Washing stringencies required are very probe-dependent.)

    The background of Northerns hybridized with SP6 probes can be reduced dramatically by RNase washing the blot (although the blot cannot be reused after RNase treatment). Use 2 μg/ml RNase A in 2x SSC for 20 min at room temperature.

^{35}S SP6 Probes

The protocol for ^{35}S SP6 probes is basically the same as for ^{32}P probes except that there is no UTP in the rNTP mix. Add 9 μl of ^{35}S-UTP (>1000 Ci/mmol: 10 mCi/ml) to the synthesis reaction.

The G-50 for the spin column should be resuspended in TE + 10 mM DTT.

REFERENCE

Johnson, M.T., and B.A. Johnson *Biotechniques* (May/June 1984):156.

OLIGONUCLEOTIDE PURIFICATION

Following synthesis on the DNA synthesizer the oligo can be removed from the silica support by treatment with concentrated NH_4OH. The purification described here uses a polyacrylamide gel to isolate the full-length oligo. It is also possible to purify oligos by HPLC. For relatively short oligos (less than 30 bases) many procedures should work fine. However if your oligo is long and is to be used in the construction of a gene, it is usually important to have a pure full-length oligo. The quality of oligos, especially long ones produced by the synthesizer, can vary. This procedure is very easy and it is possible to examine the quality of the oligos on the gel, purify the full-length oligo, and estimate the amount of oligo synthesized.

1. Draw about 0.25 ml NH_4OH into a 1-ml disposable syringe. Remove the needle and attach the oligo column. Also attach a double luer connector to the other end of the column and finally an 18-gauge needle. Hold the column above the syringe and push the NH_4OH into the column so that the entire column is filled with solution and the solution is also about halfway through the connector. Place on a horizontal surface at room temperature and leave for about 30 min. Longer times are OK.

2. Push the solution into a screw-cap 1.5-ml microfuge tube.

3. Repeat steps 1 and 2 three more times.

4. Place cap on tube and incubate at about 56° for at least 8 hr. Longer times up to 16 hr are better.

5. Divide the solution into two microfuge tubes and dry down in a speed vac which usually takes at least 3 hr.

6. Resuspend the oligo in a total of 100 μl and read the OD_{260} of a 1/1000 dilution in ddH_2O. The conversion is 33 mg/OD unit.

Acrylamide gel purification

7. Prepare an acrylamide/urea sequencing gel (see DNA sequencing section) generally 40 cm in length and about 2 mm thick. For oligos 50 nucleotides or greater an 8% gel is good and for shorter oligos a 12% gel is suitable. Prerun the gel about 30 min at 800 volts.

8. Add an equal volume of 100% formamide without any dyes to the oligonucleotide in H_2O. Heat the mixture at 55° for about 5 min prior to layering the gel. The capacity of the gel is about 50 mg per cm of well.

Layer some bromophenol blue and xylene cyanol dyes in formamide in a adjacent lane as a marker for size and flush out the wells just prior to loading the samples.

9. Generally run the gel until the bromophenol blue dye is about 3/4 the length of the gel. With experience the necessary distance to optimally separate oligos of a certain size can be determined for your particular gels.

10. After stopping the gel, remove one glass plate and place saran wrap over the gel. Flip the gel over and remove the second glass plate from the gel and again place saran wrap over the other side of the gel.

11. Place the wrapped gel over a fluorescent TLC plate (Brinkmann Instruments #68–16–000–6; Merck #5776 silica gel 60 F_{254} precoated plastic sheets).

12. Visualize the DNA by using a hand-held UV lamp using shortwave UV. Excise the desired band with a razor.

13. Add 5 ml of elution buffer (0.5 M ammonium acetate, 10 mM magnesium acetate) to a 15-ml polypropylene tube containing the gel slice and incubate the sealed tube at 37° for at least 12 hr in a shaking incubator if available.

14. Remove the solution and wash the slice with another 1 ml of elution buffer and add to the first solution.

15. Filter this solution through a Millex HV filter and collect in a fresh tube. This removes any small gel particles.

Purification of the oligo with a Sep-pak column

16. Prepare the Sep-pak column by passing 10 ml of HPLC grade acetonitrile slowly through the column using the plunger of a 10 ml syringe. Avoid passing air back through the Sep-pak column. Pass 10 ml of filtered ddH$_2$O through the column. Finally pass 2 ml of the elution buffer through the column.

17. Slowly pass the sample through the column. One pass is sufficient. Then pass 10 ml of filtered ddH$_2$O through the column.

18. Elute the oligo from the column using 60% methanol. Perform three separate 1-ml elutions and collect in three separate screw-cap microfuge

tubes. Dry down on a speed vac and resuspend in an appropriate volume of ddH$_2$O. If yields of the oligo are good then 50–100 ml is appropriate. Determine the amount of oligo by measuring the OD$_{260}$. If there is a small amount of oligo then smaller volumes would be better.

SYNTHETIC OLIGOMER: 5′ END LABELING

1. Assemble the following reaction:
   7 pmol oligomer
   3 μl 10x buffer
   10 μl [γ-^{32}P]rATP
   1 μl T4 polynucleotide kinase (5–10 units)

   Bring to final volume of 30 μl with ddH$_2$O.

2. Incubate at 37° for 30 min.

3. Purify on P6 spin column (BioRad 200–400 mesh #150–0750) or a G-50 spin column.

   10x Kinase buffer

   0.5 M Tris·HCl (pH 7.6)
   0.1 M MgCl$_2$
   50 mM DTT
   10 mM spermidine

G-50 SEPHADEX SPIN COLUMNS

1. Swell 3–4 g of Sephadex G-50 in 100 ml ddH$_2$O by autoclaving for 10 min. G-100 is *not* suitable, as beads will crush. Use 0.005 M EDTA, not sodium azide, as a preservative. The washes are not sufficient to get rid of the azide. The set up and use of a G-100 column is described in the section on cDNA cloning.

2. Remove the plunger and end-cap from a 1-ml plastic syringe. Plug the narrow end with a small amount of glass wool.

3. Squirt in 1 ml of G-50, spin 2–4 min, at setting 4 or 5 in a clinical centrifuge using a 15-ml conical tube as a support. Add more G-50 and spin again to get a column of about 1 ml volume. The resin will look dry and shrunken after centrifugation. Relax—this is how it should be.

4. Wash the column once or twice with one-tenth column volume of ddH$_2$0 (or buffer). Spin as above after each wash.

5. Empty the conical support tube if you wish to collect the sample into it. This works fine. You may also put a decapitated microfuge tube in the bottom of the conical tube and collect into the microfuge tube.

6. Apply the sample to the column in one-tenth column volume and spin as before. The flow through is now in the collection tube. The first tenth-volume is the only fraction of interest—don't bother to elute again.

Comments: A particular advantage of spin columns in addition to speed, reproducibility, and minimum exposure to radioactivity, is that the sample elutes in the same volume in which it was applied. This protocol is written for 0.1 ml samples but sample volumes of less than or more than 0.1 ml may be used. The lower column volume that seems to work is 0.3 ml. Just remember: apply the sample in a volume equal to one-tenth the column volume. Spin columns are also useful for desalting; in this case, slurry the G-50 in buffer and wash the column 4 or 5 times with buffer before applying the sample. Material in Sephadex (probably dextran) may inhibit some reactions—notably reverse transcription. Using an extensively washed column or EtOH precipitation of the eluate may be necessary in such cases. Be careful as some dextran is EtOH-precipitable.

M13 Probes, Mutagenesis, and Maintenance

M13 CLONING

The single-stranded DNA phage M13 has become a very important vector in performing dideoxy DNA sequencing, in making DNA probes for hybridization and S1 analysis, and in site-directed mutagenesis. The use of the Bluescript vector from Stratagene has many advantages over M13 phage. The plasmid DNA is much more convenient for subcloning and storage. It certainly works well for DNA sequence analysis on automated sequencers because the production of single-strand template is readily achieved with helper phages. We describe here the general handling of the phage and its use in these techniques.

M13 cloning reagents

Minimal media plates

Autoclave the following reagents separately and cool before mixing.

a) 1 liter M9 salts with 15 g agar

1 L M9 salts: 6 g Na_2HPO_4

3 g KH_2PO_4

1 g NH_4Cl

0.5 g NaCl

b) 1 ml 1 M $MgSO_4$

c) 1 ml 0.1 M $CaCl_2$

d) 1 ml 1 M thiamine·HCl

e) 10 ml 20% glucose (or 5 ml 40% glucose)

YT Media
per liter: 8 g tryptone

5 g yeast extract

5 g NaCl

Adjust pH to 7.2—7.4 with NaOH.

YT Plates
YT media that contains 15 g agar/L

YT Top Agar
YT media that contains 6 g agar/L

X-gal (5-bromo-4-chloro-3-indolyl-β-D-galactoside) Sigma #B-4252 2% solution in dimethylformamide stored in a glass container at -20°

247

IPTG (isopropyl-β-D-thiogalactopyranoside) Sigma #I-5502 100 mM solution in H_2O (23.8 mg/ml). Store in aliquots at -20°.

1. Preparation of insert and vector

A suitable vector is prepared from RF (double-stranded) M13 DNA according to the same protocol used for preparation of plasmid vectors (i.e., restriction enzyme digestion, treatment with CIP, purification by phenol extraction, and EtOH precipitation). It is often desirable to clone the insert in both directions. If the cloning is asymmetric (vector and insert cut with two different enzymes) it is necessary to prepare two vectors (i.e., mp18 and mp19) which have linkers in the opposite directions.

The insert is prepared according to standard methods.

2. Ligation

Ligate 40 ng vector with a 5-fold excess of insert in 10 μl. To determine the background of the vector, ligate 40 ng of cut + CIP'd vector (no insert).

H_2O	
vector	n μl (40 ng or 0.8 pmol)
insert	n μl (n ng or 4 pmol)
4x ligation buffer	2.5 μl
BSA (1 mg/ml)	0.5 μl
RNase (5 mg/ml)*	1.0 μl
	10 μl

*Necessary only if insert DNA contains RNA. If used, incubate at 37° for 10 min, then cool. Add 0.5–1 μl ligase and incubate at 15° for 6 hr for sticky ends or for 24 hours for blunt ends.

3. Transformation

E. coli strain JM103 is the host for M13. It is necessary to ensure that the bacteria maintain the plasmid necessary for synthesis of the F pilus as this structure is essential for M13 infection. Since this plasmid also carries a gene coding for proline and the proline region has been deleted on the chromosome, growth on minimal media selects for those cells that have retained the plasmid. The procedure described below is for a $CaCl_2$ transformation procedure. One may also electroporate JM103 cells with the ligated DNAs and then perform an infection. Just mix the transformed cells with an excess of JM103 in top agar (see step 5 under transformation).

To make competent cells:

a) Pick a single colony of JM103 from a glucose/minimal medium plate. Grow overnight in 10 ml YT media, shaking at 37°.

b) To 75 ml of YT media add 0.75 ml of an overnight culture of JM103. Grow at 37° , shaking, to OD_{600} 0.5–0.7. Remove 50 ml.

c) Gently spin down the cells (7000 x g for 2 minutes). Use the remaining 25 ml of cells for the plating culture (see below).

d) Resuspend cells in 1/2 volume (25 ml) of sterlized 50 mM $CaCl_2$ pre-chilled on ice. Leave on ice for 20 min.

e) Gently spin down cells (7000 x g for 2 min).

f) Resuspend in 1/10 volume (5 ml) of cold 50 mM $CaCl_2$.

These competent cells will keep on ice for some hours. After 24 hours, the efficiency of transformation begins to decrease, although cells may still be usable 4–5 days later.

Plating culture: Grow cells at 37°, shaking, to OD_{660} 0.9–1.0. Store at 4°.

Transformation

a) To 45 μl TE in cooled, sterile, capped tubes add 5 μl of the ligated DNAs. As a positive control, prepare one tube containing 45 μl TE and 1 ng M13 RF (supercoiled) DNA.

b) Add 300 μl competent JM103.

c) Incubate on ice for 40 min.

d) Heat shock at 42° for 2 min.

e) Immediately before plating, prepare a stock of plating mix sufficient for all reactions. Minimize the exposure of the cells to the X-gal solution which is dimethylformamide. It is generally better to pour plates containing X-gal and omit it from this mixture. Each reaction requires:

200 μl JM103 plating culture
40 μl 2% X-gal
40 μl 100 mM IPTG

Dispense 3 ml YT top agar into sterile tubes (one per reaction) and equilibrate at 50° in a heating block. Add 270 μl plating mix to the top agar and vortex. Add this to tube containing DNA and competent JM103. Vortex. Pour onto a YT plate. When top agar has hardened, invert plate and incubate at 37° overnight.

If the ligation and transformation worked, expect to see hundreds of blue plaques on the M13 wild-type plate, very few, if any, blue plaques on the vector-only plate, and many white plaques (and a few blue plaques) on the experimental plates. The white plaques contain inserts.

4. Selection of recombinants

Recombinants should not be stored as plaques but may be stored as purified single-stranded DNA.

a) Dilute an overnight culture of JM103 1:100 in YT media.

b) Dispense 2-ml aliquots into sterile 10-ml culture tubes.

c) Inoculate each tube with a colorless plaque using a 100-µl glass capillary pipette.

d) Shake the tubes vigorously at 37° for 5–6 hours. Transfer 1.5 ml to microcentrifuge tubes. Save the remaining 0.5 ml for a glycerol stock. (See below in step 6.)

e) Centrifuge for 15 min. This and subsequent steps are performed at room temperature. Pour the supernatant into a fresh tube, being very careful not to pick up any cells—do not take all of the supernatant. Store at 4° for preparation of single-stranded DNA. Aspirate any remaining liquid from the cell pellet. Pellet can be frozen if minipreps are not to be done immediately.

Typically, positive clones are identified by analyzing double-stranded phage DNA isolated from the bacterial pellet. However, if a large number of clones must be screened, the following method is an easy and quick way to identify clones with inserts (will not provide information about the size of the insert).

To 20 µl supernatant add: 1 µl 10% SDS and incubate at 68° for 30 min. Add 5 µl of 5x sample buffer and electrophorese on a 0.7% agarose gel overnight. DNA from recombinants migrates more slowly than wild-type single-stranded M13 DNA. Because this method relies on comparing the migration of wild-type and recombinant DNA, be sure to prepare some wild-type M13 (usually used as a positive control in the transformation).

Bacteria in the pellet contain both the single- and double-stranded form of the recombinant phage DNA. The double-stranded form can be extracted using one of the plasmid miniprep protocols, digested with the appropriate restriction endonuclease, and analyzed on a minigel.

If the cloning was symmetric (vector and insert cut with a single restriction enzyme) and it is necessary to have the insert cloned in both orientations (i.e., for sequencing), use the following protocol to identify complementary clones. Mix together 20 µl of the supernatant from each of two phage growths known to contain the desired insert (from minipreps). To this add 1 μl 10% SDS and incubate at 65° for 30 min. Add sample buffer and electrophorese on a 0.7% agarose gel overnight. Under these annealing conditions the two phage DNAs will form a figure-eight dimer if the inserts are complementary. The annealed DNA migrates with a lower mobility than either of the two DNAs electrophoresed by themselves. Typically, one clone that contains the insert is designated as a standard and is hybridized with the other positive clones. Hybridization of the standard with itself serves as a negative control.

5. Preparation of single-stranded DNA

a) Recentrifuge supernatant as before, to ensure that all cells are removed.

b) Add supernatant to 200 μl of 20% PEG in 2.5 M NaCl. Shake, then leave to stand for 15 min at 4°.

c) Centrifuge at 4° for 10 min. Discard supernatant.

d) Centrifuge for 2 min. Carefully remove all remaining traces of PEG on mouth of tube with tissue. A viral pellet should be observable at this stage.

e) Add 100 μl of TE to the viral pellet. Add 100 μl of phenol saturated with TE buffer. Vortex 15–20 seconds.

f) Stand tubes for 15 min at room temperature. Vortex 15 sec.

g) Centrifuge for 3 min.

h) Remove and transfer upper (aqueous) layer to a fresh microfuge tube. Phenol-extract again. Ether-extract twice.

i) Add 10 μl 3 M sodium acetate and 250 μl of ethanol.

j) Leave overnight at -20° to precipitate the DNA.

k) Centrifuge for 10 min. Wash the pellet with 1 ml cold (-20°) ethanol. Pour off ethanol and leave to drain until dry.

l) Redissolve in 25 μl of TE buffer. Expect 2.5–5 μg of DNA.

m) Determine the concentration of the DNA on a minigel using single-stranded M13 DNA as a standard.

n) Store at 4°.

6. Preparation of glycerol stock

To the reserved 0.5 ml of the 2-ml miniculture (see step d in section 4 above, Selection of Recombinants) add 0.5 ml of glycerol. Store at -70°.

To obtain more of the bacteria containing the recombinant phage, it is necessary to infect new JM103. To 2 ml of a 1:100 dilution of JM103 in YT media, add 50 µl of the reserved 0.5 ml miniculture. Shake vigorously at 37° for 5–7 hr.

7. Large-scale preparation of RF (double-stranded replicative form) DNA

a) Inoculate 3 ml of fresh JM103 cells (overnight culture diluted 100-fold in YT media) with 100 µl of glycerol stock containing the bacteria previously infected by the phage (see section 7). If you haven't such a glycerol stock, transform competent cells (see section 3 above, Transformation) with single-stranded DNA template or RF DNA (10–20 µg/plate). Pick a single plaque, and use one to inoculate 3 ml of fresh JM103.

b) Shake vigorously for 5–6 hours at 37°.

c) Spin in microfuge for 10 min. Store supernatant at 4°.

d) Inoculate 250 µl of YT media with 2.5 ml of the supernatant and 2.5 ml of an overnight culture of JM103 cells.

e) Shake vigorously for 5–6 hours at 37°.

f) Spin down cells 2.5 krpm for 10 min at 0° and isolate RF DNA by means of standard plasmid preparation method. A 250-ml culture should yield 80–100 µg RF DNA. (You can freeze the cell pellets at -20° before RF DNA extraction.)

S1 MAPPING USING UNIFORMLY LABELED SINGLE-STRAND PROBE

The cloning of a DNA fragment in a vector derived from the M13 phage permits the isolation of the single-strand template necessary for the synthesis of a uniformly labeled single-stranded probe. The use of this probe, which is complementary to the single-strand DNA fragment cloned in the phage, permits the identification of the extent of all transcribed regions within this fragment. (The use of an end-labeled probe will give you only the extent of continous transcribed regions from the labeled end.)

Briefly, the different steps are:

1. Cloning of a given fragment in M13 phage and preparation of the single-strand template.

2. Synthesis of the labeled single-strand probe after annealing the oligonucleotide primer. The primer 5′ end is localized 36 nucleotides downstream of the 3′ ends of the polylinker.

3. Selection for the complete labeled probe: digestion by a restriction enzyme, which can be the 5′ cloning site if this site remained intact after the cloning, or a site 5′ from this cloning site. Whatever the enzyme you use, this site must not exist in the insert to prevent the probe from being cut into different fragments.

4. Running the whole digestion on an acrylamide sequencing gel. While the template (about 0.7–0.8 kb) will remain on the top of the gel, the single-strand probe (50 bp–1 kb) will run further into the gel. The single-strand probe detected by a short autoradiography, is eluted from the gel and is then ready to use.

5. Hybridization of the probe to the RNA.

6. Nuclease S1 digestion.

7. Analysis of protected fragments on acrylamide sequencing gel.

Protocols

In order to obtain a single-strand probe complementary to the RNA, the DNA coding strand needs to be in the right orientation in the single strand-template. For this purpose, you have to clone the double-strand DNA fragment with the 3′ end of the gene near the primer. When the cloning sites are asymmetric, you can force the orientation of the insert during the cloning using an appropriate polylinker. If the cloning sites are symmetric you can't force the orientation, so you have to isolate from the recombinant phage population two clones in opposite orientations and use each of them as a single-strand probe to hybridize to the RNA. Only one will give you a protected fragment with RNA. If you don't know the orientation of the gene on the genome, you also have to prepare the single-strand probe in both orientations. You should use a single-strand probe only up to 800–900 bp and if you expect that the whole probe can be protected, use single-strand probe up to 500–600 bp in order to have a good resolution in a 5% acrylamide gel.

1. Hybridize the primer by mixing the following:
   250 ng single-strand template
   1 μl primer hybridization buffer
   1 μl primer (10 ng/μl)
   7 μl

   Heat for 2 min at 95° to denature any secondary structure and then hybridize for 30 min at 68°. Do a quick spin after 15 min for 1 sec in the microfuge.

2. Synthesize the DNA by adding:

   5 μl dXTP (about 800 Ci/mmol)
   0.5 μl 10 mM mix of the 3 other cold dXTP (3.3 mM each)
   0.5 μl Klenow enzyme (5 units/μl)

   Incubate for 15 min at 25°, keep on ice while you check nucleotide incorporation by TCA precipitation of 0.5 μl of the reaction. Mix 1 ml TE + 2 μl tRNA + 0.5 μl of the reaction mixture. Add 1 ml 10% TCA, place on ice for 10 min and then put through manifold. Wash manifold slot with 5% TCA. Count filter with scintillation fluid.) You should obtain 0.8 to 1.3 10^7 cpm total (real counts or about 1/3 as many Cherenkov cpm).

   Chase: Add 0.5 μl 5 mM dXTP (the nucleotide that is hot during synthesis) and incubate for 5 min at 25°.

   Heat at 68° for 8–10 min to inactivate the Klenow polymerase.

3. Excise the synthesized DNA from the M13 template by restriction enzyme digestion. To the 12.5 μl of the synthesis reaction, add 2 μl 10x buffer necessary for the activity of the restriction enzyme of your choice, 1 μl enzyme (15–20 u/μl) + 3 μl ddH$_2$0 = 20 μl. Incubate 1 hr at 37°.

   Add 3 μl of 0.5 M EDTA and 20 μl formamide dye (you can freeze the sample at -20° at this point).

4. Purify the labeled fragment by heating the sample for 5 min at 90° and load immediately on a 5% acrylamide sequencing gel that has been poured in the normal polyacrylamide apparatus (2 mm-wide spacers). Use the comb with 1 cm-wide wells and run between 250–300 V (not over 0.3 mA).

For insert up to 600 bp, stop the gel when the bromophenol blue reaches the bottom, for 600–900 bp insert stop gel when XC reaches the bottom. Expose gel to autoradiograph film for 1 min by wrapping the gel and glass plate with saran wrap. Place a few hot dots on the wrapped gel to be able to determine the location of the S1 probe. One intense band is seen near the top of the film. This is the vector. Your S1 probe is a fainter band located somewhere down the gel. Make a tracing of the autoradiograph onto a piece of tracing paper and lay the tracing paper on top of the gel, lining up the hot dots. The S1 probe is cut out with a sharp razor blade. The gel can be re-exposed if you are uncertain if you cut out your band.

Place the gel slice onto a piece of parafilm and dice it up with a razor blade. Place the pieces of gel into a 200 µl microfuge tube that has a pin hole in the bottom. Place this tube into a 1.5 ml microfuge tube and spin for 30 sec. The gel slice should all transfer into the larger microfuge tube. Add 750 µl of elution buffer and incubate 1–2 hrs at 55°, longer fragments requiring longer periods of time. Vortex every 20 min during the elution process. Spin 10 min in microfuge in cold room and take the supernatant (500–600 µl). You should obtain 0.7—7.5 10^6 cpm (Cherenkov). Don't wait to use the probe.

Use of the probe for hybridization to RNA

The amount of RNA used for the hybridization depends on its level of expression and depends also if you use cytoplasmic RNA, cytoplasmic poly(A)$^+$ or total RNA.

The condition of hybridization DNA:RNA depends on the sequence of the DNA probe. If you use the probe for the first time, you should test the following four conditions: 50% formamide at 42° and 50° and 80% formamide at 42° and 50°.

Then you should be able to estimate if you can use only one of these conditions or even a more drastic condition (i.e. 80% formamide at 60° for probe with high GC content) in future experiments with the probe.

Mix the following:

20 ng-1 µg RNA cytoplasmic poly(A)$^+$ (or 10 µg-15 µg cytoplasmic RNA or 20 µg-30 µg total RNA)
3 µl yeast tRNA 5 mg/ml (only if you use less than 10 µg of RNA in the hybridization)
50,000 cpm of probe (Cherenkov cpm)
elution buffer up to a final volume of at least 50 µl

Add 2.5 volumes of 100% EtOH. Precipitate in dry ice for 30 min. Make a duplicate of the probe at each hybridization condition with only tRNA.

Spin, wash with 70% EtOH.

Resuspend the dry pellet in 20 µl of the formamide-hybridization mix.

Incubate overnight or 12–15 hrs at the appropriate temperature.

Analysis by S1 digestion

Dilute each sample to 500 µl with 50 µl 10x S1 Buffer, 430 µl H_2O. Mix well. Add 0.5 µl S1 enzyme (Boehringer 400 u/µl). Incubate 1 hr at 37°.

Precipitate in EtOH with 3 µl of 5 mg/ml tRNA but without adding salt (30 min on dry ice). Wash with 70% EtOH and speed-vac. The pellet is resuspended in 2.4 µl H_2O, 3.6 µl formamide dye. Heat sample at 90°–95° for 3 min and load on a 5% acrylamide sequencing gel. As a marker, run 100–1000 cpm of an intact probe and 5000 cpm of end-labeled markers. Run at 1000–1200 V until the bromophenol blue reaches the bottom. Let the gel cool and take plates apart. Transfer gel to an exposed X-ray film which serves only as a backing and put on film.

S1 Mapping Reagents

1. *Primer hybridization buffer*

Tris·HCl (pH 7.6)	54 mM
NaCl	270 mM
$MgCl_2$	54 mM
DTT	6 mM

   Store at -20°.

2. *Primer pentanucleotide:* 3'-TGCAGCACTGACCCT-5'

3. *Formamide dye*

   100% deionized formamide
   0.03% xylene cyanol
   0.03% bromophenol blue
   20 mM EDTA

4. *Elution buffer*

   500 mM ammonium acetate
   10 mM magnesium acetate
   1 mM EDTA
   0.1% SDS

Before using it add tRNA to a final concentration of 10 μg/ml.

5. *Formamide-hybridization mix*

| *80% formamide mix:* (one sample) | 16 μl deionized formamide 100% 2 μl 10x hybridization buffer 2 μl H₂O |

80% formamide mix:
(one sample)

16 μl deionized formamide 100%
2 μl 10x hybridization buffer
2 μl H₂O

50% formamide mix:
(one sample)

10 μl deionized formamide 100%
2 μl 10x hybridization buffer
8 μl H₂O

10x hybridization buffer:

4 M NaCl
400 mM PIPES (pH 6.4)
10 mM EDTA

First dissolve PIPES in water—you have to add NaOH to dissolve completely. Then add NaCl and EDTA, adjust pH to 6.4, then filter, store at 4°.

6. *S1 buffer 10x*

2.8 M NaCl
0.3 M sodium acetate (pH 4.5)
30 mM ZnCl₂
Store at 4°.

MUTAGENESIS: SITE DIRECTED BY OLIGONUCLEOTIDES

M13 phage is ideally suited for site-directed mutagenesis using oligonucleotides because a single-stranded phage provides a template. Recently an improvement in the method by Kunkel has made this means of mutagenesis the method of choice for many experiments. The improvement is the creation of a uracil-substituted template. As a consequence there is a strong selection for the newly synthesized mutant DNA strand over the parental DNA template. The frequency of mutants generated is increased from a few percent to 50%-80%. In many cases we have obtained 100% mutant phages.

The procedure is so efficient that the decision to use it or just use synthetic double-stranded oligonucleotides may be made based on technical grounds. The decision of which method to use may be made in some cases on the complexity of subsequent subcloning steps. If one plans to make many mutants in a defined region the M13 method is better in that only a single oligonucleotide is needed to generate a mutant or even a series of mutants. Redundancy can be synthesized in the preparation of an oligonucleotide. If the region of interest lacks convenient restriction enzyme sites that might be used to insert sequences not only does the M13 method not need sites for insertion but it can be used to generate new useful restriction sites. Large insertions or deletions can be made by maintaining about 15 bp on each side at the point of insertion or deletion.

The template is prepared by growing your recombinant wildtype sequence in a strain, CJ236, which is *dut-* and *ung-*. The *dut-* phenotype is due to a deficient dUTPase which increases the intracellular dUTP pool. The dUTP competes with TTP for incorporation into DNA. The *ung-* mutation results in a deficient uracil glycosylase which can remove uracil bases from DNA. The consequence of growing your wild-type phage in CJ236 is to generate a uracil-substituted template that now grows well in CJ236 but very poorly in a wild-type strain such as MV1190.

The MV1190 strain carries an F' with a pro marker which is lacking in the bacterial chromosome. This selects for the maintanence of the F'. A second DNA strand is synthesized using an oligonucleotide that has the desired mutation. Upon transformation of strain MV1190 there is a strong selection of the mutant DNA strand because it is all DNA. The uracil-containing strand is inactivated presumably by the uracil glycosylase. Individual plaques are picked and screened by DNA sequence analysis. The frequency of mutants is so high there is no need to screen with oligonucleotides under very precise hybridization conditions to identify mutants. Kits are available from many vendors to perform these procedures. A kit from Amersham uses a different method of selection for recombinants and works with comparable efficiency. It has in some cases produced additional mutations than the ones desired.

Growth of the template: uracil-containing phage

1. Grow 20 ml of CJ236 for 6 hr by adding 10 μl of an overnight culture.

2. Add about 10^6 phage and shake overnight at 37°.

3. Pellet the cells by centrifugation.

4. Add to the supernatant 100 μg RNase A for 30 min.

5. Add 1/4 volume of 3.5 M ammonium acetate in 20% PEG-8000. Mix and place on ice for 1 hr.

6. Centrifuge 12 krpm for 15 min at 4°. Remove all the supernatant.

7. Resuspend in 200 μl of high-salt buffer (0.3 M NaCl, 0.1 M Tris·HCl [pH 8.0], 1 mM EDTA).

8. Spin 2 min to remove insoluble material.

9. Titer the phage stock on CJ236 and MV1190. The titer on CJ236 should be at least 5 x 10^{11} pfu/ml and on MV1190 it should be at least 10^4 lower.

10. Extract the DNA with phenol and then chloroform until the interphase is clear.

Synthesis of the mutant strand

1. Mix 0.1 pmol of the template DNA, 2–3 pmol of the mutant primer, 1 μl of the 10x annealing buffer and H_2O to a total of 10 μl.

2. Heat to 70° for 5 min. Allow to cool to 30° over 1 hr. Place on ice.

3. Add 1 μl 10x synthesis buffer, 1 μl T4 DNA ligase (2–5 units), 1 μl T4 DNA polymerase (1 unit). Incubate on ice for 5 min, then transfer to room temperature for 5 min and finally incubate at 37° for 90 min.

4. Add 90 μl TE and freeze at -20°.

Transformation of MV1190

1. Add 10 μl of *in vitro* synthesized double-stranded DNA to 0.2 ml of competent cells.

2. Place on ice for 30 min.

3. Heat-shock the cells by incubating at 37° for 150 sec and then return to ice.

4. Plate with 200 μl of a fresh overnight culture of cells.

5. After an overnight incubation of the plates at 37° pick pure M13 plaques.

6. Using dideoxy DNA sequencing procedures determine the sequence of the region of interest in individual plaques. The frequency of generating mutants is usually greater than 80%.

Annealing buffer

0.02 M Tris·HCl (pH 7.4)
0.05 M NaCl
0.002 M $MgCl_2$

Synthesis buffer

17.5 mM Tris·HCl (pH 7.4)
3.75 mM $MgCl_2$
0.75 mM rATP
0.40 mM each dNTP
21.5 mM DTT

REFERENCE

Kunkel, T. A., J. D. Roberts, and R. A. Zakour *Methods in Enzymol.* 154:367–382 (1987).

Nucleic Acid Sequencing

INTRODUCTION

There are two basic methods for determining DNA sequences. The Maxam-Gilbert procedures involve base-specific chemical cleavage of DNA that has been labeled at one terminus prior to cleavage. The Sanger method makes use of dideoxy necleotides which when incorporated into DNA cause specific chain termination at a particular nucleotide. For both methods the reaction products are separated on denaturing polyacrylamide gels. The Sanger method is used so commonly now that many sequencing kits are available from numerous vendors. For this reason the Sanger procedures for conventional DNA sequencing are not described here.

DNA sequencing machines have been designed that make use of the Sanger procedures. The sequencer from Applied Biosystems uses a dye labeled primer and is best used on Bluescript or M13 subclones. The Dupont sequencer makes use of specific fluorescent base analogues that result in chain termination when incorporated. These machines will increasingly be used in areas beyond DNA sequence determination.

In this section two methods are described. The Maxam-Gilbert procedures are presented because some parts of them are used in DNA footprinting. The second protocol described is the direct sequencing of cDNA from total RNA using the Sanger procedures. If one is familiar with the various procedures outlined here there is a tendency to use the simplest method for a given experiment. In practice many or all of the available methods are used in a lab.

MAXAM-GILBERT DNA SEQUENCING PROCEDURES

These procedures have been described in many articles. The purpose of their inclusion here is to provide a flowchart that is an adequate guide to performing the technique at the bench. In addition, these procedures are also used in DNA footprinting. In the case of methylation protection experiments, the fragment to be used for the DNA binding experiment can be labeled in the plasmid using ^{32}P and then methylated just prior to running the gel to purify the probe. The isolated DNA fragment is then used in a mobility shift assay. After the protein-DNA complex is purified one proceeds with the piperidine cleavage and sequencing gels for analysis. The sequencing of DNA has four steps: preparing the end-labeled DNA fragments, performing the chemical procedures on the fragments, running the sequencing gels and analyzing the data.

Preparing the end-labeled fragments

Preparative labeling of DNAs for sequencing is generally done by labeling the 5' end of a DNA strand using γ-ATP and polynucleotide kinase or labeling the 3' end using dNTPs and the Klenow DNA polymerase. Both procedures work well but the "fill-in" reaction with the large fragment of DNA polymerase I (Klenow polymerase) works very well and is more reliable. Because polymerases always synthesize in the 5' to 3' direction one must chose a site to label that has a 5' protruding terminus. Blunt-end sites do work using the exchange reaction but it is less efficient. A procedure is given here.

1. Digest 3 μg of a plasmid DNA containing the sequence of interest with the restriction enzyme that cleaves at that site usually in a volume of 100 μl. All of the enzymatic reactions are performed in this first microfuge tube prior to layering the preparative gel. After the appropriate time of incubation (usually 60 min) place the tube at room temperature.

2. Add the [α-^{32}P] dNTPs that are needed to copy the bases completely in the 5' overhang restriction site and at least 3 units of the Klenow polymerase and incubate an additional 30 min at room temperature. The enzyme is processive so that in the case of *Eco*R I for instance one needs to add both A and T. If one only added T there would be no appropriate polymerization. For this amount of DNA, assuming a limited number of restriction sites, we routinely add 3 μl of each labelled base having a specific activity of about 600 Ci/mmol in aqueous solution at a concentration of 10 mCi/ml.

3. In case there was incomplete copying of a terminal sequence excess unlabeled dNTPs (5 μl of a solution containing each dNTP at a concentration of 0.5 mM) are added for an additional 15 min at room temperature.

    Note: If you wish to label your DNA using polynucleotide kinase, steps 1–3 can be substituted with the following procedure. Digest 10 μg of plasmid DNA with the appropriate enzyme for 60 min. Add 1 unit of CIP (calf intestine phosphatase) for an additional 30 min at 37°. Phenol-extract the sample twice and EtOH-precipitate. Wash the precipitate with 70% EtOH and dry in air or under a vacuum. Resuspend in 18 μl TE and add 5 μl 5x kinase buffer (see general enzyme buffers), 2 μl [γ-^{32}P]rATP (ICN crude [γ-^{32}P]rATP), and 5 units of T4 polynucleotide kinase. Incubate for 60 min at 37°.

4. The Klenow polymerase (or kinase) is now heat-inactivated by incubation at 65° for 15 min. This is necessary to prevent subsequent filling-in at any other restriction site that is produced.

5. Because fragments must be generated that are labeled at only one terminus we must now cleave the plasmid DNA again using a different restriction enzyme that will cleave between the two labeled ends of the fragment that you wish to sequence. This second digest is performed for an additional 60 min at 37°. Many enzymes will work in moderate- to low-salt buffer conditions. If the two enzymes used really have drastically different buffer conditions then one can EtOH-precipitate the DNA and resuspend in the appropriate buffer. Sometimes the digest patterns are complex so it is often useful to save 10%–25% of the sample prior to the second digestion to compare the fragments produced after the first digest on the preparative acrylamide gel.

6. Add sample loading buffer and layer directly on a 5% or 8% polyacrylamide gel usually 30-cm long. Electrophorese until the BPB is near the bottom of the gel. Process for autoradiography. For fragments less than 250 bp an 8% gel is better. Larger fragments are best separated on a 5% gel. As a general rule fragments less than 250 bp can easily be soak-eluted and larger fragments should be electroeluted from the gel slices. After elution the samples are EtOH-precipitated using 2 μg of herring testis DNA carrier and *always* rinsed with 70% EtOH. The amount of subsequent additions of carrier DNA are adjusted for this amount of carrier.

The chemical procedures

A series of reactions are carried out on 5 different aliquots of a given DNA fragment, which have specificity for G, G + A, C + T, C and A > C. We have found that potential errors in identifying purines can be avoided by including the A > C reaction especially in cases where the bases are compressed in the gel. After the sample has been resuspended in 50 μl of H_2O it is aliquoted in to 5 color-coded tubes as indicated in the flowchart. The G reaction (DMS) and the pyrimidine reactions (hydrazine) are performed for 5 min on short fragments (100 bp or less) and for 3 min on longer DNA fragments. The A > C reaction is always performed for 8 min and the G + A reaction for 60 min regardless of the length of the fragment. At the end of the procedure resuspend the precipitated samples in 10 μl of loading buffer lacking BPB. The region of 8–10 bp is obscured by BPB. Use the loading dye containing BPB only for a marker on 15% gels.

Useful reminders

1. The flowchart for the chemical cleavages indicates the chilling and centrifugation times of 5 min each. Be sure to monitor the tubes with a Geiger counter to be sure the labeled DNA has precipitated under your condi-

tions. If the DNA didn't precipitate freeze the reactions for at least 15 min in an EtOH/dry-ice bath and centrifuge for 15 min at 4°.

2. When pouring off the EtOH be careful to pour off most of it especially in the first precipitation. Chemicals carried over can cause further modification.

3. Dilute piperidine in a glass tube. The stock is 10 M.

4. Resuspend the samples for the piperidine in screw-cap microfuge tubes if available; the piperidine is volatile.

5. Keep the tubes on ice if not in the microfuge.

DNA sequencing reagents for the Maxam-Gilbert procedures

DMS buffer (G-go)

0.5 M sodium cacodylate (pH 8.0)
0.01 M MgC1$_2$
0.001 M EDTA

DMS stop (G-stop)

1.5 M sodium acetate (pH 7.0)
1.0 M 2-mercaptoethanol
40 μg/ml carrier DNA

Hz-stop

0.3 M sodium acetate
0.0001 M EDTA
10 μg/ml carrier DNA

A > C-go

(should be replaced every 1–2 months)

1.2 N NaOH
0.001 M EDTA

A > C stop

1 N acetic acid (glacial acetic acid is 17.5 N)

0.3 M sodium acetate (sodium acetate from British Drug House)

5 M NaCl

Loading buffer	*50 ml*
90% (v/v) deionized formamide	45 ml formamide
0.001 M EDTA	0.1 ml 0.5 M EDTA
0.05% XC (xylene cyanol)	0.025 g XC
0.05% BPB (bromophenol blue)	0.025 g BPB
Make with and without BPB.	ddH$_2$O to 50 ml

10% ammonium persulfate

10-ml solution can be stored at 4° and replaced every 3 to 4 weeks.

TBE 1 (M)
(No pH adjustment necessary; it will be 8.3) per L:

121 g Trizma Base
3.7 g Na$_2$ EDTA
51.4 g boric acid

Piperidinium formate

1. Mix: 0.45 ml formic acid + 9.55 ml H$_2$O

2. Dilute piperidine 1:10 which results in a 1 M solution. The stock solution is 10 M.

3. Add 15 µl 1 M piperidine to the 10 ml of formic acid and water and mix. The pH should be 2.0.

Sonicated carrier DNA

1 mg/ml herring sperm DNA

DMS waste (DMS is dimethyl sulfate)

5 N NaOH

Hydrazine waste (Hz is Hydrazine)

3 M FeCl$_3$

Running the Gels

For most of the analysis two different percentage gels can be used. After some experience individuals develop preferences partly based on available equipment so many variations exist. We have found that a 40 cm 15% gel allows reading of 2–60 bp on most fragments. This is then followed by 2 sets of long runs on 8% gels which are 83-cm long. In each of these gels approximately 100 bp per lane is usually readable and the separation between bases in these long gels is very good.

The 15% gels are electrophoresed such that the BPB dye is about 25 cm down the gel which usually takes 3 hr at 1500 V. The long 8% gels are first run such that the XC dye is 10 cm from the bottom of the gel which usually takes 7 hr at 1500 V(or about 12 hr at 1000 V). The second long gel is run about twice as long so after the XC has reached the point in the first gel more dye is layered on a side lane and the run continued for a total of about 15 hr. For these long gels the actual gel must be removed from the glass plates for autoradiography.

After the gel is dismantled one plate is pried off. A dry piece of previously exposed film is gently applied to the bottom half of the gel. The gel is cut along the top edge of the film with a single-edge razor blade. The edge of the film may be used now to peel off the gel from the bottom plate. The procedure is repeated for the top section of the gel. Saran wrap is placed over the gels and they are autoradiographed using an enhancing screen at -70°.

DNA Sequencing Gels

	8% Gel		15% Gel	12.5% Gel
	(75ml)	*(125 ml)*	*(75 ml)*	*(75 ml)*
Urea	31.5 g	52.3 g	31.5 g	31.5 g
Acrylamide (40% stock)	15.0 ml	25.0 ml	28.5 ml	23.7 ml
Bisacrylamide (2% stock)	15.0 ml	25.0 ml	15.0 ml	15.0 ml
1 M TBE	7.5 ml	12.5 ml	7.5 ml	7.5 ml
H_2O	13.5 ml	22.5 ml	—	4.8 ml
Ammonium persulfate 10%	0.5 ml	0.5 ml	0.5 ml	0.5 ml

Reagents are mixed and then filtered through a 0.45-μm filter unit. Then 30 μl of TEMED is added while the filtered mixture is being stirred and the gel is then poured. For the large 8% gels use 75 μl of TEMED. After the comb has been inserted add strong clamps on the glass plates near the comb to form the wells properly. Let the gel polymerize for at least 1 hr. Prerun the gel at least 30 min and then layer 1.5 μl (no more that 3 μl) per lane. Heat the samples for 3 min at 90° before layering them.

Analyzing the data

Reading the sequence is usually straightforward. It is a good idea to label the autoradiographs well so they can be retrieved at a later time. It is advisable to immediately record the information either directly in the computer or on paper. It should be written so that the polarity of the sequence is immediately obvious. Reading samples that have been prepared by kinasing yields sequence that is 5' to 3' as one reads up the gels but the filled-in labeling procedure does the opposite. After a sequence has been compiled in a final form on the computer it is valuable to reread the gels and compare them with the computer printout. One of the most common sequence errors made in Maxam-Gilbert sequencing is the failure to recognize the sequence CCA/TGG. In the bacteria the second C is methylated and becomes resistant to the chemical procedures. The result is the absence of a band corresponding to the C residue but usually a gap at the site in the sequence. The consequence may be to read the sequence incorrectly as CA/TGG instead of CCA/TGG.

There are many methods of handling the large amount of data by computer. We have found that a Macintosh computer can be used to enter data using Microsoft Word. This can then be transferred to a mainframe VAX computer that has the Wisconsin and Staden programs for analysis. After analysis the data can be downloaded back to the Macintosh for printouts. Also files can be modified by Microsoft Word to forms suitable for publication.

DIDEOXY SEQUENCING OF PRIMER-EXTENDED cDNAs

The dideoxy sequencing reactions are most accurately applied to DNA fragments cloned into M13 and copied by the large fragment (Klenow) of *E. coli* DNA polymerase. There are ambiguities in such copying reactions that are due to the primary structure of the template rather than to reaction conditions and real confidence in this method of sequencing depends on sequencing *both* strands. Dideoxy sequencing has been adapted for use with DNA primers on RNA templates, with AMV reverse transcriptase making a cDNA copy of the RNA. Here there is only one strand available to sequence, so while these reactions are very rapid and convenient, they do not produce sequence information with 100% accuracy.

Good sequence data depends mainly on using the right ratio of dideoxy to deoxy triphosphate in each reaction. It is possible, at the correct ratios of all 4 dideoxy-containing solutions to read several hundred bases of sequence from a single set of reactions.

The protocols below are guidelines only: you may need to vary dideoxy concentrations by a factor of 2 to 4 in either direction. As written, the protocols call for the dideoxy and deoxynucleoside triphosphates to be mixed and stored together. Making the solutions this way is more work initially, but because it is the ratio of dideoxy to deoxy that is critical, such solutions should enhance the reproducibility of the reactions. Not everyone pipettes alike, so it is advantageous to make up your own solutions, test them, and aliquot concentrations as necessary.

Solutions

Store at -20° except where indicated:

10x AMV RT mix

1 ml of 10x   *Final concentration*

0.25 ml 2 M Tris·HCl (pH 8.3)   0.05 M Tris·HCl (pH 8.3)
0.12 ml 5 M NaCl   0.06 M NaCl
0.06 ml 1 M MgCl$_2$ 0.006 M MgCl$_2$
0.20 ml 1 M DTT   0.02 M DTT
0.37 ml ddH$_2$O

Primer at 25 ng/µl

2.5 mM each dNTP—make in sterile ddH$_2$O, adjusted to neutral pH, and concentration determined by absorbance.

500 µM each ddNTP—make up from premeasured stocks (ddNPTs are *very* expensive).

20µM ddCTP

20µM ddTTP

Chase solution: 500 µM all four dNTPs

>50 µl 2.5 mM dATP
>50 µl 2.5 mM dCTP
>50 µl 2.5 mM dGTP
>50 µl 2.5 mM dTTP
>50 µl ddH$_2$O

For C- labeling: "3 of 4 no C"	*For T-labeling: "3 of 4 no T"*
830 µM each dATP, dGTP, dTTP	*830 µM each dATP, dCTP, dGTP*
80 µl 2.5 mM dATP	80 µl 2.5 mM dATP
80 µl 2.5 mM dGTP	80 µl 2.5 mM dCTP
80 µl 2.5 mM dTTP	80 µl 2.5 mM dGTP

STOP	*For 25 ml*
0.3 M sodium acetate (sequencing grade)	2.5 ml of 3 M
0.002 M EDTA	0.1 ml of 0.5 M
20 µg/ml sonicated DNA	0.05 ml of 10 mg/ml
	to 25 ml with ddH$_2$O

>Store at 4°.

95% EtOH at 4° (diluted from 100% in a glass container)

Formamide + 5 mM EDTA + xylene cyanol + bromophenol blue

Store at 4°—aliquots may be kept at room temperature.

10x d + dd solutions: separate for each label

C*		3 of 4, no dCTP	ddH₂O	Dideoxy
	A°	30 µl	15 µl	5 µl 500 µM ddATP
	G°	30 µl	15 µl	5 µl 500 µM ddGTP
	T°	30 µl	15 µl	5 µl 500 µM ddTTP
	C°	30 µl	15 µl	5 µl 20 µM ddCTP
T*		3 of 4 no dTTP	ddH₂O	Dideoxy
	A°	30 µl	15 µl	5 µl 500 µM ddATP
	C°	30 µl	15 µl	5 µl 500 µM ddCTP
	G°	30 µl	15 µl	5 µl 500 µM ddGTP
	T°	30 µl	15 µl	5 µl 20 µM ddTTP

Note: The rule of thumb is that dideoxynucleotide triphosphates are present at 15%–20% the concentration of deoxynucleotide triphosphates in the final reaction. Here the final concentrations are:

	Deoxy	Dideoxy
unlabeled	50 µM	10 µM
labeled	1.5 µM	0.2–0.4 µM

When adjusting dideoxy concentrations, be sure to keep the final unlabeled deoxy concentration at 500 µM in the 10x d + dd, either by making a stock of 500 µM 3 of 4 especially for dilutions, or by calculating the appropriate amount of 830 µM 3 of 4 to add. For a final concentration of 500 µM: 830 µM 4 of 4 should be 60% of the final solution, i.e., 30 µl in 50 µl.

CAUTION: Any cross-contamination of ddNTP, dNTP, or primers will provide uninterpretable data. Make the solutions and cherish them.

Reactions

When sequencing more than one RNA, it is convenient to set up color-coded microfuge tubes containing 10x d + dd, and add 9 µl of reaction mix to each. Use a plastic pipette tip to deliver 1 µl of 10x d + dd to the bottom of each color-coded tube, and then add 9 µl of reaction mix to the side of each of four tubes, about 5 mm above the bottom. Doing this carefully, one may use the same pipette tip to deliver the 9-µl aliquot to all four tubes.

These reactions are written for a final volume of 10 µl. Smaller volumes— down to 5 µl—work fine, and are appropriate if you feel comfortable pipetting very small volumes. Plastic pipette tips are generally a better choice than the glass micropipettes for measuring these small volumes. This is not due to any inherent inaccuracy in the glass tips, but because glass may carry excess volumes on the surface and wiping the tip before delivering is not advisable with labeled solutions.

1. *For 4x 10-μl reactions*

   14 μl ddH₂O (sterile)
   4.4 μl 10x AMV RT mix
   4.4 μl primer at 25 ng/μl
   8.8 μl RNA (Total cellular RNA at 5 μg/μl works very well or poly(A)-containing RNA at 0.5 μg/μl.)

   Mix and incubate at 65° for 5 min, then 42° for 5 min, then room temperature for 5 min and then place on ice.

2. Add 4.4 μl [α-³²P]dNTP and 4 μl AMV reverse transcriptase. Mix well but gently.

3. Deliver 9 μl/tube to 4 microfuge tubes, each of which contains 1 μl of 10x d + dd—A°, C°, G° or T°.

4. As soon as the reaction mix is added to each tube, mix it well but gently, close the top and place it in a 42° water bath. This staggers the starts of the reactions.

5. Incubate at 42° for 15 min.

6. Add 2 μl chase (500 μM all 4 dNTPs).

7. Incubate at 42° for 15 min.

8. Add 100 μl STOP plus 300 μl 95% EtOH and vortex *very* well.

9. Place tubes in dry ice for 15 min.

10. Spin 10 min at full speed in the microfuge.

11. Decant the supernatant *gently*, being careful not to dislodge the pellet. Keep the tube inverted and let it drain onto a sheet of Benchkote for 5–10 min.

12. Wipe the mouth of the tube while still inverted, turn right-side up and place in uncovered 37°–42° water bath until *all* liquid evaporates. This takes 15–30 min. The liquid will evaporate at room temperature but this takes several hours (the tubes cool slightly as EtOH evaporates). The liquid must evaporate completely or the sequencing gel will be trashed.

13. Take up sample in 4–8 μl formamide, EDTA, dye solution and vortex well.

14. Before electrophoresis, place samples in a 90°–95° water bath for at least 3 min. Do not cool before loading. Load 1.5 μl per lane. Store samples at -20°.

Gel Electrophoresis

An 8% acrylamide TBE gradient gel, 40-cm long, is very convenient for checking out the reactions, and with care such a gel produces nice sequence data. Run at 1400 V for 2.5–3 hr (XC about 25–28 cm). The sharpness of bands on these gels improves greatly when autoradiographed without an intensifying screen.

A 12% acrylamide 80-cm long gel produces data more reliably and is much easier to read than a shorter gel. Run at 2000 V for 12–14 hr (XC about 55—60 cm; the XC runs at 65–70 bp).

TBE gradient gel (short)

10x TBE (Peacock-Dingman)

108 g Tris base
55 g boric acid
9.3 g Na$_2$EDTA
per liter of ddH$_2$O

0.5x TBE gel mix

75 ml 40% acrylamide stock
(39:1, acrylamide: bisacrylamide)
25 ml 10x TBE
230 g urea
ddH$_2$O to 500 ml

2.5x TBE gel mix

15 ml 40% acrylamide stock
25 ml 10x TBE
46 g urea
5 g sucrose
3 ml 2.5 mg/ml bromophenol blue
ddH$_2$O to 100 ml

1. Filter both gel mixes, store at 4°.

    For a 30-cm x 40-cm gel:

    70 ml 0.5x TBE gel mix
    140 µl 25% ammonium persulfate
    20 µl TEMED

    14 ml 2.5x TBE gel mix
    28 µl 25% ammonium persulfate
    5 µl TEMED

2. Add TEMED just before pouring. The gel will polymerize in about 15 min.

3. With propipette or electric pipetter, draw up 8 ml 0.5x into a 25-ml disposable pipette. Do not dispense. In the same pipette draw up 12 ml of the 2.5x mix (blue). To form the gradient: holding the pipette vertically, use pipetter to draw several air bubbles through the solution. You will see the blue 2.5 mix disperse through the 0.5x mix to form a gradient.

4. Pipette into assembled gel plates, stand the gel straight up to flatten the surface of the gradient.

5. Tilt gel, fill with the remaining 0.5x mix. This may disrupt the gradient: stand the gel straight up again to flatten its surface. While the gel is vertical, tap out air bubbles. The usefulness of the gradient gel depends entirely on getting an even gradient—an even blue layer at the bottom of the gel. Lay gel down flat, insert comb, clamp tight and **DO NOT TOUCH** for at least 30 min. The gel may be stored overnight at 4°, covered with saran wrap.

    12% acrylamide gel (long)

    63 g urea
    45 ml 40% acrylamide stock (39:1, acrylamide; bisacrylamide)
    15 ml 10x TBE
    44 ml ddH$_2$O

    0.7 ml 100 mg/ml ammonium persulfate (freshly dissolved)
    45 µl TEMED

Mix the first four ingredients and stir until the urea dissolves. Add the ammonium persulfate, filter through a 0.45 µm Nalgene filter unit and degas. Add the TEMED just before pouring.

Pouring a long gel is most conveniently done using a peristaltic pump to introduce the gel mix at a constant rate. A needle may be inserted on the end of the tubing and held in place between the gel plates. With a clamp, start with the sandwich tilted at a fairly high angle, and lower it to near-horizontal as it fills with gel mix. A striker can be used to dislodge bubbles that may form, but don't overdo it. The gel is ready to use after 1–2 hr, but may be kept overnight if necessary after covering the exposed end with saran wrap.

After running, the top and bottom halves of a long gel are autoradiographed separately; use an intensifying screen on the bottom half and develop the film after an overnight exposure. No screen should be used on the top half because resolution will be lost. The film may be developed after 4–5 days.

Troubleshooting the reactions

1. *Products are too large or too small.* When the dideoxy concentration is too low, there will be abundant synthesis of large, even full-length, molecules. When the dideoxy concentration is too high, synthesis terminates very early, or it may even look as if there has been no synthesis at all. Because the reactions must be properly tuned *in all four bases* to read sequence from a gel, it can be very useful to run parallel reactions with a given dideoxy at two different concentrations in order to be sure to get readable sequence information.

2. *Products are a smear.* Many sorts of problems with the gel itself can cause this. In particular, samples that have not been EtOH precipitated or that have been washed with 95% EtOH seem to smear on gradient gels. If smearing is due to the reverse transcription reaction, it is probably because the RNA is degraded. Make new RNA.

3. *Ambiguous sequence.* Apparent stops in more than one lane may be due to RNA secondary structure or to the conditions of the reaction. The labeled dNTP is present at very low concentration (1.5 μM), and reverse transcriptase, like some other polymerases, seems to pause at particular sites when working so far below its Km. Three strategies are useful in this regard.

a) Choose the reactions with a high concentration (100 μM) of all four dNTPS. This seems to be essential.

b) Run eight rather than four reactions for each RNA and primer, labelling one set of four with one dNTP (e.g., [α^{32}P]dCTP) and the other with a second dNTP (e.g., [α^{32}P]TTP). Pauses in more than one lane with one label may resolve to single stops in the other label.

c) Cut the labeled dNTP 3- to 4-fold with cold dNTP so the final concentration of this dNTP is 6–8 μM, specific activity 100–150 Ci/mmol.

The booklet from Amersham or Boehringer-Mannheim on M13 sequencing contains a great deal of useful information on dideoxy sequencing, sequencing gels, etc. Those particular reaction conditions are for the Klenow polymerase, not for reverse transcriptase, and are not transferable. The reaction conditions described above derive from the following references.

REFERENCES

Hamlyn, P. H., G. G. Brownlee, C. S. Cheng, M. J. Gait, and C. Milstein *Cell* 15: 1067–1075 (1978).

Hamlyn, P. H., M. M. Gait, and C. Milstein *Nucl. Acids Res.* 9: 4485–4494 (1981).

Kaartinen, M., G. M. Griffiths, P. H. Hamlyn, A. F. Markham, K. Karjalainen, J. L. T. Pelknonen, O. Makela, and C. Milstein *J. Immunol.* 130: 937–945 (1983).

Kaartinen, M., G. M. Griffiths, A. F. Markham, and C. Milstein *Nature* 309: 320–325 (1983).

TBE Gradient gel:

Briggin, M. D., T. J. Gibson, and G. F. Hong *Proc. Nat. Acad. Sci. USA* 80: 3963–3965 (1983).

Immunologic Methods and Cell Culture

SURFACE STAINING OF CELLS WITH ANTIBODIES

This protocol is used routinely to stain surface molecules of cells normally grown in suspension. It assumes that stock antibodies have previously been titered for optimal staining. Commercially obtained antibodies usually come pretitered, although titrations are simply done by trying different dilutions of stock antibody (e.g., 1/10, 1/100, 1/1000, etc.). Usually this will be a two-layer staining, the first layer being antibody-specific for the surface molecule of interest, and the second a fluorescein-conjugated antibody directed against the constant domain of the first. Thus, for example, to stain for surface IgM the first layer may be a rabbit antibody directed against murine IgM, and the second layer might be fluorescein-conjugated goat anti-rabbit antibody. There obviously are many variations including the use of directly conjugated first layer antibodies (useful for two- or three-color fluorescence studies).

1. Harvest the cells assuming 0.5–1 x 10^6 cells per stained sample. Wash cells once in staining buffer. Resuspend at about 0.5 x 10^6 cells/ml in staining buffer. Add 2 ml/sample (i.e., 1 x 10^6 cells/tube) to Falcon 2058 tubes. Spin cells down, pour off the supernatant and blot dry by briefly inverting on a paper towel. Flick pellet to resuspend.

2. Add the appropriate dilution of the primary antibody in 50–100 μl staining buffer. Incubate on ice for 20–30 min keeping tubes on ice. This prevents internalization and capping of antibodies.

3. Wash cells 3x with staining buffer. After the third wash, pour off the supernatant and blot the tube dry on a paper towel. Flick the pellet to resuspend.

4. Add an appropriate dilution of the secondary antibody in 100 μl staining buffer. Incubate on ice for 20–30 min.

5. Wash 3x in staining buffer, or if the cells are to be fixed, in PBS + 0.02% sodium azide without FCS. All protein must be removed prior to fixation.

6. Resuspend the final pellet in 100–200 μl 1% paraformaldehyde solution to fix the cells. Stained cells can be stored for at least two weeks at 4° in the dark after fixation. For fluorescence activated cell sorter (FACS) analysis, the cells should be diluted in PBS-D + 0.02% sodium azide to obtain a cell density of about 1 x 10^6 cells/ml.

Solutions and Materials

Staining buffer is PBS-D (PBS lacking Ca^{++} and Mg^{++}), 2% fetal calf serum (FCS), 0.02% sodium azide, ice-cold.

1% paraformaldehyde: Add 1 g paraformaldehyde to 100 ml 0.85% NaCl. Heat to 70° in a fume hood until paraformaldehyde dissolves. Allow the solution to cool to room temperature. Adjust the pH to 7.4 using 0.1 N NaOH or 0.1 N HCl as needed. Store at 4°.

Tubes for FACS analysis must be Falcon 2058 tubes.

CYTOPLASMIC STAINING OF CELLS WITH ANTIBODIES

1. Prepare cells for the cytospin centrifuge. Count cells. You will need 10^6 cells/sample. Spin down cells, wash with PBS (cold) and then resuspend at 10^6 cells/ml in 1% BSA/PBS/0.1% sodium azide (cold).

2. For cytospinning you must prewet the slide with 1% BSA/PBS. Put filter and glass slide (it is easier to label the slides before starting, to avoid confusion later) into cytospin and put 50 µl of 1% BSA/PBS into chamber. Cytospin to wet slide (let speed reach 1 krpm and then shut off).

3. Add 100 µl of well-resuspended cells into chamber. Cytospin for 8 min at 1 krpm.

4. Remove slide and circle where cells are with a diamond point pen. Allow cells to dry 1 hr at room temperature.

5. Place slides into 95% EtOH (-20°; VERY IMPORTANT). Place in freezer for 30 min.

6. Remove slides. Blot on paper towel. Place in PBS at 4° for 20 min.

7. Place in 0.1% BSA/PBS for 10 min.

8. One at a time: remove slides, wipe around cells with Kimwipe and apply 20 µl of the appropriate dilution of the first antibody. Place in moist chamber for 30 min at room temperature.

9. Repeat steps 6 and 7.

10. Repeat step 8 with 20 µl of the second antibody.

11. Repeat steps 6 and 7.

12. Wipe around cells with Kimwipe. Place 1 drop of Aquamount on the cells and apply a cover slip to the slide. Press out any air bubbles and allow to dry.

13. Slides should be stored at 4° in a slide box with a moist piece of paper towel inside.

Cytoplasmic staining of cells for FACS

1.   Use 10^6 cells for staining. Spin down cells in 15-ml capped tubes.

2.   Wash once with PBS at 4°.

3.   Resuspend cells in 1 ml of 95% EtOH/5% acetic acid (-20°; VERY IMPOR-TANT) per sample (i.e., if you are staining one cell line with three different first antibodies you have 3 x 10^6 cells in the tube and you add 3 ml of the EtOH/acetic acid). Put in the freezer at -20° for 30 min.

4.   Wash 3x using 6 ml 1% BSA/PBS/0.1% sodium azide at 4°. After last wash aliquot cells into 5-ml capped tubes.

5.   After pouring off blot tubes on paper towel. Add 100 µl of the appropriate dilution of the first antibody.

6.   Stain 30 min at room temp.

7.   Wash 3x using 2 ml of BSA/PBS at 4°.

8.   Stain as in step 5 with appropriate dilution of the second antibody.

9.   Wash as in step 7.

10. Resuspend cells in 1 ml of BSA/PBS. Cells are ready for FACS analysis.

ELISA ASSAY

This is a very commonly used assay for determining the specificity of antibodies. The antigen binds to the plastic plate and is then detected with an antibody. This antibody can be detected by a variety of secondary reagents. An enzyme is generally coupled to the secondary reagent and the antigen is detected by the associated enzyme activity. The assay described here has very good sensitivity. There is an Elisa Amplification Kit available from BRL which is about 10-fold more sensitive.

1. Coat 96-well plates (Dynatech Immulon #011–010–3450, flat bottom, Dynatech Labs, Alexandria, VA) with the antigen of interest. Try starting with 100 ng/well of antigen and titrate to find an optimal concentration. The antigen is diluted in ddH$_2$O. The total volume per well is 50 μl. The antigen is usually dried onto the well using a hair dryer on the hot setting. Alternatively, the antigen in solution may be incubated in wells at 37° for 2 hrs. Control wells are coated with BSA for 2 hr at 37° for specificity controls.

2. Wash the wells 3x with borate-buffered saline (BBS). A Nunc ImmunoWash eight-channel washer is used for all washing steps.

3. Block wells with 1 mg/ml BSA (Pentex Bovine Albumin Fraction V, Miles) in BBS. After filling the wells, incubate 10 min to 2 hrs at 37°. Gelatin at 5 mg/ml can be used for blocking or as a carrier because some antibodies bind BSA.

4. Remove the block by aspirating off the BSA but don't wash the wells. The plates may be covered with parafilm and stored at 4° at this point.

5. Add the antibody. The antibody may be diluted into BSA/BBS (the BSA is 1 mg/ml in BBS) + 0.05% Tween 20 (Sigma). Tween reduces nonspecific antibody binding. Include a negative and positive antibody control. Nonspecific binding to various plate coats or by different antisera or culture supernatants will often dilute out at concentrations where specific binding persists. Add 50 μl/well. Cover the plates with parafilm. Incubate overnight at 4° or 2 hr at 37°. Overnight incubation often gives stronger signals, notably when screening hybridoma supernatants.

6. Wash wells 5x with BBS.

7. Add 50 μl/well alkaline-phosphatase-conjugated second antibody reagent. We use protein A-alkaline phosphatase (Zymed), which binds mouse and rabbit IgG. The protein A-alkaline phosphatase is diluted

1:1000 to 1:2000 in BSA/BBS with no Tween 20, but should be titrated for each new lot. Incubate 2 hr at 37°.

8. Wash 6x with BBS.

9. Add the substrate paranitrophenylphosphate (PNPP)(Sigma 104 phosphatase substrate). It comes in 5 mg/ml tablets which should be stored dessicated at -20° in the dark. Improper storage causes spontaneous hydrolysis and high background. Dissolve 1 tablet per 5 ml diethanolamine buffer (DEA buffer) for a final concentration of 1 mg/ml. Add 50 ml/well. The reaction is time-dependent so add the substrate as rapidly as possible to all wells. Yellow color development may occur immediately or may take longer. Incubation at 37° will decrease the development time. Read the color intensity on an Elisa reader at 405 nm. Warm the Elisa machine before use.

DEA buffer

9.85 ml diethanolamine (from Kodak #1598, equals 10.7 g)
0.1 ml 1 M $MgCl_2$

Make up to 100 ml with ddH_2O and pH to 9.8 with conc HCl.

BBS (pH 8.4)   *per 4 L*

35 mM borate	41 g H_3BO_3
80 mM NaCl	29.2 g NaCl
	7 g NaOH
	Bring to 4 L with ddH_2O.

IMMUNOPRECIPITATION OF METABOLICALLY LABELED PROTEINS

1. Label the cells in a T-75 or T-25 flask.

2. Lyse the cells in detergent buffer using 1 ml if from a T-25 flask or 2–3 ml if from a T-75 flask.

3. Centrifuge to remove the nuclei.

4. Add 5 μl normal mouse serum to 1 ml of cell lysate at 4°; shake 30 min.

5. Add 40 μl washed Pansorbin and shake for another 30 min at 4°.

6. Spin 2 min and add another 40 μl Pansorbin to the supernatant.

7. Spin 2 min and pass the supernatant through glass wool.

8. Add SDS to the precleared cell lysate to a final concentration of 0.25%. This amount of SDS is efficient in reducing background. The percentage of SDS that maintains the activity of the antibody and reduces background varies. For some antibodies 0.1% or 0.2% works better.

9. Add 5 μl of the specific antibody; shake at room temperature for 1 hr.

10. Add 40 μl of protein A-Sepharose in PBS (50% v/v) and shake for 1 hr at room temperature.

11. Spin 5 min. Wash the pellets 4x with the detergent buffer containing 0.25% SDS.

12. Resuspend the pellets in 500 μl 0.05 M Tris·HCl (pH 6.7). Layer on top of 500 μl of a 20% sucrose cushion in 0.05 M Tris·HCl (pH 6.7).

13. Spin 5 min. Resuspend the pellet in 40 μl of SDS-PAGE loading buffer and load a portion of an SDS gel.

Detergent buffer

0.02 M Tris·HCl (pH 8.0)
2 mM EDTA
0.5% NP-40
0.5% desoxycholate
50 mM iodoacetamide
0.15 M NaCl
2% α-methyl-D-mannoside
1 mM PMSF

Preparation of Staph A "washed bacteria"

1. Place 9 ml of Pansorbin (Calbiochem) in a Corex tube.

2. Add 1 ml of 20% SDS and 100 μl of 2-mercaptoethanol and boil for 15 min.

3. Centrifuge for 5 min at 10 krpm.

4. Resuspend the pellet in 10 ml H_2O containing 2% SDS and 1% 2-mercaptoethanol as above and boil for 15 min.

5. Centrifuge for 10 krpm for 5 min.

6. Wash the pellet 5x with 10 ml of TR-HS buffer with 5 min centrifugation steps between the washes.

7. Resuspend in 9 ml TR-HS buffer.

TR-HS buffer

0.02 M Tris·HCl (pH 8.0)
1 M NaCl
1% Triton X-100 or NP-40
0.02% sodium azide

PREPARATION OF POLYCLONAL ANTIBODIES USING SMALL AMOUNTS OF ANTIGEN

This procedure describes the immunization of rabbit popliteal lymph nodes and is good when there are limited amounts of antigen available for immunization. Alternatively, the use of double-stranded RNA (poly[A]·poly[U]) has been shown to be a remarkably effective adjuvant for producing antibodies using very small amounts of antigen (see Hovanessian et al. 1988, *Immunol. Today* 9:161–162).

1. 2–3 hr prior to immunization inject 0.5 ml of 1% Evans blue or Trypan blue in PBS between the toes of each foot. This is a subcutaneous injection with a 26-gauge needle. Rinse the area to be injected with 80% ethanol and give a single injection per foot. This dye will accumulate in the nodes and facilitate identification.

2. Anesthetize the rabbit with sodium pentobarbital. First inject 1 ml in the marginal ear vein. After a minute or two check the corneal reflex. Inject 0.2 ml of barbital and wait about 2 min. Check the corneal reflex again. Repeat this routine until there is a loss of the corneal reflex. A dose between 1.5 and 2.5 ml should be sufficient.

3. Shave the fur behind both knees. An area approximately 6–10 cm should be shaved. Be sure to use a vacuum during the procedure to remove the fur. Rinse the hind leg just behind the knee with ethanol. With scissors (sterilized by immersion in 70% ethanol) gently break the skin just behind the knee. Search for the node. The node should be about 0.4–0.8 cm in diameter and be a blue color. Cut the tissue above the node and tease the node out and lay it on the outside of the incision. Be especially careful to avoid blood vessels. Inject the node with 0.1 ml of antigen in complete Freund's adjuvant (CFA) using a 23-gauge needle. The node should turn a cream color due to the white color of CFA. Replace the node. Use about four 9-mm autoclamps to close the incision and rinse with ethanol. Repeat the procedure on the other hind leg. Apply an antibiotic cream or mercurichrome to minimize the possibility of subsequent infection.

4. Inject another portion of the antigen subcutaneously in the back of the rabbit in 0.05-ml to 0.1-ml aliquots. Two to four injections would be appropriate.

5. Allow the rabbit a couple of hours or until it recovers from the anesthesia before returning it to an unsupervised cage.

6. Observe the rabbit daily to check for infection.

Equipment needed

Autoclip applicator and autoclips (Clay-Adams)
Animal clipper (Oster-Harvard)
Vacuum cleaner
Scissors and forceps with hooks on ends

PREPARATION OF MOUSE MONOCLONAL ANTIBODIES AS ASCITES

When useful monoclonal antibodies have been identified they can be expanded as ascites in mice. If the monoclonal antibodies were made in BALB/c or C57BL/6 mice the F1 animals from a cross between C57BL/6 and DBA/2 referred to as B6/D2 can be used. Occasionally one may need to use antibodies produced by rat monoclonals. The cells producing these antibodies are the fusion products of a mouse myeloma and a rat spleen cell. For the rat monoclonals one should use nude mice.

The procedure for generating ascites is to inject 0.5 ml pristane (2,6,10, 14 tetramethylpentadecane) i.p. using a 26-gauge needle into 8- to 10-week-old mice, rested at least 4–5 days after delivery from the breeder. Older mice are better suited for this because they are bigger and less affected by the ascites. After 2 weeks the mice should be injected i.p. with 5×10^6 cells producing a given monoclonal antibody. The mice should be watched to determine when the ascites have expanded but the mouse is not yet sick. At that point, usually 2–3 weeks (only 1–2 weeks for nude mice), a 16-gauge needle can be used to remove ascites fluid. Mice can usually be tapped 3 times after which they can be euthanized by cervical dislocation. Usually 10 ml of ascites fluid can be removed during each tap. The second and third taps are taken at 3-day intervals. This is a short enough interval such that the mouse experiences no obvious discomfort. The ascites fluid is centrifuged in a clinical centrifuge for 10 min and usually stored in 1-ml aliquots at -20° (if not a frost-free freezer) or -70°.

LIMITING DILUTION CLONING

Cloning provides a homogenous cell population, and encourages cells to continue producing or secreting factors of interest by removing selective pressures that otherwise might operate against such cells. Early and persistent cloning is often crucial to establishing a cell line. Begin cloning as soon as "fusoma" is identified as interesting.

Cloning by limiting dilution requires that a single well be seeded with one and only one cell. From the Poisson distribution, one can calculate that this will be the case when 30% or less of the seeded wells are positive for growth. Because cell viability under cloning conditions is always less than 100%, one sets up a limiting dilution cloning with three separate microtiter plates at three different cell densities: 0.3 cells/well = 0.12 ml, 1 cell/0.12 ml, and 3 cells/0.12 ml. Once cells have grown up, wells will contain clones *only at those dilutions* where 30% or less of the wells are positive for growth. Plates with more than 30% of the wells positive for growth will not contain true clones. It is the cloning efficiency *per plate*, not over the whole experiment, that is relevant.

Not infrequently less than 30% of all the wells on all three of the cloning plates are positive for growth, but on one plate, (the least dilute) all the wells have cells growing.

For B-cell hybridoma cloning at limiting dilution, it is necessary to include either a feeder or peritoneal exudate cells, or an extract of such cells. We have been using endothelial cell growth factor from Collaborative Research at 100 μg/ml. For T cell hybrids, the feeder does not seem to be necessary.

Cloning medium

RPMI 1640
20% FCS
10 mM HEPES
100 μg/ml feeder
(Glutamine, antibiotics, antimycotics, β-mercaptoethanol as desired)

1. Count viable cells in trypan blue.

2. Dilute cells to a density of 10^5 viable cells/ml, in one ml RPMI or PBS.

3. Dilute cells 1:100 (10 μl into 1 ml, or 0.1 ml into 10 ml) into RPMI or PBS. Cell density is now 10^3/ml.

4. Dilute cells 1:40 (0.45 ml into 18 ml cloning medium): density is now 25 cells/ml or 3 cells/0.12 ml. This dilution will serve to seed plate A.

5. Dilute cells used to seed plate A 1:3 (6 ml into 12 ml cloning medium): density is now 1 cell/0.12 ml, and this dilution will seed plate B.

6. Dilute cells used to seed plate B 1:3.3 (4.5 ml into 9 ml cloning medium): density is now 0.3 cells/0.12 ml, and this dilution seeds plate C.

7. Pipette 0.12 ml/well from dilutions A, B, and C into three 96-well microtiter plates correspondingly labeled A, B, and C. Two drops from a 5-ml pipette is 0.12 ml.

8. Wrap plates in saran wrap, incubate 10 days to 2 weeks at 37° in 5% CO_2.

9. Assay all the wells on all the plates containing true clones. Pick at least six positive clones for expansion (more is better).

10. Expand into 1-ml wells, omitting feeder from the medium but maintaining serum at 20%. Assay these wells after they have grown up. If a low proportion are positive, or if they are less than before, it may be prudent to reclone immediately.

11. Expand to 10 ml in 20% serum. This is conveniently done in a T-75 flask incubated upright rather than on its side.

12. Expand to 40 ml by feeding 30 ml to the T-75 flask, and incubating on its side. This is a good time to drop the serum concentration, using medium containing 10% serum for this feeding.

13. Assay this culture, and freeze cells from it in liquid nitrogen.

FREEZING AND THAWING CELL LINES

Freezing

Freeze Medium:

90% horse serum
10% DMSO

or RPMI
20% fetal calf serum
10% DMSO

The horse serum containing DMSO is now a standard freezing medium but previously the RPMI/FCS/DMSO has been used routinely. DMSO, dimethyl sulfoxide $(CH_3)_2SO$, sometimes labeled methyl sulfoxide) is sterile as it comes from the reagent bottle. It has a relatively high melting temperature and may crystallize at room temperature. This doesn't hurt: just melt at 37° before use.

Cells must be growing happily prior to freezing or their chances of thawing out will be much reduced. Pellet cells and resuspend at approximately 5 x 10^6/ml in freeze medium at 4°. Usually a 10-fold concentration of a healthy culture is fine. Pipette 1 ml per vial into prelabeled Nunc cryovials, and immediately put vials on ice. Either transfer directly to the liquid nitrogen freezer, or freeze stepwise, starting the cells in a styrofoam box at -70° and transferring to liquid nitrogen after several hours.

It is good practice to have at least three copies of any frozen cell line, and more of important or frequently used lines. Some people keep copies in different freezers to reduce the chance of losing a cell line in case of freezer failure.

Thawing

Remove vial from liquid nitrogen and thaw quickly at 37°. Transfer contents to a centrifuge tube containing 10 ml RPMI (no serum) or PBS at room temperature. Pellet cells. This washes out the DMSO, which is toxic. Pour off the supernatant, take up cell pellet in about 2–3 ml growth medium supplemented with 20% FCS. Aliquot 1 ml per well in wells of 24-well cluster plates, and incubate at 37° and watch for growth. Cells may begin growing at once, or they may take up to 2 to 3 weeks. It may help to feed with several drops of fresh medium every few days.

Expand the culture only once the cells are sufficiently well established that the spent medium looks slightly yellow. Always replace a thawed vial by freezing away some of the newly grown culture; a good policy is to freeze three vials for each thawed one.

Appendix A
Lab Reagents and Materials

Dialysis tubing

1. Cut a roll of tubing into approximately 1-m pieces and place in a 2- or 4-L beaker containing 1.5–2 L of 2% sodium bicarbonate. Two standard sizes are: 1.0 cm x 100 ft, m.w. cutoff 12,000–14,000 (Fisher No. 08–667A), and 1 inch x 100 ft, m.w. cutoff 12,000–14,000 (Fisher No. 08–667B).

2. After boiling for 5–10 min turn off the flame and let cool for about 20 min. Pour off the solution.

3. Repeat the boiling procedure in 10 mM EDTA.

4. Repeat the boiling procedure with H_2O.

5. Rinse the tubing with distilled water and then store at 4° in TE or approximately 25% EtOH.

5x sample gel loading buffer

50% glycerol
0.1 M Tris·HCl (pH 7.5)
0.1% SDS
0.1 M EDTA
0.1 ml/10 ml saturated xylene cyanol
0.5 ml/10 ml saturated bromophenol blue

rNTP and dNTP solutions

1. Dissolve rNTP or dNTP in water at approximate concentration of 0.2 M.

2. Using 0.05 M Tris base and a micropipette, adjust pH to 7.0 by spotting on pH paper. Determine the actual concentration spectro-photometrically using the extinction coefficient.

   Optical densities of rNTPs and dNTPs

Base	Wavelength	Extinction coefficient ($M^{-1}cm^{-1}$)
A	259 nm	1.54×10^4
C	271 nm	9.1×10^3
G	253 nm	1.37×10^4
T	260 nm	7.4×10^3
U	262 nm	1.0×10^4

3. Dilute to final concentration of 0.1 M.

4. Aliquot stock solutions of 0.1 M, 0.02 M, 0.01 M and store at - 20°.

   For 0.1 M rATP dissolve 300 mg of ATP in 4 ml of H_2O. Using NaOH and pH paper adjust the pH to 7.0. Bring the final volume to 5 ml with ddH_2O and store frozen in aliquots.

Equilibration of phenol

Many molecular biologists used to redistill phenol prior to use in extractions of nucleic acids. Now it is much more sensible to purchase pure phenol prepared for use in molecular biology experiments. However, many times it is purchased as recrystallized phenol. It needs rehydration and an adjustment of the pH to near neutrality. The following procedure can be used.

1. Phenol can cause severe burns. Wear gloves, lab coat, and safety glasses. If you do get phenol on your skin attempt to clean your skin as soon as possible. The phenol will cause burns on the skin and peeling of the surface layer may occur. To remove the phenol most effectively rub the area on the skin with a paper towel that is soaked with 70%–95% EtOH, or H_2O will work. Do not use 100% EtOH because the phenol won't be removed from your skin no matter how hard you rub. If you scrub an area quickly, preferably with 95% EtOH, there are frequently no significant aftereffects of a phenol spill on your skin.

2. If your phenol is in a crystalline form add ddH_2O and shake it, usually on a mechanical device, until it is all dissolved. Alternatively you may have purchased 88% liquified phenol and it is ready to be equilibrated.

3. To each 100 ml of liquified phenol add 0.1 g of 8-hydroxyquinoline. This is added as an antioxidant. Also add an excess of 0.1 M Tris·HCl (pH 8) (100 ml). The use of the antioxidant is highly recommended but not essential. The equilibration of phenol to approximately pH 8 is absolutely essential.

4. Mix the solution well for about 10 min and let the phases separate by letting the container sit at room temperature.

5. Remove the upper excess aqueous phase with a glass pipette using a suction device. Do not use a plastic pipette.

6. Add another 100 ml of 0.1 M Tris·HCl (pH 8) to the phenol and mix well for about 10 min, let the phases separate, and remove the excess aqueous phase.

7. Repeat this procedure another two times or until the pH is 8 as judged by indicator paper.

8. Store in foil-covered or brown bottles in the refrigerator. Leave a layer of buffer on top of the phenol.

Appendix B
Basic Lab Solutions

0.5 M EDTA

Dissolve 186.1 g EDTA and NaOH pellets (about 20–25 g) in about 900 ml ddH$_2$0 and stir. This will dissolve the EDTA. The pH is adjusted to 8.0 and the solution poured through filter paper into the stock bottle. Adjust volume to 1 L with ddH$_2$O. Alternatively, put 186.1 g Na$_2$EDTA into 500 ml ddH$_2$O. Dissolve by adding conc NaOH and adjust the pH to 8.0. Add ddH$_2$O to 1 L.

10x TBE

10x	*per L*
0.89 M Tris-borate	108 g Tris base
0.89 M boric acid	55 g boric acid
0.02 M EDTA	3.72 g EDTA or 4 ml of 0.5 M EDTA

20x E

20x	*per L*
0.8 M Tris-acetate	97 g Tris base
1.0 M sodium acetate	136 g sodium acetate
0.02 M EDTA	7.4 g EDTA

Adjust to pH 7.9 using about 36.8 ml conc HCl.

20x SPE

20x	*per 10 L*
0.2 M HPO$_4$	2 L 1 M Na$_2$HPO$_4$ (pH 7.6)
3.6 M NaCl	2090 g NaCl
20 mM EDTA	400 ml 0.5 M EDTA (pH 8.0)

20x SSCPE

20x	*per L*	*per 20 L*
2.4 M NaCl	140 g NaCl	2800 g NaCl
0.3 M Na citrate	88 g Na citrate	1763 g Na citrate
0.2 M KPO$_4$	35 g KH$_2$PO$_4$	708 g KH$_2$PO$_4$
0.02 M EDTA	7.4 g EDTA	148 g EDTA

Adjust pH to 7.2 with NaOH.

20x SSC

20x	*per L*	*per 20 L*
3 M NaCl	175 g NaCl	3500 g NaCl
0.3 M Na citrate	88.1 g Na citrate	1763 g Na citrate
Adjust pH to 7.0.		

10x PBS (phosphate buffered saline)

10x, per L

80 g NaCl
2 g KCl
11.5 g $Na_2HPO_4 7H_2O$
2 g KH_2PO_4

3 M sodium acetate

408 g sodium acetate·$3H_2O$ dissolved in about 800 ml ddH_2O
Adjust pH to 5.2 with glacial acetic acid and add ddH_2O to 1 L.

100x Denhardt's solution

Make three separate 100-ml solutions containing 6 g per 100 ml in ddH_2O of Ficoll 400, Polyvinylpyrrolidone, and Bovine serum albumin (Pentax Fraction V). After each is dissolved thoroughly mix all three solutions and store at 4°. This is far superior to mixing all three ingredients together and then attempting to dissolve them.

50% dextran sulfate

Add 50 g dextran sulfate (Pharmacia) to about 50 ml H_2O in a 100-ml glass bottle. Heat at 65° and shake the capped bottle periodically. After 2–3 hr the powder should be dissolved. Add H_2O to the bottle to a total of 100 ml and again mix well by shaking and heating. Store at 4°.

Ethidium bromide (10 mg/ml)

Dissolve 200 mg in 20 ml ddH_2O. Shake until well mixed, wrap the container with foil, and store at 4°. It is also useful to make a 10-fold dilution of this stock to 1 mg/ml. This compound is a mutagen so wear gloves and a mask when weighing it.

λ dil

10 mM Tris·HCl (pH 8.0)
10 mM MgSO$_4$
1 mM EDTA

TE

10 mM Tris·HCl (pH 8.0 usually, but other pHs may be specified)
1 mM EDTA

1 M dithiothreitol

Dissolve 3.09 g of DTT in 20 ml of 0.01 M sodium acetate (pH 5.2).
Sterilize by filtration.
Dispense into 1 ml aliquots and store at -20°.

SEVAG

Chloroform plus isoamyl alcohol in a ratio of 24 to 1

Appendix C
Bacterial Culture Media

L Broth

For liquid medium
per liter:

10 g Bacto tryptone
5 g NaCl
5 g yeast extract
1 ml 1 N NaOH

Autoclave.

For plates

1. Make liquid medium as above.

2. Add 14 g Bacto agar per liter.

3. Autoclave.

4. Swirl so that agar is evenly dissolved.

5. Keep at 68° to pour plates.

6. Pour 30 ml/100-mm petri dish.

NZY Broth

For liquid medium
per liter:

5 g NaCl
2 g $MgCl_2 \cdot 6H_2O$
10 g NZ amine
5 g yeast extract

Autoclave.

For plates

1. Make liquid medium as above.

2. For bottom agar, add 14 g agar/liter.
   For top agar, add 8 g agar/liter.
   For top agarose, add 8 g agarose/liter.

3. Autoclave.

4. Swirl to distribute agar evenly, pour 30 ml per plate.

Note: It usually makes sense to store top agarose in aliquots of 100 ml or 250 ml. There is a limit to the number of times it can be microwaved (2 g agarose/250 ml NZY broth). For bottom agarose plates, add 14 g/liter agarose.

SOC medium

per liter	*final concentration*
20 g Bacto tryptone	2%
5 g yeast extract	0.5%
2.5 ml 4 M NaCl	10 mM
2.5 ml 1 M KCl	2.5 mM

Mix the above in 970 ml of ddH_2O and autoclave. Then add the following ingredients which have been filter-steriled through a 0.2 μm sterile filter unit. The $MgSO_4$ and $MgCl_2$ can be mixed prior to filtration or added separately. A 2 M stock containing both reagents is convenient, in which case one would add 10 ml per liter.

10 ml 1 M $MgSO_4$	10 mM $MgSO_4$
10 ml 1 M $MgCl_2$	10 mM $MgCl_2$
10 ml 2 M glucose	20 mM glucose

IDENTIFICATION OF β-GALACTOSIDASE EXPRESSION IN RECOMBINANTS

For both phage and bacterial colony screening, X-gal plus IPTG are used to identify recombinants for parental vectors. IPTG is not always required. Certainly the pUC plasmids don't need IPTG and in fact the use of MacConkey agar is simpler and much less expensive. The transformants containing the parental pUC19 vector are red and the recombinants having insertions into the polylinker are white. Be aware that at least some isolates of pUC18 do not work on MacConkey agar but they do work fine with X-gal selection. Just combine the MacConkey agar mix plus lactose to pour plates and eliminate the X-gal and IPTG. When using X-gal dissolve it at 20 mg/ml in dimethylformamide in a glass tube. Use that solution as 1000x for plates. You can also add 40 μl to the surface of an individual plate for screening. When IPTG is used again make a 20 mg/ml solution in sterile ddH$_2$O and use that at 1000x. Both of these reagents can be stored at -20°. The X-gal is good for a few weeks at -20°.

ANTIBIOTICS

Ampicillin

Prepare a 35 mg/ml solution of the sodium salt of ampicillin in water. Sterilize by filtration and store in aliquots at -20°. In order to add to media, allow media to cool. Add ampicillin to 35 μg/ml for plates or liquid media. Plates with ampicillin can be stored for only 1–2 weeks at 4°. Ampicillin powder should be stored dessicated at 4°.

Tetracycline

Prepare a 15 mg/ml solution of tetracycline hydrochloride in ethanol/water (50% v/v). Sterilize by filtration and store in aliquots at -20° in the dark. To add to media, first allow media to cool. Add tetracycline to 15 μg/ml for plates or liquid media. Store plates in the dark at 4°.

Chloramphenicol

Dissolve in 95% EtOH usually at 200 mg/ml. It can be stored at -20°. For plasmid amplification it is usually used at 200 μg/ml and for selection at 30 μg/ml.

Kanamycin

Prepare a 1000x solution at 30 mg/ml in 50% EtOH.

Appendix D
General Enzymology

RESTRICTION ENZYME DIGESTION

1. Enzyme digestions are usually done according to buffer indicated as optimal from the source of the enzyme. Slightly different conditions often won't matter much if you want to combine enzymes in double digestions. For example, 100 mM NaCl, 10 mM Tris·HCl usually works for BamH I, Pst I, EcoR I, and Hind III.

2. Never vortex enzymes.

3. Don't forget to heat-kill EcoR I (10 min at 68°) before changing salt concentration to avoid EcoR I star activity.

4. Note: Not all enzymes can be heat-killed. (For example, BamH I, Bcl I, BstN I, Hind III, Sal I).

10x Restriction Enzyme Buffers

Commonly four buffers are made as 10x stock solutions which differ in the amount of NaCl that is present (0, 50, 100, and 150 mM NaCl are used as the final 1x concentration).

	0 mM	50 mM	100 mM	150 mM
1 M Tris·HCl (pH 7.8)	2.5	2.5	2.5	2.5
4 M NaCl	0.0	1.25	2.5	3.75
1 M MgCl$_2$	1.0	1.0	1.0	1.0
50 mg/ml BSA	0.2	0.2	0.2	0.2
1 M DTT	0.1	0.1	0.1	0.1
Sterile ddH$_2$O	6.2	4.95	3.7	2.45

The numbers in the table are the ml used to make a 10-ml stock of each 10x buffer. These stocks are made as 10-ml volumes and aliquoted in 0.5 ml in color-coded tubes and stored at -20°. A given vial is used until all the solution is gone or any problems in digestion are encountered before starting a new 10x vial.

304

CIP (CALF INTESTINE PHOSPHATASE)

This enzyme is used for removing terminal 5' phosphates.

CIP is currently purchased from Boehringer-Mannheim as a ready-to-use solution, cat. no. 713 023. Note that CIP preparations in the catalog come as an ammonium sulfate precipitate that must be prepared before use. Store the enzyme at 4°. According to the manufacturer, it should be stable at this temperature for 6 months.

Dilute the enzyme to 1 unit/µl in:

30 mM triethanolamine
1 mM $MgCl_2$
0.1 mM $ZnCl_2$
3 M NaCl

Store this dilution at 4° as well.

To perform actual CIP reaction (prior to kinasing or ligating):

1. Heat-inactivate restriction enzyme.
    Dilute up using 1x CIP buffer (see below).

2. Add CIP: 0.0125 units CIP:picomole ends.
    We usually do not do these calculations but routinely use 1 u CIP for most reactions such as vector construction (1–3 µg) or for kinasing (10–20 µg).
    Incubate at 45° for 45 min.

3. Before the next reaction (usually a kinase), the CIP must be removed:

    2X Phenol-extract
    2X Ether-extract

    Add salt and EtOH, precipitate, wash, resuspend in TE.

    10x CIP Buffer

    0.5 M Tris·HCl (pH 8.1)
    0.1 M $MgCl_2$

LIGATIONS

4x Buffer

20 μl 10 mM rATP (stored frozen at -20°)
20 μl 200 mM DTT (stored at -20°)
10 μl 1 M Tris·HCl (pH 7.4) /0.2 M MgCl$_2$

Incubate ligation reactions at 17° at least 3 hr.
Do in small volume (5–10 μl).
Keep vector concentration constant and vary insert ratios.

    For plasmid vector use 100 ng in 5 μl reaction.
    For phage vector use l μg in 6 μl reaction.

Do not forget control ligation of digested and CIP'd vector alone.

DNA is prepared for ligation by:

2x phenol-extract
2x ether-extract

Ethanol-precipitate, wash.
RNA can inhibit ligation: one can add RNase directly to the ligation reaction.

KINASING (OF 3', 5', AND BLUNT ENDS)

1.   After CIPing, wash pellet with 70% EtOH.
    Dessicate and resuspend in TE.
    We routinely kinase 10 μg of plasmid which we resuspend in 15 μl TE.

2.   Kinase is performed as follows:

    15 μl digested and CIP'd DNA in TE
    7 μl ddH$_2$0
    6 μl 5x kinase buffer
    2 μl [γ^{32}P]-ATP (ICN crude, cat. no. 35020, aqueous soln: 150 μCi/μl >90% of specific activity)
    0.5 μl T4 kinase (BRL 200 u/17 μl)
    ―――――――――――――――――――
    30 μl TOTAL

    Incubate at 37° for 1–1.5 hr.

    5x kinase buffer

    250 mM Tris·HCl (pH 8.7)
    50 mM MgCl$_2$
    50 mM DTT

3. *a)* After kinasing, DNA can be recut directly by heat-inactivating kinase, diluting several-fold with appropriate restriction buffer, and adding excess of enzyme.

    This whole reaction can then be loaded on a gel to purify the desired end-labeled fragment (see below).

    b) If no second restriction site exists to separate labeled ends, the desired fragment can be strand-separated (see below).

4. We have found that kinasing of 3′ ends can be done using the 5x buffer above as 10x buffer quite satisfactorily without denaturing the ends to be labeled; however, we provide a denaturing protocol to be used in labeling blunt and 3′ ends if desired.

Denaturing protocol for labeling 3′ and blunt ends

Denature: Boil 15 μl DNA for 3 min.
           Cool in ice-water immediately.

Kinase: As above.

Renature: Add 7.5 μl 5 M NaCl to make 1 M final concentration.
           Incubate at 85° for 15 min (heating block).
           Let cool slowly on bench 30 min–1 hr.
           Add 65 μl ddH$_2$O to reduce salt to 330 mM.
           EtOH-precipitate with 250 μl EtOH.

Can then do a second cut in 20–30 μl.

2. Sample preparation (for 200–1000 bp fragments):

    a) EtOH-precipitate and wash with 70% EtOH *twice* to completely remove salt.

    b) Resuspend in 30–40 μl sample buffer.

    c) 90° for 2 min.

    d) Quick-chill in ice.

    e) Load.

Sample Buffer

30% DMSO
1 mM EDTA
0.05% xylene cyanol
0.05% bromophenol blue

Appendix E
Ethanol Precipitation of DNA

One of the most common manipulations is the precipitation of DNA using salt plus alcohol. The most common is probably the use of a final concentration of 0.3 M sodium acetate plus 2 1/2 volumes of EtOH. There are protocols in which ammonium acetate has been substituted for sodium acetate at a final concentration of 2.5 M in the aqueous solution. Both of these methods work fine but there are several guidelines worth remembering.

1. The precipitation works better if the volume is smaller.

2. Amounts of DNA in excess of 1 μg in volumes up to 200 μl are relatively easy to precipitate while lesser amounts may need longer centrifugation conditions.

3. After the addition of EtOH the length of time on ice can be relatively short. A few minutes to equilibrate the temperature is sufficient. Incubation at -20° or -70° doesn't improve the recovery of DNA. Recovery of DNA after centrifugation at room temperature is very good.

4. One of the most important factors is the length of the microfuge spin. Maximal recoveries are obtained after a 30-min centrifugation.

5. The use of ammonium acetate is generally fine *except* when the products are to be used in a ligation. Ammonium acetate is better than sodium acetate for achieving separation from unincorporated dNTPs. They are more soluble in the ammonium acetate solution especially at room temperature. Sometimes 2 to 3 successive ammonium acetate precipitations can be used to clean up either genomic DNA or plasmid DNAs that are difficult to cleave with restriction enzymes.

6. It is common practice to do an EtOH rinse with 70% EtOH to remove residual salt after the precipitation. It is a good idea to include 100 mM sodium chloride in the rinse. If all salt is removed the plasmid DNA will sometimes partially or almost completely denature. This can affect reactions such as preparation of DNA for subcloning or SP6 probes.

7. Sodium chloride can be used instead of sodium acetate especially if there seems to be a problem with recovery of DNA. The salt may contribute to larger pellets which should be rinsed. If significantly larger

volumes of EtOH are used than needed (2 1/2 volumes) you may see increased precipitation of salt.

8. If DNA is to be resuspended in a high-salt buffer it is sometimes advisable to first resuspend it in H_2O or low-salt buffer and then add the high salt.

9. Magnesium acetate or chloride (at 10 mM) can also be added to facilitate precipitation.

Appendix F
Common *E. coli* Lab Strains

Commonly used for transformation of plasmids or cosmids

DH1	C600
DH5	HB101
DH5α	GM161
TB1	MC1061
JM83	MC1061/p3

Plasmid transformations were commonly done using C600 and HB101 or MC1061. The MC1061/p3 strain has the very large (57 kb) p3 plasmid which is Kan^R and has amber mutations in its *Tet* and *Amp* genes. It is used to select for plasmids containing tRNA suppressors such as cDNA libraries constructed in CDM8. Later DH1 was selected as a highly transformable strain and DH5 was even better. DH1 is a *recA-* host used for both plasmids and cosmids. The DH5α strain was made to express α complementation. JM83 and TB1 are also suitable for selection using α complementation. TB1 is a r-m- derivative of JM83. These three strains produce constitutively defective β-galactosidase and can be used without IPTG. When pUC plasmids are transformed into DH5α the result is a complementation producing blue colonies in the presense of X-gal. If the pUC plasmid contains an insert subcloned into the polylinker the α complementation capability is lost and the colony is white. Strain GM161 lacks the *Dam* methylase which normally methylates the sequence GATC. This strain can be used when it is necessary to cleave a plasmid DNA at sites that are normally methylated and therefore protected from cleavage by enzymes such as *Cla* I and *Bcl* I. Another strain, GM2929, is reported as being *Dam-* but in our hands doesn't render *Bcl* I sites sensitive to that enzyme.

Commonly used for λ phages

LE392	Y1089
(P2)392	Y1090
KM392	C600
NM538	C600*hflA*
NM539	BHB2688
NM646	BHB2690
Y1088	

Strain LE392 is su^+ and can be used with λ phage vectors. KM392 is derived from LE392 and lacks a functional β-galactosidase gene. It is thus used for screening λgt11 libraries. The strains Y1088, Y1089, and Y1090 are also used for analyzing λgt11 clones. Strains NM539 and (P2)392 are used for screening genomic libraries (usually EMBL3 or related vectors) in which the Spi phenotype is used to select for recombinant phages. They are often used in parallel with either NM538 or LE392 to determine the total number of phages present and thus determine the quality of the library. The strain NM646 is the preferred strain in which to generate a genomic library now using the EMBL3cos vector because the *mcr* mutations increase the yield of recombinant phages up to 10-fold. The C600 and C600*hflA* strains are used to screen and analyze λgt10 libraries. The *hflA* mutation forces the parental phages into lysogeny and only the recombinant phages produce clear plaques. The BHB2688 and BHB2690 strains are used to make *in vitro* packaging extracts.

Strains used with M13 phages

A series of strains JM101 to JM109 are often used and their characterisics are described in detail in Yanisch-Perron et al., *Gene* 33:103–119 (1985). Two other strains, MV1190 and CJ236, are used to generate M13 mutants. CJ236 is *dut-* and *ung-* and therefore deficient in incorporated uracil residues. The MV1190 is a relatively wild-type strain used to select for oligonucleotide-created mutants (see M13 mutagenesis section 10).

Appendix G
Synthesis of an Oligonucleotide Probe Based on Amino Acid Sequence

This table can be used to predict the nucleotide sequence of a gene based on amino acid sequence data. These predictions are based on human codon usage frequencies but have been used to clone genes successfully from other mammalian species.

Amino acid	Code	Predicted Codon	Codon when the next codon begins with G
Methionine	Met (M)	ATG	nc
Tryptophan	Trp (W)	TGG	nc
Tyrosine	Tyr (Y)	TAC	TAT
Cysteine	Cys (C)	TGC	TGT
Glutamine	Gln (Q)	CAG	nc
Phenylalanine	Phe (F)	TTC	TTT
Aspartic acid	Asp (D)	GAC	GAT
Asparagine	Asn (N)	AAC	AAT
Histidine	His (H)	CAC[a]	CAT
Glutamic acid	Glu (E)	GAG	nc
Lysine	Lys (K)	AAG	nc
Alanine	Ala (A)	GCC	GCT
Isoleucine	Ile (I)	ATC	ATT
Threonine	Thr (T)	ACC	ACA
Valine	Val (V)	GTG[b]	nc
Proline	Pro (P)	CCC[c]	CCT
Glycine	Gly (G)	GGC	nc
Leucine	Leu (L)	CTG	nc
Arginine	Arg (R)	CGG	nc
Serine	Ser (S)	TCC	TCT

The following exceptions are noted:

[a] CAT when followed by C
[b] GTC when followed by T
[c] CCA when followed by T

The ability to predict the correct codon is listed in order of decreasing certainty with Met being the highest. This information is taken directly from Lathe, R., *J. Mol. Biol.* 183:1–12 (1985).

Appendix H
Codon Identities

	2nd base			
	T	**C**	**A**	**G**
1st base				
	TTT Phe (F)	TCT Ser (S)	TAT Tyr (Y)	TGT Cys (C)
	TTC Phe	TCC Ser	TAC Tyr	TGC Cys
T				
	TTA Leu (L)	TCA Ser	TAA Ochre	TGA Umber
	TTG Leu	TCG Ser	TAG Amber	TGG Trp (W)
	CTT Leu	CCT Pro (P)	CAT His (H)	CGT Arg (R)
	CTC Leu	CCC Pro	CAC His	CGC Arg
C				
	CTA Leu	CCA Pro	CAA Gln (Q)	CGA Arg
	CTG Leu	CCG Pro	CAG Gln	CGG Arg
	ATT Ile (I)	ACT Thr (T)	AAT Asn (N)	AGT Ser
	ATC Ile	ACC Thr	AAC Asn	AGC Ser
A				
	ATA Ile	ACA Thr	AAA Lys (K)	AGA Arg
	ATG Met (M)	ACG Thr	AAG Lys	AGG Arg
	GTT Val (V)	GCT Ala (A)	GAT Asp (D)	GGT Gly (G)
	GTC Val	GCC Ala	GAC Asp	GGC Gly
G				
	GTA Val	GCA Ala	GAA Glu (E)	GGA Gly
	GTG Val	GCG Ala	GAG Glu	GGG Gly

Appendix I
Polylinker Sequences

pUC19 POLYLINKER SEQUENCE

5'-AAGCTT GCATGC CTGCAG GTCGAC TCTAGA
3'-TTCGAA CGTACG GACGTC CAGCTG AGATCT
  Hind III   *Sph* I   *Pst* I   *Sal* I   *Xba* I
                                       Acc I
                                       Hinc II

          Sma I
GGATCC CCG GGTACC GAGCTC GAATTC-3'
CCTAGG GGC CCATGG CTCGAG CTTAAG-5'
*Bam*H I   *Kpn* I   *Sac* I   *Eco*R I

Assuming pUC19 to have 2686 bp and the *Hind* III sites to be at bp 447 and the EcoR I site at bp 396 the following enzymes cut once or twice in the pUC19 plasmid: *Nar* I(235), *Nde* I(183), *Sca* I(2177), *Ssp* I(2501), *Xmn* I(2294), *Ava* II(1837, 2059), *Bgl* I(245, 1813), *Fsp* I(256, 1919), *Pvu* I(276, 2066), and *Pvu* II(306, 628).

The following enzymes do not cut pUC19: *Apa* I, *Avr* II, *Bal* I, *Bcl* I, *Bgl* II, *Bss*H II, *Bst*E II, *Bst*X I, *Cla* I, *Eag* I, *Eco*R V, *Hpa* I, *Mlu* I, *Mst* II(*Bsu*36 I), *Nae* I, *Nco* I, *Nhe* I, *Not* I, *Nru* I, *Nsi* I, *Rsr* II, *Sac* II, *Sfi* I, *Spe* I, *Stu* I, *Sty* I, *Tth*111 I, and *Xho* I.

Reading frame for pUC19

The polylinker between the two underlined sites is also in pGEM-3 with SP6 transcription initiating 6 bp 5' to the *Hind* III site and the T7 transcription initiating 9 bp 3' to the *Eco*R I site. The pGEM-4 plasmid has the polylinker in the opposite orientation with respect to the sites of SP6 and T7 transcription initiation. For procedures on inducing pUC fusion proteins in E. coli see Pallas et al. *J. Virol.* 60:1075 (1986).

5' ATG ACC ATG ATT ACG CCA AGC TTG CAT GCC TGC AGG TCG ACT
                                 Hind III
CTA GAG GAT CCC CGG GTA CCG AGC TCG AAT TCA CTG GCC-3'
                                   *Eco*R I

Reading frame for pUC18

5'-ATG ACC ATG ATT ACG AAT TCG AGC TCG GTA CCC GGG GAT CCT
          <u>   </u>
          *Eco*R I
CTA GAG TCG ACC TGC AGG CAT GCA AGC TTG GCA ATG GCC-3'
                                <u>   </u>
                                *Hin*d III

Reading frame for pUC13

The polylinker between the two underlined sites is also in pSP64 with RNA inititation occurring 6 bp 5' to the *Hin*d III site.

5'-ATG ACC ATG ATT ACG CCA AGC TTG GGC TGC AGG TCG ACT
                        <u>   </u>
                        *Hin*d III
CTA GAG GAT CCC CGG GCG AGC TCG AAT TCA CTG GCC-3'
                                <u>   </u>
                                *Eco*R I

Reading frame for pUC12

The polylinker between the two underlined sites is also in pSP65 with the RNA initiation occurring 9 bp 5' to the *Eco*R I site.

5'-ATG ACC ATG ATT ACG AAT TCG AGC TCG CCC GGG GAT CCT
          <u>   </u>
          *Eco*R I
CTA GAG TCG ACC TGC AGC CCA AGC TTG GCA ATG GCC-3'
                        <u>   </u>
                        *Hin*d III

Reading frame for pUC9

5'-ATG ACC ATG ATT ACG CCA AGC TTG GCT GCA
                        <u>   </u>
                        *Hin*d III
GGT CGA CGG ATC CCC GGG AAT TCA CTG GCC-3'
                        <u>   </u>
                        *Eco*R I

Reading frame for pUC8

5'-ATG ACC ATG ATT ACG AAT TCC CGG GGA TCC
                        <u>   </u>
                        *Eco*R I
GTC GAC CTG CAG CCA AGC TTG GCA CTG GCC-3'
                   <u>   </u>
                   *Hin*d III

The reading frames for pUC9 and pUC8 for sites within the polylinker differ from those in pUC19 and pUC18 and are useful for generating certain fusion proteins.

Index

317